ELEMENTARY LINEAR ALGEBRA
with applications

ELEMENTARY LINEAR ALGEBRA

with applications

Adil Yaqub University of California at Santa Barbara
Hal G. Moore Brigham Young University, Provo, Utah

 ADDISON-WESLEY PUBLISHING COMPANY
Reading, Massachusetts • Menlo Park, California
London • Amsterdam • Don Mills, Ontario • Sydney

This book is in the
ADDISON-WESLEY SERIES IN MATHEMATICS

Lynn H. Loomis
Consulting Editor

Library of Congress Cataloging in Publication Data

Yaqub, Adil, 1928-
  Elementary linear algebra with applications.

  Includes bibliographical references and index.
  1. Algebras, Linear. I. Moore, Hal G., 1929–
joint author. II. Title.
QA184.Y36   512′.5   79-18743
ISBN 0-201-08825-8

Reprinted with corrections, August 1981

ISBN 0-201-08825-8
EFGHIJ-HA-8987654

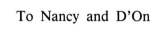
To Nancy and D'On

INTRODUCTION

Linear algebra is indispensible for the study of most topics in the physical, biological, social, and natural sciences. In this book we have attempted to give the student an introduction to the basic techniques and facts of the subject without an overwhelming rigorous description. Our emphasis is on computational techniques and applications rather than on abstract concepts and proofs for their own sake. On the other hand, linear algebra leads naturally into the beauty and elegance of mathematics itself. Because its applications are near at hand, it forms an ideal vehicle for introducing the student to the incredible power of generalization and abstraction. We have, therefore, given some proofs and have developed an adequate amount of theoretical material when it was felt that this would aid the understanding of the subject matter.

For the most part, we have assumed that a student has had the equivalent of two years of high-school algebra. Thus, the text might be suitable for high-school seniors as well as college freshmen and sophomores. There are some examples and exercises—clearly labeled—for those who have studied calculus. These can, however, be easily omitted without disrupting the flow of the material. They are included because they give additional examples of the wide application of linear algebra and because most students will study linear algebra after a year (or a semester) of calculus.

The entire text can be covered in a semester course which meets four hours per week. However, the first five chapters, which are the heart of the material, can be covered in a one-quarter course meeting four hours per week. These will give the student a thorough knowledge of all the basic facts he is likely to need in his discipline. The last two chapters contain additional applications of linear algebra which are both interesting and easily accessible. The following table gives some explicit suggestions for various course organizations.

Amount of time available	Cover chapters
One quarter— three meetings per week, or	Chapters 1, 2, 3, 4 (except 4.5) plus
One semester— two meetings per week	Sections 5.1, 5.2, and 6.1
One quarter— four meetings per week	Chapters 1, 2, 3, 4, 5 plus Section 6.1
One quarter— five meetings per week or	Chapters 1, 2, 3, 4, 5 plus Sections 6.1, 6.2, 6.3
One semester— three meetings per week	with selection from rest of Chapters 6 and 7
One semester— four meetings per week	Chapters 1, 2, 3, 4, 5, 6, 7

Throughout the text we have stressed geometric considerations and interpretations of linear algebra whenever such interpretations are possible. In particular we have given a substantial number of examples of a geometric nature. Numerous illustrations can be found in every chapter and each section concludes with a large number of exercises—more than any student will want to do in one assignment. Thus, the instructor can add whatever emphasis he pleases to the course: computation, application, or abstraction. The chapters are ordered with the thought that one should proceed from the familiar to the unfamiliar. Briefly they are as follows:

Chapter 1 begins with systems of linear equations and their solution, leading to matrix algebra.

Chapter 2 discusses determinants and Cramer's rule for solving systems of equations. This chapter could possibly be postponed until just before Chapter 6, if so desired.

Chapter 3 begins with intuitive notions of vectors and develops the concepts of vector spaces by looking first at the space R^n.

Chapter 4 develops the ideas of length and angle in R^3 into a consideration of real inner-product spaces in general.

Chapter 5 discusses linear transformations and ties together the ideas of vectors and matrices. It does not use the inner product until the final section.

Chapter 6 uses the ideas developed in the preceding chapters as it discusses eigenvalues and their applications to diagonalization, quadratic forms, quadric surfaces, and solutions to systems of differential equations. Calculus is required only for Section 6.6. The final section discusses partitioning matrices into blocks.

Chapter 7 could be covered any time after Chapter 3. It develops some simple applications of matrix algebra. Sections 7.3 and 7.4 require a little knowledge of probability. Section 6.7, on block multiplication of matrices, would be useful before this chapter.

An Appendix gathers together some of the computational algorithms developed in the main part of the book. These provide an easy reference for the student to the more computational aspects of the material.

The diagram illustrates the interdependence of the chapters and suggests ways in which the material may alternatively be presented. We, of course, prefer the way in which it appears in the text.

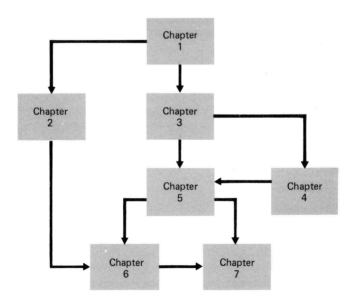

Interdependence of the chapters

We are very appreciative of the many people who have aided in the preparation of the text. To Steve Quigley, our editor, and to Lynn Loomis who went over the preliminary manuscripts very carefully and made many valuable suggestions, we express our sincere thanks. We also appreciate the many helpful suggestions given by N. Eric Ellis from the Essex Community College, Mark P. Hale, Jr. from the University of Florida, Stacy G. Langton from the University of San Diego, Bruce Palka from the University of Texas at Austin, John W. Petro from the Western Michigan University, and Steven Pruess from the University of New Mexico.

Our gratitude extends also to the staffs of the Mathematics Department and the Algebra Institute at the University of California, Santa Barbara, for their excellent typing of the manuscript. We also appreciate the forbearance of our students at BYU and UCSB who used the material in its preliminary form and learned linear algebra. Finally, to the production staff of Addison-Wesley for their fine cooperation and professional efforts in the publication of the book we express our sincere appreciation.

December, 1979

A. Y.
H. G. M.

CONTENTS

3
VECTOR SPACES

4
REAL INNER–PRODUCT SPACES

5
LINEAR TRANSFORMATIONS

6
EIGENVALUES, EIGENVECTORS, AND QUADRATIC FORMS

7

OTHER APPLICATIONS

SYSTEMS OF LINEAR EQUATIONS AND MATRICES

Linear algebra has many applications. Its notational economy and rules for analysis are indispensable for meaningful interpretation of much raw data. This is no less true in the behavioral, management, and biological sciences than it is in the physical sciences, where these techniques have long been used.

In this text we shall study those parts of linear algebra that provide the vocabulary and skill necessary to construct and manipulate linear mathematical models. The nature of an actual model usually depends upon many factors and frequently involves an interplay between linear algebra and other branches of mathematics. We shall discuss some of these models as we proceed.

1.1 ELEMENTARY IDEAS—SYSTEMS OF LINEAR EQUATIONS

The value of linear algebra quickly becomes apparent in the study of solutions to a system of linear equations. These systems arise when one wants to determine several quantities subjected to a number of different constraints. Such problems are very common in all branches of biological, social, and physical sciences. Let us begin by examining a very simple problem from elementary algebra.

1

Example 1   A rectangular area has a perimeter of 56 linear feet. If the width of the area is doubled and the length is increased by half, then the perimeter will be 96 feet. What are the original dimensions of the area?

Let w be the width of the area in question and let u represent the length of the area. The conditions stated can then be expressed by the system of equations:

$$\begin{cases} 2u + 2w = 56, \\ 3u + 4w = 96. \end{cases} \tag{1.1}$$

Several different techniques are available to solve this system. We shall explore three of them here. The first of these techniques, *substitution*, is perhaps the simplest for this example. The second technique, *graphing*, has its greatest value in giving geometric insight into the nature of the solutions; however, if the number of variables is larger than three (two, for some people), geometric intuition is severely strained (nevertheless, these insights will be exploited in our discussion). The third technique, *elimination*, will be the one that is best generalized to handle systems involving a large number of equations and variables.

A way to solve the system (1.1) using the substitution method is to solve the first equation for u in terms of w. This gives

$$u = 28 - w,$$

which may be substituted for u in the second equation, yielding

$$3(28 - w) + 4w = 96.$$

This is an equation with but one variable, and solving it gives $w = 12$. Therefore, $u = 28 - 12 = 16$.

In the graphical method one thinks of each of the equations in (1.1) as the equation of a line in the plane. Thus, the system itself gives the equations for *two* straight lines. Each line is the set of all points (u, w) that satisfy the given equation, and the solution to the system is the point (u_0, w_0) of intersection of both lines; Fig. 1.1 illustrates this.

The third method for solving a linear system, elimination, is easily accomplished for the system of Example 1 by the following sequence of steps. First, the system (1.1) is

$$\begin{cases} 2u + 2w - 56, \\ 3u + 4w = 96. \end{cases}$$

Multiply the first equation by 2 to obtain a new system

$$\begin{cases} 4u + 4w = 112, \\ 3u + 4w = 96, \end{cases}$$

which has the same solutions as the original. Now subtract the first equation from

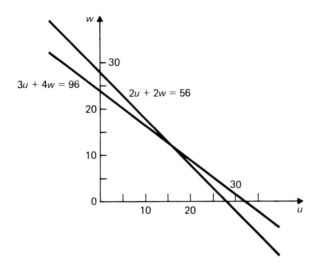

Figure 1.1

the second and use the result to replace the second equation. The system

$$\begin{cases} 4u + 4w = & 112, \\ -u & = -16 \end{cases}$$

has the same solutions as the original. The value of w can now be obtained by substituting in the first equation the value given for u.

As an alternative approach, we could write

$$\begin{cases} u & = 16, \\ u + w = 28. \end{cases} \tag{1.2}$$

This system results from interchanging the equations in the previous step, and then dividing the first equation by (-1) and the second equation by 4. Then, subtracting the first equation from the second and substituting the result for the second equation gives the system

$$\begin{cases} u = 16, \\ w = 12, \end{cases}$$

which displays the solutions to the equations.

The discussion above is much more detailed than was actually warranted by the problem, but it illustrates the general ideas to be developed below.

To be able to discuss systems of equations of arbitrary size, we need some general terminology.

First of all, a *linear equation* in n variables is an equation of the form

$$a_1 x_1 + a_2 x_2 + \ldots + a_n x_n = b,$$

where b and $a_i, i = 1, 2, \ldots, n$, are all real numbers (constants) and $x_i, i = 1, 2, \ldots, n$, are the variables. A **system of linear equations** is a collection of such equations. A **solution** to a system of linear equations is any ordered n-tuple $(c_1, c_2, \ldots, c_n)$ of real numbers such that each of the equations of the system is satisfied when the values $c_1, \ldots, c_n$ are substituted for $x_1, \ldots, x_n$, respectively.

Two systems of linear equations in n variables are called **equivalent** if they have precisely the *same set* of solutions. Consider an example.

Example 2 Find all the solutions to the system of equations

$$\begin{cases} x + y + z = 0, \\ x + 2y + 2z = 1, \\ x - 3y - z = 0. \end{cases} \tag{1.3}$$

Using the method of elimination, as we did in Example 1, we subtract the first equation in (1.3) from the second equation to obtain the system

$$\begin{array}{ll} \text{a)} & x + y + z = 0, \\ & y + z = 1, \\ & x - 3y - z = 0. \end{array}$$

Since subtracting an equal amount from both sides of an equation does not change the equality, we have not altered the solutions to the system. Therefore, the system in step (a) is equivalent to the system (1.3). For the same reason so is the following system. What did we do?

$$\begin{array}{ll} \text{b)} & x + y + z = 0, \\ & y + z = 1, \\ & -4y - 2z = 0. \end{array}$$

Then if we multiply both sides of the third equation in step (b) by $-\frac{1}{2}$, we also do not alter the solutions, so that the following system is still equilvalent to (has the same solutions as) (1.3):

$$\begin{array}{ll} \text{c)} & x + y + z = 0, \\ & y + z = 1, \\ & 2y + z = 0. \end{array}$$

Finally, if we subtract two times equation two in step (c) from the third equation of that system, we have the equivalent system

$$\begin{array}{rl} x + y + z = & 0, \\ y + z = & 1, \\ -z = & -2. \end{array} \tag{1.4}$$

The last equation of the system (1.4) immediately gives us that $z = 2$. At this point $z = 2$ can be substituted in the second equation of (1.4) to obtain $y = -1$, and then the two values can be substituted in the first equation to obtain $x = -1$.

Therefore, the system

$$\begin{cases} x & = -1, \\ & y & = -1, \\ & & z = 2, \end{cases} \qquad (1.5)$$

is equivalent to the system (1.3) and the solution to (1.3) is the triple $(-1, -1, 2)$.

This example shows that, to *solve* a system of equations, one can successively replace it by equivalent systems with successively *simpler* equations until, finally, such a simple system appears that the solutions are displayed as in (1.5).

The following theorem summarizes the allowable manipulations in using this technique. This theorem is quite plausible, and we omit its proof.

Theorem 1.1

Each of the following elementary operations on the equations of a given system of linear equations produces a system equivalent to the original system:

   i) *interchanging the order of any two equations in the system;*
  ii) *multiplying both sides of any equation by a nonzero real number;*
 iii) *replacing any equation in the system by its sum with a constant multiple of any other equation in the system.*

Consider, therefore, a system of m equations in n variables:

$$\begin{cases} a_{11}x_1 + a_{12}x_2 + \ldots + a_{1n}x_n = b_1, \\ a_{21}x_1 + a_{22}x_2 + \ldots + a_{2n}x_n = b_2, \\ \quad\vdots \qquad \vdots \qquad\qquad \vdots \qquad \vdots \\ a_{m1}x_1 + a_{m2}x_2 + \ldots + a_{mn}x_n = b_n. \end{cases} \qquad (1.6)$$

A word or two is in order about the notation used in (1.6). Note that each of the coefficients in this array is given a double subscript. The first subscript designates the equation (row) and the second designates the variable (column) in that row of (1.6) where it appears. One can think of these subscripts as the *address* of the coefficient; thus, a_{24} is the coefficient of x_4 in the second equation.

Our goal, then, is to substitute for this system of equations an equivalent system that has the special form obtained by equations (1.4) in Example 2. This particular form is called echelon form.

A system of equations is said to be in **echelon form** when the first variable with a nonzero coefficient in any equation is missing (has zero coefficient) in every following equation.

That is, if a_{ik} is the first nonzero coefficient occurring in the ith equation of the system, then $a_{jk} = 0$ for all $j > i$. As you can see, the system in (1.4) has this form, while the following system does not:

$$2y - z = 1,$$
$$3x \quad + 2z = 5,$$
$$x - 5y \quad = 4.$$

We wish to replace a given system of equations, such as (1.6) with an equivalent system in echelon form. There is no "best" tactic for doing this, but we can use Theorem 1.1 judiciously, as was illustrated in Example 2. We will also illustrate its use in the next example. It is generally easier for hand calculation when the first nonzero coefficient in any row is a 1. Although this is not a rigid requirement, we shall generally adhere to this practice in what follows. The step-by-step process of reducing a system to echelon form (as illustrated by this next example) is called **Gaussian elimination**.

Example 3 Reduce the following system of equations to an equivalent system in echelon form and find a solution to the system:

$$\begin{aligned} x_1 - 3x_2 + x_3 - x_4 &= 1, \\ 2x_1 - 9x_2 - x_3 + x_4 &= -1, \\ x_1 - 2x_2 - 3x_3 + 4x_4 &= 5, \\ 3x_1 - x_2 + 2x_3 - x_4 &= -2. \end{aligned} \tag{1.7}$$

To accomplish the desired reduction, we must replace the second, third, and fourth equations of (1.7) with new equations each of which has a zero for the coefficient of x_1. We use Theorem 1.1(iii) to accomplish this.

Replace equation two with $-3x_2 - 3x_3 + 3x_4 = -3$, which is obtained by adding equation two to the result of multiplying both sides of equation one by (-2). Replace equation three with $x_2 - 4x_3 + 5x_4 = 4$, which is the sum of the third equation and (-1) times the first equation. Next, replace the fourth equation with $8x_2 - x_3 + 2x_4 = -5$, its sum with (-3) times the first equation. An equivalent system is, therefore,

$$\begin{aligned} x_1 - 3x_2 + x_3 - x_4 &= 1, \\ -3x_2 - 3x_3 + 3x_4 &= -3, \\ x_2 - 4x_3 + 5x_4 &= 4, \\ 8x_2 - x_3 + 2x_4 &= -5. \end{aligned} \tag{1.8}$$

This system is, of course, not yet in echelon form. We have, however, taken care of the first step. It is now necessary to eliminate the x_2 terms from the third and fourth equations. This will be easier if we first multiply the second equation by $(-\frac{1}{3})$, obtaining a new equation

$$x_2 + x_3 - x_4 = 1.$$

If the third equation of (1.8) is replaced by its sum with (-1) times this *new* second equation, and if equation four is replaced by its sum with (-8) times this *new* second equation, we have the following system that is equivalent to (1.8) and therefore to (1.7):

$$
\begin{aligned}
x_1 - 3x_2 + x_3 - x_4 &= 1, \\
x_2 + x_3 - x_4 &= 1, \\
-5x_3 + 6x_4 &= 3, \\
-9x_3 + 10x_4 &= -13.
\end{aligned}
\tag{1.9}
$$

If we continue by replacing the fourth equation of (1.9) by its sum with $(-9/5)$ of the third equation, we obtain a system in echelon form:

$$
\begin{aligned}
x_1 - 3x_2 + x_3 - x_4 &= 1, \\
x_2 + x_3 - x_4 &= 1, \\
-5x_3 + 6x_4 &= 3, \\
-\tfrac{4}{5}x_4 &= -\tfrac{92}{5}.
\end{aligned}
\tag{1.10}
$$

From the fourth equation of (1.10) it is apparent that $x_4 = 23$; therefore the solution to (1.10) and, consequently, to (1.7) can be found by successive substitutions in the equations of (1.10), similar to the ones in Example 2. This process is often called **back substitution**. This can be done in a systematic way by continuing the reduction process:

a)
$$
\begin{cases}
x_1 - 3x_2 + x_3 = 24, \\
x_2 + x_3 = 24, \\
-5x_3 = -135, \\
x_4 = 23;
\end{cases}
$$
b)
$$
\begin{cases}
x_1 - 3x_2 + x_3 = 24, \\
x_2 + x_3 = 24, \\
x_3 = 27, \\
x_4 = 23;
\end{cases}
$$

c)
$$
\begin{cases}
x_1 - 3x_2 = -3, \\
x_2 = -3, \\
x_3 = 27, \\
x_4 = 23;
\end{cases}
$$
d)
$$
\begin{cases}
x_1 = -12, \\
x_2 = -3, \\
x_3 = 27, \\
x_4 = 23.
\end{cases}
$$

From Theorem 1.1, you should be able to supply the reasons why these systems of equations are equivalent to the one in the preceding step and therefore to (1.10). Either way, the quadruple (4-tuple) $(-12, -3, 27, 23)$ is the solution to (1.7). The last step, (d), resembles the system (1.5) of Example 2.

Example 4   Use Gaussian elimination to find the solution (if it exists) to the system

$$
\begin{cases}
x_1 + x_2 + x_3 = 3, \\
x_1 - x_2 - x_3 = -1, \\
3x_1 + x_2 + x_3 = 7.
\end{cases}
\tag{1.11}
$$

To find the solution (if it exists), we replace (1.11) by a system in echelon form. This is accomplished in the following steps (you should supply the reasons from

Theorem 1.1 why each system is equivalent to the system (1.11)):

a) $\begin{cases} x_1 + x_2 + x_3 = 3, \\ \quad -2x_2 - 2x_3 = -4, \\ \quad -2x_2 - 2x_3 = -2; \end{cases}$ b) $\begin{cases} x_1 + x_2 + x_3 = 3, \\ \quad x_2 + x_3 = 2, \\ \quad x_2 + x_3 = 1; \end{cases}$ c) $\begin{cases} x_1 + x_2 + x_3 = 3, \\ \quad x_2 + x_3 = 2, \\ \quad 0 = -1. \end{cases}$

The last equation in step (c) is, of course, nonsense. Nevertheless, this system is equivalent to (1.11). Therefore, (1.11) has no solutions since no values of the variables can produce $0 = -1$. Such a system is called **inconsistent**. Systems of this type and other special systems will be discussed further in Section 1.3.

Often nonlinear systems may be treated as linear systems and solved by the methods described above. Usually this is done by making a substitution that changes the variables and makes the system appear to be linear.

Example 5 Solve the following system of equations:

$$\begin{cases} \dfrac{1}{x} + \dfrac{1}{y} - \dfrac{1}{z} = 0, \\[2mm] \dfrac{2}{x} - \dfrac{2}{y} + \dfrac{1}{z} = 3, \\[2mm] \dfrac{3}{x} - \dfrac{4}{y} + \dfrac{2}{z} = 4. \end{cases} \tag{1.12}$$

To solve this system, first substitute $u = 1/x$, $v = 1/y$, $w = 1/z$. The resulting system is linear:

$$\begin{cases} u + v - w = 0, \\ 2u - 2v + w = 3, \\ 3u - 4v + 2w = 4. \end{cases}$$

This linear system is reduced by the following sequence of steps first to echelon form and then further (you can supply the reasons from Theorem 1.1):

a) $\begin{aligned} u + v - w &= 0, \\ -4v + 3w &= 3, \\ -7v + 5w &= 4; \end{aligned}$ b) $\begin{aligned} u + v - w &= 0, \\ v - \tfrac{3}{4}w &= -\tfrac{3}{4}, \\ -\tfrac{1}{4}w &= -\tfrac{5}{4}; \end{aligned}$ c) $\begin{aligned} u + v - w &= 0, \\ v - \tfrac{3}{4}w &= -\tfrac{3}{4}, \\ w &= 5; \end{aligned}$

d) $\begin{aligned} u + v &= 5, \\ v &= 3, \\ w &= 5; \end{aligned}$ e) $\begin{aligned} u &= 2, \\ v &= 3, \\ w &= 5. \end{aligned}$

From step (e) we conclude that $1/x = 2$, $1/y = 3$, and $1/z = 5$. Therefore $x = \tfrac{1}{2}$, $y = \tfrac{1}{3}$, $z = \tfrac{1}{5}$, and thus the triple $(\tfrac{1}{2}, \tfrac{1}{3}, \tfrac{1}{5})$ is a solution to (1.12).

Example 6 Let us look now at a fairly simple allocation problem; it is stated initially in verbal form but can be modeled by a system of linear equations. The solution to the problem is then obtained from the solution to the linear system.

A certain bakery makes three kinds of specialty pies: Adam's Apple costs $2.50 for the ingredients and requires 20 minutes of the baker's time to prepare it; Boston Brown costs $3.50 for ingredients and requires 15 minutes of the baker's time to prepare, and Coconut Custard costs $2.00 for the ingredients and requires 10 minutes of the baker's time to prepare. Experience has shown that the bakery can sell a total of two dozen of these special pies per day, that the baker can allot six hours of his time to preparing them, and that $64.00 per day can be spent on ingredients for these specialty pies. How many of each pie should be prepared?

To solve the problem posed here we set up several equations that model the various pieces of information given. First, select three variables to represent the numbers of each type of pie to be baked each day. Let these variables be a, b, and c (we could just as well use x_1, x_2, x_3 or any other three notations). Since a total of two dozen pies are sold each day, we model this fact with the simple equation

$$a + b + c = 24.$$

Now $64.00 is spent for ingredients each day. This gives rise to the equation

$$2.5a + 3.5b + 2c = 64$$

because each Adam's Apple pie costs $2.50, so a of them will cost $2.5a$ dollars, and so forth for the other two.

Finally, since six hours can be devoted to baking the pies, we have the third equation

$$\tfrac{1}{3}a + \tfrac{1}{4}b + \tfrac{1}{6}c = 6$$

because each Apple pie requires 20 minutes $= \tfrac{1}{3}$ hrs, so a of them will require a total of $\tfrac{1}{3}a$ hours, etc. Thus, the pie problem can be represented by the system of equations

$$
\begin{aligned}
a + \quad b + \quad c &= 24, \\
2.5a + 3.5b + 2c &= 64, \\
\tfrac{1}{3}a + \quad \tfrac{1}{4}b + \tfrac{1}{6}c &= \quad 6.
\end{aligned}
$$

Now let us reduce this system to echelon form. Multiply the second equation by 2 and the third equation by 12 to obtain the following equivalent system with integer coefficients (this, of course, is not a requirement, but it makes hand calculation a little easier):

$$
\begin{aligned}
a + \quad b + \quad c &= \quad 24, \\
5a + 7b + 4c &= 128, \\
4a + 3b + 2c &= \quad 72.
\end{aligned}
$$

Then, by using Gaussian elimination we can solve the system (check this and give the reasons for each step):

a)
$$\begin{aligned} a + b + c &= 24, \\ 2b - c &= 8, \\ -b - 2c &= -24; \end{aligned}$$

b)
$$\begin{aligned} a + b + c &= 24, \\ b + 2c &= 24, \\ 2b - c &= 8; \end{aligned}$$

c)
$$\begin{aligned} a + b + c &= 24, \\ b + 2c &= 24, \\ -5c &= -40; \end{aligned}$$

d)
$$\begin{aligned} a + b + c &= 24, \\ b + 2c &= 24, \\ c &= 8. \end{aligned}$$

Step (d) is in echelon form. We can finish the solution by back substitution of the value $c = 8$ into the second equation to find b, and then the values of b and c into the first equation to find a. As an alternative, we may continue our use of Theorem 1.1, backwards now, to obtain the next two equivalent systems:

e)
$$\begin{aligned} a + b &= 16, \\ b &= 8, \\ c &= 8; \end{aligned}$$

f)
$$\begin{aligned} a &= 8, \\ b &= 8, \\ c &= 8. \end{aligned}$$

From the simple system in step (f) we read the solutions to our original system, namely, $a = b = c = 8$. From the solution to the model we conclude that, given the conditions as stated, the bakery should bake eight of each type of pie.

We have presented the solution to this simple problem in some detail to show you how the process can be used for many applications of linear algebra. These techniques illustrate several general principles for solving "word problems." Such principles are included in the following suggestions:

1. Read (or listen to) the description of the problem very carefully.

2. Determine those parts of the problem that can be quantified or represented by simple variables.

3. Let the variables represent the quantities asked for in the problem, where this is practical.

4. Formulate equations by representing the same quantity symbolically in two different ways.

5. If possible, sketch the situation described by the problem and label all the known quantities on the sketch.

6. Often the problem will require information that is not given explicitly but should be part of the general knowledge of any literate individual; e.g., 60 minutes $= 1$ hr, $A = \pi r^2$, etc. Use these facts in formulating the equations.

7. Solve the resulting equations.

8. Check the resulting solutions against the original problem to see if the answers make sense. For example, why could the solution $b = 10, c = 18, a = -4$ never

be a solution to the pie-baking problem, even if it were a solution to the system of equations modeling the problem?

These general principles will be illustrated in several examples throughout this text and will also be required to solve some of the exercises. For a discussion of the general problem of mathematical modeling you should consult the books by Lancaster, Roberts, Malkevitch and Meyer, or Rubinstein listed in the References at the end of the book. Also, your instructor will surely have some good suggestions for you.

EXERCISES (1.1)　————————————————————

In Exercises 1–6, interpret the system of equations geometrically and determine if a solution exists. Then approximate the solution from the graph.

1. $x - y = 3$
   $2x + y = 6$

2. $x + y = 2$
   $10x + y = 11$

3. $x - 3y = 7$
   $2x + 6y = 8$

4. $2x + y = 6$
   $4x + 2y = 6$

5. $2x + y = 0$
   $x + 3y = 0$

6. $x^2 + y^2 = 4$
   $y = 2$

In Exercises 7–12 solve the systems of equations by substitution.

7. $x + y = 4$
   $2x - y = 11$

8. $2x - y = 8$
   $3x + 2y = 20$

9. $3x + 5y = 6$
   $2x + 4y = 8$

10. $\frac{x}{2} - y = 6$
    $x + \frac{y}{2} = 8$

11. $x^2 + y^2 = 4$
    $x - 2y = 1$

12. $xy = 1$
    $x + y = 5$

In Exercises 13–26 solve the systems of equations by Gaussian elimination.

13. $x - y = 5$
    $x + 2y = 2$

14. $x + 2y = 6$
    $2x - y = 8$

15. $2x - y = 4$
    $3x + 5y = -7$

16. $x + y + z = 3$
    $x + 2y - z = 2$
    $x - 2y + z = 0$

17. $x + y - z = 2$
    $x - y + z = 1$
    $2x - y + 3z = 3$

18. $x - 2y + 2z = 2$
    $x + 2y - 2z = 2$
    $3x - y + 5z = 2$

19. $x + y - z = 3$
    $x - y + z = -1$
    $2x - 3y - 4z = 3$

20. $x + 2y + z = 2$
    $-x + 4y + z = 4$
    $3x + 5y - 3z = 0$

21. $x - y + z = 0$
    $x - 2y + z = 1$
    $3x + 2y - 4z = 0$

22. $5x - 6y - 2z = -5$
    $3x - 2y + z = 2$
    $4x + y + 2z = 1$

23. $x_1 + x_2 + x_3 - x_4 = -2$
    $2x_1 - x_2 + x_3 + x_4 = 0$
    $3x_1 + 2x_2 - x_3 - x_4 = 1$
    $-x_1 - 4x_2 - 3x_3 + 3x_4 = 5$

24. $2x_1 - x_2 + x_3 - x_4 = 3$
    $3x_1 - 2x_2 + 4x_3 - x_4 = 4$
    $5x_1 + 2x_2 - 3x_3 - 4x_4 = 0$
    $-x_1 - x_2 + 3x_3 + 4x_4 = 2$

25.
$$x + y + z - w = 2$$
$$x - y - z - w = 2$$
$$x + 2y + 2z - 2w = 3$$
$$2x - y - z - 3w = 5$$

26.
$$2x_1 - x_2 - x_3 + x_4 = 1$$
$$3x_1 - 2x_2 + x_3 + x_4 = -5$$
$$-2x_1 + 3x_2 + 2x_3 - x_4 = -1$$
$$3x_1 + x_2 + x_3 + x_4 = -2$$

27. If $10,000 is invested, part at 5% and part at 6%, and if the yearly interest on the 5% investment is $60 more than that on the 6% investment, how much is invested at each rate?

28. The Wednesday-evening performance at the local theater is sold out. The price of adult tickets is $2.00. Student tickets are $1.50 each. If the gross receipts were $600 and the theater has 400 seats, how many of each type of ticket was sold?

29. A firm has an alloy of copper and tin that contains 10% tin. It has a second alloy of these metals containing 25% tin. How much of each alloy should be combined to produce two tons of a copper-tin alloy consisting of 20% tin?

30. A father told his son: "Right now, I am three times as old as you are, but in fifteen years I'll only be twice as old as you will be." Find the present age of each.

31. A milling company has two feeds. The first feed contains 5% protein and 15% carbohydrates. The second feed contains 15% protein and 25% carbohydrates. How many pounds of each should be used to make 100 pounds of a mixture containing 10% protein? What will be the carbohydrate content of this mixture?

32. One food contains 8 units per oz. of vitamin B_1 and 12 units per oz. of vitamin C. A second food contains 12 and 18 units per oz. of vitamins B_1 and C, respectively. How many ounces of each are required for a meal that will contain 100 units of vitamin B_1 and 150 units of vitamin C?

33. A man purchases a watch, a necklace, and a ring for a total expenditure of $225.00. The watch sold for $50.00 more than the necklace. The ring sold for $25.00 more than the watch and the necklace together. What was the individual price of each item?

Make a substitution that will transform the nonlinear systems in Exercises 34–39 into linear systems and then solve them.

34.
$$\frac{1}{x} + \frac{1}{y} + \frac{3}{z} = 0$$
$$\frac{2}{x} - \frac{2}{y} - \frac{2}{z} = -4$$
$$\frac{3}{x} + \frac{1}{y} + \frac{1}{z} = 4$$

35.
$$\sqrt{x} - \sqrt{y} + \sqrt{z} = 3$$
$$2\sqrt{x} + \sqrt{y} - \sqrt{z} = 3$$
$$\sqrt{x} - \sqrt{y} + 2\sqrt{z} = 7$$

36.
$$x^3 - 3y^3 - z^3 = -4$$
$$2x^3 + y^3 + z^3 = 9$$
$$5x^3 - 3y^3 - z^3 = 0$$

37.
$$3\sqrt{x^2 - 1} - 2y = \sqrt{3}$$
$$5\sqrt{x^2 - 1} - 4y = \sqrt{3}$$

38.
$$\frac{2}{x-y} + \frac{1}{x+y} = \frac{2}{3}$$
$$\frac{5}{x-y} + \frac{6}{x+y} = \frac{1}{4}$$

39.
$$\frac{1}{3x-y} + \frac{2}{x+3y} = 2$$
$$\frac{10}{3x-y} - \frac{9}{x+3y} = 7$$

40. Show that the system

$$a_1 x + a_2 y = 0$$
$$b_1 x + b_2 y = 0$$

always has at least one solution and that, if $a_1 b_2 - a_2 b_1 \neq 0$, there is exactly one solution.

41. What can you say if $a_1 b_2 - a_2 b_1 = 0$ in Problem 40?

For Exercises 42 and 43, suppose that the n-tuple of real numbers $(r_1, r_2, \ldots, r_n)$ is a solution to the system of equations

$$a_{11} x_1 + a_{12} x_2 + \ldots + a_{1n} x_n = b_1,$$
$$a_{21} x_1 + a_{22} x_2 + \ldots + a_{2n} x_n = b_2,$$
$$\vdots \qquad \vdots \qquad\qquad \vdots \qquad \vdots$$
$$a_{m1} x_1 + a_{m2} x_2 + \ldots + a_{mn} x_n = b_m,$$

and the n-tuple $(s_1, s_2, \ldots, s_n)$ is a solution to the system

$$a_{11} x_1 + a_{12} x_2 + \ldots + a_{1n} x_n = c_1,$$
$$a_{21} x_1 + a_{22} x_2 + \ldots + a_{2n} x_n = c_2,$$
$$\vdots \qquad \vdots \qquad\qquad \vdots \qquad \vdots$$
$$a_{m1} x_1 + a_{m2} x_2 + \ldots + a_{mn} x_n = c_m.$$

42. Show that for each real number k, the n-tuple $(kr_1, kr_2, \ldots, kr_n)$ is a solution to the system

$$a_{11} x_1 + a_{12} x_2 + \ldots + a_{1n} x_n = kb_1,$$
$$a_{21} x_1 + a_{22} x_2 + \ldots + a_{2n} x_n = kb_2,$$
$$\vdots \qquad \vdots \qquad\qquad \vdots \qquad \vdots$$
$$a_{m1} x_1 + a_{m2} x_2 + \ldots + a_{mn} x_n = kb_m.$$

43. Show that the following system has a solution and find it:

$$a_{11} x_1 + a_{12} x_2 + \ldots + a_{1n} x_n = b_1 + c_1,$$
$$\vdots \qquad \vdots \qquad\qquad \vdots \qquad \vdots$$
$$a_{m1} x_1 + a_{m2} x_2 + \ldots + a_{mn} x_n = b_m + c_m.$$

44. Determine a and b so that the point $(1, 2)$ lies on the graphs of both $ax + by = 3$ and $ax^2 + by^2 = 5$. Sketch both graphs. Are there any other points of intersection? If so, find them.

1.2 MATRIX METHODS

The method for solving a system of equations by finding an equivalent system in echelon form, as outlined in the preceding section, has a simplification that greatly expands its usefulness. You have probably already observed that it is the coefficients in each equation that are actually involved in the computations, rather than the variables $x_1, x_2, \ldots$, etc. themselves. We shall develop here a routine method for working with these coefficients.

Example 1 Suppose that we wish to reduce the following system to echelon form:

$$\left\{\begin{array}{l} 3x_1 - x_2 + x_3 = 4, \\ x_1 + x_2 - x_3 = 4, \\ x_1 - 2x_2 + 3x_3 = -5. \end{array}\right. \tag{1.13}$$

The left side of this system can be abbreviated by the following array of its coefficients:

$$\begin{bmatrix} 3 & -1 & 1 \\ 1 & 1 & -1 \\ 1 & -2 & 3 \end{bmatrix}. \tag{1.14}$$

Any rectangular array of numbers is called a **matrix**. The array in (1.14) is called the **coefficient matrix** of the system (1.13). The members of the left-hand side of the equations in the system (1.13) correspond to **rows** of the matrix (1.14), while the coefficients of the same variable x_i in (1.13) all lie in the same **column** of (1.14). This particular matrix is **square**; it has three rows and three columns, and is called a three-by-three (3×3) matrix. The numbers in the matrix are referred to as **entries**.

The constant terms on the right-hand side of (1.13) can also be written in matrix form as the 3×1 matrix

$$\begin{bmatrix} 4 \\ 4 \\ -5 \end{bmatrix}. \tag{1.15}$$

When the coefficient matrix of a system is combined with the column matrix of the constant terms of the system, the resulting matrix is called the **augmented matrix** of the system. Thus, the 3×4 matrix

$$\begin{bmatrix} 3 & -1 & 1 & 4 \\ 1 & 1 & -1 & 4 \\ 1 & -2 & 3 & -5 \end{bmatrix}. \tag{1.16}$$

is the augmented matrix of the system (1.13).

Example 2 Write the augmented matrix for the system

$$\begin{array}{l} 2x_1 + 3x_3 = x_4 + 4, \\ 2x_2 + x_4 = 6 - 2x_3, \\ 3x_1 - x_4 = 5x_2 + 1, \\ 3x_2 + x_3 = 5x_1 - 2. \end{array}$$

To do this, first find an equivalent system in which each variable is in its own column on the left side of each equation and the constant terms are on the right side of each equation. This gives the following system:

$$
\begin{aligned}
2x_1 + 3x_3 - x_4 &= 4, \\
2x_2 + 2x_3 + x_4 &= 6, \\
3x_1 - 5x_2 - x_4 &= 1, \\
-5x_1 + 3x_2 + x_3 &= -2.
\end{aligned}
$$

Thus the augmented matrix for this system is

$$
\begin{bmatrix}
2 & 0 & 3 & -1 & 4 \\
0 & 2 & 2 & 1 & 6 \\
3 & -5 & 0 & -1 & 1 \\
-5 & 3 & 1 & 0 & -2
\end{bmatrix}.
$$

Note that, in the augmented matrix we always put 0 wherever a term is missing in an equation.

By arranging the equations of any given system of equations in such a way that in each column the coefficients of the same variable appear, the augmented matrix of the system can easily be written. This arrangement may necessitate substituting an equivalent system for the original system. Once the decision has been made as to which variable belongs in which column, there is a unique matrix for that system, as was illustrated in the example above.

Now, to find a system of equations in echelon form that is equivalent to a given system, one need only work with the augmented matrix. The operations on equations given in Theorem 1.1 of the preceding section translate into elementary operations on the rows of the augmented matrix. The following theorem is this translation and it will be used to reduce the augmented matrix of a given system.

Theorem 1.2

Each of the following elementary row operations on a given matrix (the augmented matrix of a system of equations) produces the augmented matrix of an equivalent system of equations:

   i) *interchange any two rows of the matrix;*

   ii) *multiply all the elements in a given row by the same nonzero number;*

   iii) *replace any row in the matrix by its sum with a constant multiple of any other row.*

By virtue of this theorem any two matrices A and B from whatever source obtained are called **row-equivalent** if one can be derived from the other by any finite sequence of elementary row operations listed in Theorem 1.2.

By judicious application of the elementary row operations of Theorem 1.2 to the matrix (1.16) of Example 1, a row-equivalent matrix in echelon form can be obtained. To do this, proceed as follows. First interchange rows one and two to obtain the matrix

$$\begin{bmatrix} 1 & 1 & -1 & 4 \\ 3 & -1 & 1 & 4 \\ 1 & -2 & 3 & -5 \end{bmatrix}. \qquad (1.17)$$

Then replace row two of (1.17) by its sum with (-3) times row one. Also replace row three by its sum with (-1) times row one. This gives the matrix

$$\begin{bmatrix} 1 & 1 & -1 & 4 \\ 0 & -4 & 4 & -8 \\ 0 & -3 & 4 & -9 \end{bmatrix}. \qquad (1.18)$$

Next, multiply row two of (1.18) by $(-\frac{1}{4})$ to obtain the matrix

$$\begin{bmatrix} 1 & 1 & -1 & 4 \\ 0 & 1 & -1 & 2 \\ 0 & -3 & 4 & -9 \end{bmatrix}. \qquad (1.19)$$

Then, replace row three of (1.19) by its sum with (3) times row two, to obtain

$$\begin{bmatrix} 1 & 1 & -1 & 4 \\ 0 & 1 & -1 & 2 \\ 0 & 0 & 1 & -3 \end{bmatrix}. \qquad (1.20)$$

This matrix is the augmented matrix of the following system of equations. This system is in echelon form and could easily be solved by successive substitutions:

$$\begin{aligned} x_1 + x_2 - x_3 &= 4, \\ x_2 - x_3 &= 2, \\ x_3 &= -3. \end{aligned}$$

On the other hand, should we choose to perform some additional elementary operations on the matrix (1.20), the following equivalent matrices result:

adding the third row to each of rows one and two:

$$\begin{bmatrix} 1 & 1 & 0 & 1 \\ 0 & 1 & 0 & -1 \\ 0 & 0 & 1 & -3 \end{bmatrix};$$

adding (-1) times the second row to the first row:

$$\begin{bmatrix} 1 & 0 & 0 & 2 \\ 0 & 1 & 0 & -1 \\ 0 & 0 & 1 & -3 \end{bmatrix}. \qquad (1.21)$$

The matrix in (1.21) is called the **reduced row-echelon form** (Hermite normal form) of the original matrix (1.16). It is the augmented matrix of the *very* simple system of equations

$$\begin{aligned} x_1 &= 2, \\ x_2 &= -1, \\ x_3 &= -3. \end{aligned}$$

This system is equivalent to (1.13); hence, the solution to (1.13) is the triple of numbers $(2, -1, -3)$.

The process of finding a matrix in reduced row-echelon form that is equivalent to a given matrix is called a **Gauss–Jordan reduction**.

To find the solution to the system of equations in Example 2, one can proceed in the same way. Begin with its augmented matrix

$$\begin{bmatrix} 2 & 0 & 3 & -1 & 4 \\ 0 & 2 & 2 & 1 & 6 \\ 3 & -5 & 0 & -1 & 1 \\ -5 & 3 & 1 & 0 & -2 \end{bmatrix}.$$

Since no number (element) in the first column of this matrix is 1, rather than dividing the first row by (2) to make it

$$\begin{bmatrix} 1 & 0 & \tfrac{3}{2} & -\tfrac{1}{2} & 2 \end{bmatrix},$$

which does have a 1 in the first position, it is a good tactic for hand calculation to replace row three by its sum with (-1) times row one. This gives the following matrix in which there are no fractions:

$$\begin{bmatrix} 2 & 0 & 3 & -1 & 4 \\ 0 & 2 & 2 & 1 & 6 \\ 1 & -5 & -3 & 0 & -3 \\ -5 & 3 & 1 & 0 & -2 \end{bmatrix}.$$

Now you should be able to supply the justification from Theorem 1.2 for the following sequence of steps. Each of these steps in the Gauss–Jordan reduction produces a matrix row-equivalent to the others:

a)
$$\begin{bmatrix} 1 & -5 & -3 & 0 & -3 \\ 0 & 2 & 2 & 1 & 6 \\ 2 & 0 & 3 & -1 & 4 \\ -5 & 3 & 1 & 0 & -2 \end{bmatrix},$$

b)
$$\begin{bmatrix} 1 & -5 & -3 & 0 & -3 \\ 0 & 2 & 2 & 1 & 6 \\ 0 & 10 & 9 & -1 & 10 \\ 0 & -22 & -14 & 0 & -17 \end{bmatrix},$$

c)
$$\begin{bmatrix} 1 & -5 & -3 & 0 & -3 \\ 0 & 2 & 2 & 1 & 6 \\ 0 & 10 & 9 & -1 & 10 \\ 0 & -2 & 4 & -2 & 3 \end{bmatrix},$$

d)
$$\begin{bmatrix} 1 & -5 & -3 & 0 & -3 \\ 0 & 2 & 2 & 1 & 6 \\ 0 & 0 & -1 & -6 & -20 \\ 0 & 0 & 6 & -1 & 9 \end{bmatrix},$$

e) $\begin{bmatrix} 1 & -5 & -3 & 0 & -3 \\ 0 & 2 & 2 & 1 & 6 \\ 0 & 0 & 1 & 6 & 20 \\ 0 & 0 & 0 & -37 & -111 \end{bmatrix}$,

f) $\begin{bmatrix} 1 & -5 & -3 & 0 & -3 \\ 0 & 1 & 1 & \frac{1}{2} & 3 \\ 0 & 0 & 1 & 6 & 20 \\ 0 & 0 & 0 & 1 & 3 \end{bmatrix}$.

The matrix in step (e) is in echelon form, as is (f). However, it is useful to proceed as follows, observing that, by Theorem 1.2 (iii), each step produces an equivalent matrix:

g) $\begin{bmatrix} 1 & -5 & -3 & 0 & -3 \\ 0 & 1 & 1 & 0 & \frac{3}{2} \\ 0 & 0 & 1 & 0 & 2 \\ 0 & 0 & 0 & 1 & 3 \end{bmatrix}$,

h) $\begin{bmatrix} 1 & -5 & 0 & 0 & 3 \\ 0 & 1 & 0 & 0 & -\frac{1}{2} \\ 0 & 0 & 1 & 0 & 2 \\ 0 & 0 & 0 & 1 & 3 \end{bmatrix}$,

i) $\begin{bmatrix} 1 & 0 & 0 & 0 & \frac{1}{2} \\ 0 & 1 & 0 & 0 & -\frac{1}{2} \\ 0 & 0 & 1 & 0 & 2 \\ 0 & 0 & 0 & 1 & 3 \end{bmatrix}$.

The last matrix tells us that

$$
\begin{aligned}
x_1 &= \tfrac{1}{2}, \\
x_2 &= -\tfrac{1}{2}, \\
x_3 &= 2, \\
x_4 &= 3.
\end{aligned}
$$

Therefore, the 4-tuple $(\tfrac{1}{2}, -\tfrac{1}{2}, 2, 3)$ is the solution to the system. The Gauss–Jordan reduction performed in the preceding example illustrates the method one would most likely use for hand calculation, since it avoids fractions as much as possible. It is not necessary to be so delicate when computer help is available.

A simplified flowchart detailing the Gauss–Jordan process is given in Chart 1 of the Appendix.

Example 3   Reduce the augmented matrix for the following system of equations to its reduced row-echelon form. Find the solutions to the system (if any).

$$
\begin{aligned}
x + y + z &= 2, \\
2x - y - z &= 1, \\
x - y - z &= 0, \\
3x + 4y + 2z &= 3.
\end{aligned}
$$

The augmented matrix for this system is

$$
\begin{bmatrix} 1 & 1 & 1 & 2 \\ 2 & -1 & -1 & 1 \\ 1 & -1 & -1 & 0 \\ 3 & 4 & 2 & 3 \end{bmatrix}.
$$

By using the Gauss–Jordan reduction techniques we find that this matrix has reduced row-echelon form:

$$\begin{bmatrix} 1 & 0 & 0 & 1 \\ 0 & 1 & 0 & -1 \\ 0 & 0 & 1 & 2 \\ 0 & 0 & 0 & 0 \end{bmatrix}.$$

Note that the final row of zeros resulted from the fact that there were more equations than unknowns in the original system. The four equations could have put too many constraints on the three variables. Such was not the case here, however. One of the equations was ultimately not essential to the solution, as this final row of zeros indicates. We have, therefore, the equivalent system represented by the matrix above:

$$x = 1,$$
$$y = -1,$$
$$z = 2.$$

Other configurations, including those with fewer equations than unknowns, will be considered in the next sections.

Example 4 Application of Kirchhoff's Laws. The techniques developed so far can be applied to describe certain problems in direct-current electrical circuits.

When systems of resistors, batteries, etc., are connected, we have examples of electrical networks. One such network, containing two "meshes", is illustrated in Fig. 1.2. To determine the current flowing in the various elements of such meshes, one makes use of one or both general principles formulated by the German physicist G. R. Kirchhoff (1824–1887).

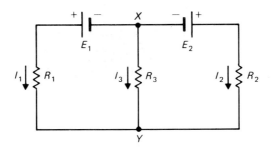

Figure 1.2

The formal statements of Kirchhoff's laws are as follows:

1. the algebraic sum of the currents that meet at any junction of a network is zero;

2. in going around any closed path of a network, from any point of the network back to the same point, the algebraic sum of all the changes in potential (voltage) encountered on the way is zero.

In effect, the first law states that no electrical charge will accumulate at any point of a network. The second law is a statement that every point of the network has, at any given instant, a unique electrical potential (voltage).

If the current in any part of the network is I, the potential (voltage) is E, and the resistance is R, we assume that Ohm's law

$$E = IR$$

is valid. We also assume that the voltage drop caused by the current passing through several resistors connected in series is the sum of the individual voltage drops in each resistor. In analyzing the network of Fig. 1.2, the first of Kirchhoff's laws, applied to either junction X or Y, gives the equation

$$I_1 + I_2 + I_3 = 0.$$

By going around the left-hand mesh counterclockwise and adding all of the voltage drops algebraically, according to the second law we arrive at the equation

$$E_1 - R_1 I_1 + R_3 I_3 = 0.$$

Going around the right-hand mesh in a clockwise direction we obtain the equation

$$E_2 - R_2 I_2 + R_3 I_3 = 0.$$

In each case we have assumed that current flows from $+$ to $-$. From these equations we obtain a system of three equations in the three unknowns I_1, I_2, and I_3.

Suppose then that in the electrical network of Fig. 1.2 the following is true: $R_1 = 3\Omega$, $R_2 = 5\Omega$, and $R_3 = 2\Omega$ (ohms), while $E_1 = 3$ V and $E_2 = 6$ V (volts). Find I_1, I_2, and I_3. In this case the three equations deduced from Kirchhoff's laws are

$$
\begin{aligned}
I_1 + I_2 + I_3 &= 0, \\
3I_1 \qquad\quad - 2I_3 &= 3, \\
5I_2 - 2I_3 &= 6.
\end{aligned}
$$

The augmented matrix for this system of equations is

$$
\begin{bmatrix}
1 & 1 & 1 & 0 \\
3 & 0 & -2 & 3 \\
0 & 5 & -2 & 6
\end{bmatrix}.
$$

Its reduced row-echelon form is found to be (verify this)

$$
\begin{bmatrix}
1 & 0 & 0 & \frac{9}{31} \\
0 & 1 & 0 & \frac{24}{31} \\
0 & 0 & 1 & -\frac{33}{31}
\end{bmatrix}.
$$

Thus, the currents are $I_1 = 9/31$ A, $I_2 = 24/31$ A, and $I_3 = -33/31$ A (amperes). The minus sign indicates that I_3 flows in the direction opposite to that indicated by the arrow in Fig. 1.2.

EXERCISES (1.2)

1. The following matrices are all row-equivalent. Give the justification for this statement using Theorem 1.2.

$$A = \begin{bmatrix} 1 & -2 & -1 & -1 \\ 1 & 1 & -1 & 1 \\ 2 & 1 & 2 & -1 \end{bmatrix} \qquad B = \begin{bmatrix} 1 & 1 & -1 & 1 \\ 1 & -2 & -1 & -1 \\ 2 & 1 & 2 & -1 \end{bmatrix}$$

$$C = \begin{bmatrix} 1 & 1 & -1 & 1 \\ 0 & -3 & 0 & -2 \\ 2 & 1 & 2 & -1 \end{bmatrix} \qquad D = \begin{bmatrix} 1 & 1 & -1 & 1 \\ 0 & 3 & 0 & 2 \\ 0 & -1 & 4 & -3 \end{bmatrix}$$

$$E = \begin{bmatrix} 1 & 1 & -1 & 1 \\ 0 & 1 & -4 & 3 \\ 0 & 0 & 12 & -7 \end{bmatrix} \qquad F = \begin{bmatrix} 1 & 1 & -1 & 1 \\ 0 & 1 & 0 & \frac{2}{3} \\ 0 & 0 & 1 & -\frac{7}{12} \end{bmatrix}$$

In Exercises 2–17, use the matrix method to solve the systems of equations.

2. $x - y = 4$
   $x + y = 6$

3. $x - 5y = 6$
   $2x - 3y = 5$

4. $x - y - z = -1$
   $2x + 2y - z = 0$
   $x + y + z = 3$

5. $u - 2v - w = 0$
   $2u + v + 2w = 7$
   $3u + 4v - w = 4$

6. $x_1 + x_2 - x_3 = 1$
   $x_1 - 2x_2 + x_3 = 2$
   $2x_1 + 3x_2 - 3x_3 = 1$

7. $x_1 - 3x_2 - 2x_3 = 1$
   $x_1 + x_2 + x_3 = 3$
   $2x_1 + x_2 + 2x_3 = 1$

8. $5x - 6y = 4$
   $7x + y = 13$
   $2x + 7y = 9$

9. $7x_1 + 3x_2 - 5x_3 = 4$
   $3x_1 + 5x_2 + 7x_3 = -2$
   $4x_1 - x_2 - 6x_3 = 5$

10. $2x_1 + 3x_2 + 4x_3 = 3$
    $3x_1 + 6x_2 - 2x_3 = 1$
    $5x_1 - 9x_2 + 6x_3 = 1$

11. $2r - 2s + 3t = -3$
    $3r + 2s + 3t = 2$
    $7r - 5s + 2t = 0$

12. $3a + 9b - 6c = 1$
    $2a + 3b + 12c = 3$
    $2a - 3b + 3c = 1$

13. $5u + 5v - w = -\frac{3}{2}$
    $7u + v - 2w = 3$
    $3u + 2v + 3w = \frac{11}{2}$
    $u + 6v + 4w = 1$

14. $x_1 - x_2 + x_3 - x_4 = 0$
    $x_1 + x_2 + x_3 + x_4 = 0$
    $x_1 - x_2 - x_3 - x_4 = 2$
    $x_1 + x_2 + x_3 - x_4 = 2$

15. $x_1 + 2x_2 + 2x_3 + x_4 = 1$
    $3x_1 - 6x_2 + 5x_3 + 2x_4 = 2$
    $2x_1 + 3x_2 - x_3 - x_4 = 1$
    $5x_1 - 5x_2 + 3x_3 - 2x_4 = -2$

16.
$$2u - v + w + 2s + 3t = -4$$
$$3u + 2v + 2w + 2s + 4t = 0$$
$$3u + 3v - 3w + 2s - 4t = 1$$
$$5u - v - w + 3s - 7t = 2$$
$$7u + v + 3w + 5s - 5t = -2$$

17.
$$x_1 + x_2 + x_3 + x_4 + x_5 + x_6 = 0$$
$$x_1 - x_2 - x_3 - x_4 - x_5 - x_6 = 2$$
$$x_1 - x_2 + x_3 - x_4 + x_5 + x_6 = 4$$
$$2x_1 + 2x_2 - 3x_3 + 4x_4 + x_5 - 2x_6 = -4$$
$$3x_1 - 2x_2 + x_3 + x_4 - x_5 + 3x_6 = 1$$
$$5x_1 + 5x_2 - 3x_3 - 3x_4 + 4x_5 + 3x_6 = 1$$

18. The equation of a parabola has the form $y = ax^2 + bx + c$. Determine the parabola passing through the points $(0, 1)$, $(1, 2)$, and $(-1, 6)$.

19–26. Use matrices to do Exercises 19–26 of Section 1.1 (pp. 11, 12).

27. Does the point $(2, 4)$ lie on the parabola given in Exercise 18? If it does not, determine the equation of the third-degree polynomial function $y = kx^3 + ax^2 + bx + c$ that passes through this point and through the three points given in Exercise 18.

In Exercises 28–31, find a matrix in reduced row-echelon form that is equivalent to the given matrix, where x is a variable.

28.
$$\begin{bmatrix} 1 & 2 & 3 & 4 & 5 \\ 2 & 3 & 4 & 5 & 1 \\ 3 & 4 & 5 & 1 & 2 \\ 4 & 5 & 1 & 2 & 3 \\ 5 & 1 & 2 & 3 & 4 \end{bmatrix}$$

29.
$$\begin{bmatrix} 1 & 2 & 3 & 4 & 5 \\ 2 & 3 & 4 & 5 & 6 \\ 3 & 4 & 5 & 6 & 7 \\ 4 & 5 & 6 & 7 & 8 \\ 5 & 6 & 7 & 8 & 9 \end{bmatrix}$$

30.
$$\begin{bmatrix} 1 & x & -1 \\ x & 1 & -1 \\ -1 & 1 & x \end{bmatrix}$$

31.
$$\begin{bmatrix} x-1 & 1 & 2 & 3 \\ 1 & x-1 & 1 & 0 \\ 3 & 2 & x-2 & 1 \\ 1 & 0 & 1 & x-2 \end{bmatrix}$$

32. In a recent election the three candidates for an office received 20%, 27%, and 53% of the vote, respectively. The winning candidate had a majority of 732 votes over the total of his opponents. How many votes did each get? (Use the matrix method to solve the resulting system of equations.)

33. A collection of 50 coins consists of nickels, dimes, and quarters. If there are three times as many nickels as dimes and the total amount is $6.50, how many quarters are there? Use the matrix method.

34. Find the electrical currents (in amperes) for the circuit depicted in Fig. 1.3 (see Example 4).

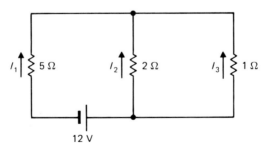

Figure 1.3

35. Three alloys X, Y, Z have the following percentages of lead, zinc, and copper:

Alloy	Lead	Zinc	Copper
X	50	30	20
Y	40	30	30
Z	30	70	

How many grams of each alloy must be combined to obtain an alloy that is 44 % lead, 38 % zinc, and 18 % copper?

36. In 1964, Pike and Erickson found out that, in the Potawatomi language, the subject and object of a transitive verb are revealed by pronomial prefixes. For example, we say "I see you"; however, in Potawatomi this is expressed by a prefix k to the Potawatomi verb for "see." By way of contrast, the prefix n means "He sees me," and the prefix w refers to a fourth party seeing him. Also, analysis of this language shows that the prefixes can indicate (for subject or object) eight different grammatical persons: I, you, he, fourth person, I and you, we, you (plural), they. The prefixes appear to relate subject and object as in the table below. This matrix can be made to look much simpler by appropriate interchange of rows and columns. Try to find suitable interchanges.

TABLE   The Potawatomi Pronomial Prefixes

	1	2	3	4	12	1p	2p	3p
1		k	n	n			k	n
2	k		k	k		k		k
3	n	k		w	k	n	k	
4	n	k	w		k	n	k	w
12		k	k					k
1p		k	n	n			k	n
2p	k		k	k		k		k
3p	n	k		w	k	n	k	

1.3 SYSTEMS WITHOUT UNIQUE SOLUTIONS

Not every system of n linear equations in n variables has a unique solution. That is, there may not always be a single n-tuple of numbers that will simultaneously satisfy all of the equations of the system. We already encountered one such system in Example 4 of Section 1.1. In this section we shall informally discuss three types of systems where a unique solution might not exist and we will see that the matrix methods developed will help us here as well.

Dependent Systems

Some systems of linear equations may have an infinite number of possible solutions. For example, the system

$$\begin{aligned} x + \ y &= 4 \\ 2x + 2y &= 8 \end{aligned} \tag{1.22}$$

has all of the points (x, y) on the single straight line $y = -x + 4$ as its graphical representation. You can see this by sketching the graph of each equation separately and noting that the same straight line results, as in Fig. 1.4.

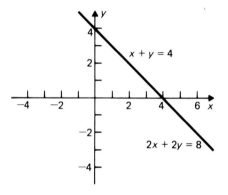

Figure 1.4

It is quite clear that the second equation of this system is merely a multiple of the first equation in the system. It gives us no additional information. Such a system of equations is called **dependent**. We shall defer the definition of dependency to a later chapter. For our present purposes we shall merely look at examples of dependent systems. Consider the following example.

Example 1   Solve the system of equations

$$\begin{cases} x - 2y + \ z = -3, \\ 2x + 3y - 2z = \ \ 5, \\ 3x + \ y - \ z = \ \ 2. \end{cases} \tag{1.23}$$

An examination of this system reveals that the third equation really gives us no new information since it is merely the sum of the first two. This fact also becomes apparent when the augmented matrix of the system is reduced to echelon form.

Indeed, the matrix

$$\begin{bmatrix} 1 & -2 & 1 & -3 \\ 2 & 3 & -2 & 5 \\ 3 & 1 & -1 & 2 \end{bmatrix},$$

can be reduced to (verify this)

$$\begin{bmatrix} 1 & -2 & 1 & -3 \\ 0 & 7 & -4 & 11 \\ 0 & 0 & 0 & 0 \end{bmatrix}.$$

The final row of zeros replaces the third row (equation). This result in the augmented matrix indicates that such a system might have infinitely many solutions. Of course infinitely many solutions are not restricted to dependent systems. The system consisting of the single equation

$$x_1 - x_2 = 5$$

clearly has infinitely many solutions, yet is not dependent.

In our present example, since a linear equation in three variables can be thought of as the equation of a plane in 3–space, each equation from the system (1.23) is the equation of such a plane. These three planes do not intersect in a single point, as they would if a unique solution existed for (1.23). Rather they intersect in a line. Hence there are infinitely many points common to all three planes. The infinite collection of these points can be expressed parametrically by the equations of the line of intersection. To determine the general form of the solution, we note that the reduced echelon form for the augmented matrix of (1.23) is (verify this)

$$\begin{bmatrix} 1 & 0 & -\frac{1}{7} & \frac{1}{7} \\ 0 & 1 & -\frac{4}{7} & \frac{11}{7} \\ 0 & 0 & 0 & 0 \end{bmatrix}.$$

This is the augmented matrix for the system

$$x - \frac{1}{7}z = \frac{1}{7},$$
$$y - \frac{4}{7}z = \frac{11}{7}.$$

Thus, if $z = t$, then

$$x = \frac{1}{7}t + \frac{1}{7},$$
$$y = \frac{4}{7}t + \frac{11}{7},$$

express the infinite collection of solutions. That is, each of the ordered triples

$$\left(\frac{1}{7}t+\frac{1}{7}, \ \frac{4}{7}t+\frac{11}{7}, \ t\right),$$

where t is any real number, is a solution to the system (1.23).

Let us now consider an example similar to Exercise 31 of Section 1.1.

Example 2 A certain feed contains 8% protein and 25% carbohydrate. A second feed contains 13% protein and 30% carbohydrate. How much of each should be used to form 100 lbs of a mixture containing 10% protein and 27% carbohydrate?

From this problem we obtain the following system of three equations in the two variables f and s (the number of pounds of the first and second feed to be used, respectively):

$$f + \quad s = 100 \qquad \text{(weight)},$$

$$0.08f + 0.13s = (0.10) \cdot 100 \ \ \text{(protein content)}, \qquad \qquad \textbf{(1.24)}$$

$$0.25f + 0.30s = (0.27) \cdot 100 \ \ \text{(carbohydrate content)}.$$

Since there are more equations than there are variables in this system, it is quite possible that no solution exists. This is because each of the equations in (1.24) corresponds to a line in the f, s plane. A unique solution to (1.24) would be their common point of intersection (in which case two of them would have been enough). Three arbitrary lines in the plane could also intersect in three different points or not at all (sketch the possible situations).

The augmented matrix for the system (1.24) will be square. We must remember that the last column is the column of constant terms. The matrix is

$$\begin{bmatrix} 1 & 1 & 100 \\ 0.08 & 0.13 & 10 \\ 0.25 & 0.30 & 27 \end{bmatrix}. \qquad \qquad \textbf{(1.25)}$$

It can be shown that the reduced echelon form of this matrix is (you should verify this)

$$\begin{bmatrix} 1 & 0 & 60 \\ 0 & 1 & 40 \\ 0 & 0 & 0 \end{bmatrix}.$$

The final row of zeros indicates that the system (1.24) is dependent, since the third equation gave no new information. In this case we in fact do have a unique solution to this system, as indicated by the matrix: 60 lbs. of the first feed should be mixed with 40 lbs. of the second.

Systems With No Solutions

In the above example we pointed out the possibility that there could have been no solution. A system of linear equations is called **inconsistent** if the equations of the system express contradictory conditions. Such a system cannot possibly have any solutions. For example:

$$x + y = 1,$$
$$x + y = 2,$$

is an obviously inconsistent system. If we sketch the graphs for each of the given equations, as in Fig. 1.5, we see that the two lines are parallel. Hence there is no common point of intersection and therefore *no solution* to the system exists.

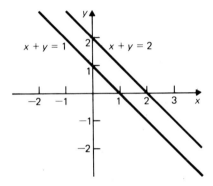

Figure 1.5

The matrix method for solving systems of equations helps to illuminate otherwise obscure inconsistencies. This is illustrated in the next example.

Example 3 Show that the following system is inconsistent:

$$x - 2y + z = 3,$$
$$2x + 3y - 2z = 5, \qquad\qquad (1.26)$$
$$3x + y - z = 6.$$

The augmented matrix for this system is

$$\begin{bmatrix} 1 & -2 & 1 & 3 \\ 2 & 3 & -2 & 5 \\ 3 & 1 & -1 & 6 \end{bmatrix}.$$

This can be reduced to the following echelon form (verify this):

$$\begin{bmatrix} 1 & -2 & 1 & 3 \\ 0 & 7 & -4 & -1 \\ 0 & 0 & 0 & -2 \end{bmatrix}.$$

The last row of this matrix corresponds to the equation

$$0 = -2,$$

which is clearly inconsistent. Therefore, the original system, being equivalent, is also inconsistent.

Some of the geometric interpretations of conceivable situations for various systems of three linear equations in three variables are illustrated by Fig. 1.6. Other configurations, for example, two of the planes coinciding, are also feasible. Of course, it is impossible to draw pictures such as these when the number of variables is larger than three. However, the algebraic concepts and the resulting solutions are analogous.

It is probably fairly clear to you that if the number of equations exceeds the number of variables ($m > n$), the danger of too many constraints is increased, but even when the number of equations is less than the number of variables, the system might still fail to have a solution, as for example the system

$$2x - 3y + 4z = 6,$$
$$2x - 3y + 4z = 7;$$

these would be two parallel planes in 3-space.

Homogeneous Systems

We turn now to a type of system that will always have a solution. A system of equations is called **homogeneous** if the right side of each equation (the constant term) is zero. Such a system as

$$a_{11}x_1 + a_{12}x_2 + a_{13}x_3 + \ldots + a_{1n}x_n = 0,$$
$$a_{21}x_1 + a_{22}x_2 + a_{23}x_3 + \ldots + a_{2n}x_n = 0,$$
$$\vdots \qquad \vdots \qquad \vdots \qquad \qquad \vdots \qquad \vdots$$
$$a_{m1}x_1 + a_{m2}x_2 + a_{m3}x_3 + \ldots + a_{mn}x_n = 0,$$

(1.27)

always has the **trivial solution** $x_1 = x_2 = \ldots = x_n = 0$, as is easily seen. It is possible that a homogeneous system may have additional **nontrivial solutions**, as is the case in the following example.

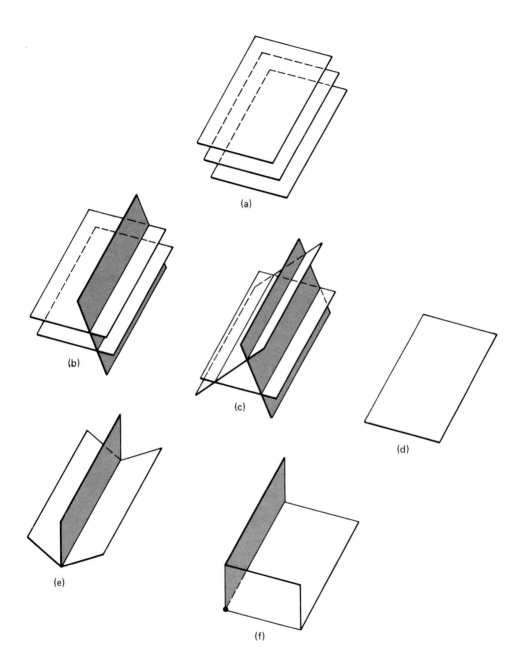

Fig. 1.6 a) no solutions (three parallel planes); b) no solutions (two planes parallel); c) no solutions (three planes intersecting in three lines); d) infinitely many solutions (three coincident planes); e) infinitely many solutions (three planes intersecting in a line); f) one solution (three planes intersecting at a point).

SYSTEMS OF LINEAR EQUATIONS AND MATRICES

Example 4 Find all the solutions to the homogeneous system

$$\begin{aligned} x + y + z + w &= 0, \\ x - y + z - w &= 0, \\ x + y - z - w &= 0, \\ 3x + y + z - w &= 0. \end{aligned} \quad (1.28)$$

The augmented matrix for (1.28) is

$$\begin{bmatrix} 1 & 1 & 1 & 1 & 0 \\ 1 & -1 & 1 & -1 & 0 \\ 1 & 1 & -1 & -1 & 0 \\ 3 & 1 & 1 & -1 & 0 \end{bmatrix}.$$

This matrix has the following reduced row-echelon form. (Verify this):

$$\begin{bmatrix} 1 & 0 & 0 & -1 & 0 \\ 0 & 1 & 0 & 1 & 0 \\ 0 & 0 & 1 & 1 & 0 \\ 0 & 0 & 0 & 0 & 0 \end{bmatrix}. \quad (1.29)$$

The final row of zeros in (1.29) indicates that the system (1.28) is dependent. It is equivalent to the following system:

$$\begin{aligned} x &= w, \\ y &= -w, \\ z &= -w. \end{aligned}$$

The solutions to (1.28) are any of the 4-tuples $(t, -t, -t, t)$ for any real number t.

Note that if the homogeneous system (1.27) has $m = n$ and the equations are not in some way dependent, the augmented matrix will have the following reduced row-echelon form:

$$\begin{bmatrix} 1 & 0 & 0 & \ldots & 0 & 0 \\ 0 & 1 & 0 & \ldots & 0 & 0 \\ 0 & 0 & 1 & \ldots & 0 & 0 \\ \cdot & \cdot & \cdot & & \cdot & \cdot \\ \cdot & \cdot & \cdot & & \cdot & \cdot \\ \cdot & \cdot & \cdot & & \cdot & \cdot \\ 0 & 0 & 0 & \ldots & 1 & 0 \end{bmatrix}. \quad (1.30)$$

This indicates that the trivial solution is the only solution. If $m > n$, a homogeneous system (1.27) might be dependent and yet still have only the trivial solution. In this case its augmented matrix will have reduced row-echelon form similar to that in (1.30) but with $(m - n)$ rows of zeros at the bottom. What happens if $m < n$?

EXERCISES (1.3) ————————————————————————

Use the matrix method to find all the solutions to the following homogeneous systems of equations.

1. $x + y + z = 0$
$\quad x - y + z = 0$
$\quad x - 3y + z = 0$

2. $x + y + z = 0$
$\quad x - y + z = 0$
$\quad x + y - z = 0$

3. $x_1 - x_2 + x_3 = 0$
$\quad 2x_1 + 3x_2 - 5x_3 = 0$
$\quad 3x_1 + 2x_2 - 4x_3 = 0$

4. $x_1 + x_2 + x_3 = 0$
$\quad x_1 + 2x_2 + 3x_3 = 0$
$\quad 2x_1 + 3x_2 + 2x_3 = 0$

5. $x + y = w$
$\quad w + x = y$
$\quad w + z = 2x$
$\quad x - y = z$

6. $s - t - u - v = 0$
$\quad 3s - t - u - v = 0$
$\quad 4s + t + u + v = 0$
$\quad s + t + u + v = 0$
$\quad 5s - 3t + 2u - 4v = 0$

Use the matrix method to find all the solutions to the following systems of equations, if solutions exist.

7. $x - 2y - 2z = -1$
$\quad 2x + 3y - z = 1$
$\quad x + y - z = 0$

8. $x - 7y = 17$
$\quad 2x + 3y = 0$
$\quad 3x - 4y = 17$

9. $x_1 + x_2 - x_3 = 3$
$\quad 2x_1 - 2x_2 + 3x_3 = 5$

10. $x_1 + x_2 - x_3 = 1$
$\quad 2x_1 - x_2 + x_3 = 4$
$\quad x_1 + 4x_2 - 4x_3 = 3$

11. $x_1 + 2x_2 - 2x_3 = 0$
$\quad 3x_1 - x_2 + 3x_3 = 1$
$\quad 4x_1 + x_2 + x_3 = 2$

12. $x_1 - x_2 - x_3 = 1$
$\quad x_1 + x_2 + x_3 = -1$
$\quad 2x_1 + 2x_2 - x_3 = 6$

13. $u + v - w - x = 0$
$\quad u - v + w - x = 0$
$\quad u + v - w + x = 0$

14. $x_1 + x_2 - 4x_3 + 2x_4 = 0$
$\quad -x_1 + x_2 - x_3 + 2x_4 + x_5 = 0$
$\quad x_1 + 2x_2 - x_3 + 4x_4 - x_5 = 0$
$\quad 2x_1 - x_2 + 3x_3 - x_4 + x_5 = 0$

15. Suppose that $(s_1, s_2, \ldots, s_n)$ and $(t_1, t_2, \ldots, t_n)$ are solutions to the system of homogeneous equations in (1.27). Show that $(ks_1, ks_2, \ldots, ks_n)$ and $(s_1 + t_1, s_2 + t_2, \ldots, s_n + t_n)$ are also solutions, where k is any real number.

16. Given the situation of Exercise 15, show that $(hs_1 + kt_1, hs_2 + kt_2, \ldots, hs_n + kt_n)$ is a solution for any pair of real numbers h and k.

17. Explain why a homogeneous system such as (1.27) with $m > n$ must be dependent. *Hint:* Consider reducing the augmented matrix.

18. Discuss what can occur in a homogeneous system such as (1.27) when $m < n$.

19. Given a system of equations whose augmented matrix is

$$A = \begin{bmatrix} a_{11} & a_{12} & a_{13} & \cdots & a_{1n} & b_1 \\ a_{21} & a_{22} & a_{23} & \cdots & a_{2n} & b_2 \\ \vdots & \vdots & \vdots & & \vdots & \vdots \\ a_{n1} & a_{n2} & a_{n3} & \cdots & a_{nn} & b_n \end{bmatrix}$$

with solution $(s_1, s_2, \ldots s_n)$. Consider also the corresponding homogeneous system (1.27) with the same a_{ij} and $m = n$ and with solution $(u_1, u_2, \ldots, u_n)$. Show that the system represented by A also has $(s_1 + u_1, s_2 + u_2, \ldots, s_n + u_n)$ as a solution.

20. Demonstrate that for every real number k and the situation described in Exercise 19, $(s_1 + ku_1, s_2 + ku_2, \ldots, s_n + ku_n)$ is also a solution to the system represented by A.

1.4 BASIC MATRIX OPERATIONS

We have seen how matrices can be used to help simplify the procedures for solving systems of linear equations. This is not, however, the only field in which matrices play an important role. The fact that they appear in many and varied contexts makes matrices, in and of themselves, objects of interest and study. In the next two sections we shall see that an *algebra of matrices* can be developed that has many similarities with and also many important differences from the usual *algebra of numbers* with which you are familiar.

Let us begin by introducing some notation. Remember that a matrix is any rectangular array of numbers. These numbers are often called *scalars* to distinguish them from the matrices and from the vectors with which we also work. Remember that the scalars in the array are called the *entries* (or *elements*) of the given matrix. Let us denote the matrix A by the array of scalars

$$A = \begin{bmatrix} a_{11} & a_{12} & \cdots & a_{1n} \\ a_{21} & a_{22} & \cdots & a_{2n} \\ \vdots & \vdots & & \vdots \\ a_{m1} & a_{m2} & \cdots & a_{mn} \end{bmatrix}. \tag{1.31}$$

Recall also that we give double subscripts to the entries of A. The first subscript indicates the (horizontal) *row* of A in which the entry is located and the second subscript locates the (vertical) *column* of A containing that entry. Since A has m rows and n columns, we call it an $m \times n$ (m by n) *matrix*. We shall frequently abbreviate the notation in (1.31) by writing

$$A = (a_{ij}),$$

where the scalar a_{ij} is a typical entry in A, appearing in row i and column j, $i = 1, 2, \ldots, m, j = 1, 2, \ldots, n$.

Matrix Equality

Two matrices A and B are called **equal** if and only if they are of the same shape (i.e., have the same number of rows and the same number of columns) and contain equal entries in the same positions. If $A = (a_{ij})$ and $B = (b_{ij})$, then $A = B$ if, and only if,

$a_{ij} = b_{ij}$ for each $i = 1, 2, \ldots, m$ and $j = 1, 2, \ldots, n$. Thus

$$A = \begin{bmatrix} 2 & -1 \\ 0 & 1 \\ 1 & 3 \end{bmatrix} \quad \text{and} \quad B = \begin{bmatrix} 1 & 3 \\ 0 & 1 \\ 2 & -1 \end{bmatrix}$$

are *not equal* matrices, even though they are row equivalent. If

$$C = \begin{bmatrix} a & b & c \\ d & e & f \end{bmatrix} \quad \text{and} \quad D = \begin{bmatrix} 1 & 0 & 2 \\ 3 & 1 & -1 \end{bmatrix}$$

are equal matrices, we can immediately conclude that $a = 1$, $b = 0$, $c = 2$, $d = 3$, $e = 1$, and $f = -1$. The matrices B and C cannot be equal to each other, nor can B and D, because, among other things, they are not of the same shape.

Example 1 Solve the matrix equation

$$\begin{bmatrix} x & 2 & x-y \\ y & z & -1 \\ -1 & 3 & x+z \end{bmatrix} = \begin{bmatrix} 1 & y & -1 \\ 2 & 3 & y-z \\ -x & z & 4 \end{bmatrix}.$$

For the two matrices to be equal, corresponding entries must be equal scalars. Thus, reading across the rows, we must conclude that

$$\begin{array}{lll} x = & 1, & y = 2, & x - y = -1, \\ y = & 2, & z = 3, & y - z = -1, \\ -x = -1, & z = 3, & x + z = 4. \end{array}$$

Since these (scalar) equations are consistent, $x = 1$, $y = 2$, $z = 3$ solves the matrix equation and the matrix is

$$\begin{bmatrix} 1 & 2 & -1 \\ 2 & 3 & -1 \\ -1 & 3 & 4 \end{bmatrix}.$$

Matrix Addition

Two matrices of the same shape, say $m \times n$ (that is, having m rows and n columns) can be added in a natural way to form a new $m \times n$ matrix called their **sum**. If $A = (a_{ij})$ and $B = (b_{ij})$, then

$$A + B = (a_{ij} + b_{ij})$$

for each $i = 1, 2, \ldots, m$ and $j = 1, 2, \ldots, n$. That is, matrix addition is performed by adding the corresponding entries in each position.

Example 2   Consider the matrices

$$A = \begin{bmatrix} 1 & 0 & 1 \\ -1 & 2 & 4 \\ 3 & 2 & -1 \end{bmatrix}; \quad B = \begin{bmatrix} 2 & 1 & -1 \\ 1 & -3 & -3 \\ 0 & 1 & 2 \end{bmatrix}; \quad D = \begin{bmatrix} 1 & 0 & 2 \\ 3 & 1 & -1 \end{bmatrix}.$$

Since both A and B are 3×3, their sum is defined and

$$A + B = \begin{bmatrix} (\ 1+2) & (0+\ 1) & (\ 1+-1) \\ (-1+1) & (2+-3) & (\ 4+-3) \\ (\ 3+0) & (2+\ 1) & (-1+\ 2) \end{bmatrix} = \begin{bmatrix} 3 & 1 & 0 \\ 0 & -1 & 1 \\ 3 & 3 & 1 \end{bmatrix}.$$

On the other hand, since A is 3×3 and D is 2×3, the sum $A + D$ is not defined; similarly $B + D$ is not defined.

Matrix addition is defined only when both matrices are of the same shape, that is, they both have the same number of rows and the same number of columns.

Since the definition of matrix addition is given in terms of addition of the scalar entries, it is not too surprising that matrix addition satisfies the same basic properties as the addition of real numbers. We have the following theorem, which summarizes the basic properties of addition in matrix algebra.

Theorem 1.3
Let A, B, C be $m \times n$ matrices with real (or complex) number entries. Then:
  i) *$A + B = B + A$ (commutative law);*
 ii) *$A + (B + C) = (A + B) + C$ (associative law);*
iii) *there exists an $m \times n$ zero matrix 0 such that for each matrix A:*

$$A + 0 = 0 + A = A;$$

iv) *for each matrix A there is a unique matrix $-A$ called the negative of A such that*

$$A + (-A) = 0.$$

The proof of this theorem is a straightforward application of the definition of matrix addition, together with the corresponding properties of real (or complex) number algebra. To prove part (iii), we choose each entry in the zero matrix to be a zero scalar. In part (iv), we define each entry of matrix $-A$ to be the negative of the corresponding entry in A; that is if $A = (a_{ij})$, then

$$-A = (-a_{ij})$$

where $i = 1, 2, \ldots, m; j = 1, 2, \ldots, n$. The rest of the proof is left as an exercise.

Example 3 If

$$A = \begin{bmatrix} 1 & -1 & 0 & 2 \\ -1 & 2 & 4 & -3 \\ 2 & 7 & -6 & 9 \end{bmatrix}, \quad \text{then} \quad -A = \begin{bmatrix} -1 & 1 & 0 & -2 \\ 1 & -2 & -4 & 3 \\ -2 & -7 & 6 & -9 \end{bmatrix}.$$

Multiplication by a Scalar

If A is a matrix, then it would be convenient to write $A + A$ as $2A$, just as we do with numbers. Therefore, from the rules of matrix addition, the matrix $2A$ is a matrix whose entries are twice the corresponding entries in A. If $A = (a_{ij})$, then $2A = A + A = (2a_{ij})$. Now let r be any scalar. Using the matrix $2A$ as a pattern, let us define rA, the multiplication of the matrix A by the scalar r, as follows:

$$\text{If} \quad A = (a_{ij}), \quad \text{then} \quad rA = (ra_{ij}),$$

where $i = 1, 2, \ldots, m;$ $j = 1, 2, \ldots, n$. That is, rA is the matrix whose entries are r times the corresponding entries of A.

Example 4 Let A be as in Example 3; then $\frac{3}{5}A$ is the matrix

$$\begin{bmatrix} \frac{3}{5} & -\frac{3}{5} & 0 & \frac{6}{5} \\ -\frac{3}{5} & \frac{6}{5} & \frac{12}{5} & -\frac{9}{5} \\ \frac{6}{5} & \frac{21}{5} & -\frac{18}{5} & \frac{27}{5} \end{bmatrix}$$

and

$$\text{if} \quad B = \begin{bmatrix} 1 & 0 & -1 \\ 2 & 5 & -3 \\ \frac{1}{2} & 7 & 6 \end{bmatrix}, \quad \text{then} \quad \pi B = \begin{bmatrix} \pi & 0 & -\pi \\ 2\pi & 5\pi & -3\pi \\ \frac{\pi}{2} & 7\pi & 6\pi \end{bmatrix}.$$

Note that this operation is *not* the same as the elementary operation (ii) of Theorem 1.2. Here *every* entry of the matrix A is multiplied by the scalar r, not just those in one row.

The following theorem lists the basic properties of multiplication by a scalar and their relation to matrix addition.

Theorem 1.4

Let A, B be $m \times n$ matrices of real (complex) numbers and let r, s be scalars i.e., real (or complex) numbers. Then:

i) $r(A + B) = rA + rB;$
ii) $(r + s)A = rA + sA;$
iii) $(rs)A = r(sA);$
iv) $1A = A.$

The proof of this theorem is again a straightforward application of the definitions. In part (i) of the theorem, if $A = (a_{ij})$ and $B = (b_{ij})$, where $i = 1, 2, \ldots, m$, $j = 1, 2, 3, \ldots, n$, then

$$r(A + B) = (r(a_{ij} + b_{ij})) = (ra_{ij} + rb_{ij})$$
$$= (ra_{ij}) + (rb_{ij}) = rA + rB,$$

as desired. The proofs of other parts are similar and are left as exercises.

Matrix Multiplication

The third operation of interest in our algebra of matrices involves the product of two matrices. One might be tempted to give a rather natural definition of this operation by suggesting multiplying corresponding scalar entries of each matrix. This simple approach is, however, not as useful for our purposes as is the more complicated definition we give here. Before actually stating a definition for the product AB of two matrices A and B, let us look at one of the situations where matrix multiplication is useful. In the first three sections of this chapter we considered systems of linear equations. Suppose we have a system of linear equations such as the following:

$$
\begin{aligned}
x_1 + 2x_2 - x_3 + x_4 &= 4, \\
2x_1 - 3x_2 + x_3 - x_4 &= -1, \\
5x_1 + x_2 + 2x_3 + 2x_4 &= 7, \\
x_1 - x_2 - x_3 - x_4 &= 0.
\end{aligned}
\tag{1.32}
$$

The coefficient matrix of this system of equations is the matrix A (see Section 1.2):

$$
A = \begin{bmatrix}
1 & 2 & -1 & 1 \\
2 & -3 & 1 & -1 \\
5 & 1 & 2 & 2 \\
1 & -1 & -1 & -1
\end{bmatrix}.
$$

Let us also consider two 4×1 (column) matrices X and B defined by

$$
X = \begin{bmatrix} x_1 \\ x_2 \\ x_3 \\ x_4 \end{bmatrix}
\quad \text{and} \quad
B = \begin{bmatrix} 4 \\ -1 \\ 7 \\ 0 \end{bmatrix}.
$$

It would be very convenient to be able to represent the system of equations (1.32) by the simple matrix equation

$$AX = B. \tag{1.33}$$

Hence, knowing A (the coefficients) and B (the constants), we seek the value of X (the solution to the system). Were the rules of high-school algebra to prevail here, we should be allowed to treat the equation (1.33) much as we would an algebraic equation in the real-number algebra with which we are familiar: Divide both sides by A. In real-number algebra this sort of procedure is justified by the existence (for each real number $a \neq 0$) of a multiplicative inverse a^{-1} with the property that $a^{-1}a = 1$. Then an equation $ax = b$ is solved by multiplying both sides by the real number a^{-1}. Thus, if there is a solution x to the equation $ax = b$, then

$$a^{-1}(ax) = (a^{-1}a)x = a^{-1}b,$$
$$1x = a^{-1}b,$$

so that the solution would necessarily be $x = a^{-1}b$.

If this same situation prevailed in matrix algebra, we could find a multiplicative inverse matrix A^{-1} for the coefficient matrix A of the system (1.32) and then solve Eq. (1.33) by the same process:

$$A^{-1}(AX) = A^{-1}B,$$
$$X = A^{-1}B.$$

This happy state of affairs is, unfortunately, not always possible in matrix algebra, as we shall see later. Nevertheless, such a matrix algebra is desirable. For this to be true at any time, however, we need a much more involved definition of matrix multiplication than simply multiplying corresponding entries. Note that if the matrix equation (1.33) is to represent the system of equations (1.32), it is necessary that the product matrix AX have the left sides of the system (1.32) as its rows. Thus,

$$AX = \begin{bmatrix} x_1 + 2x_2 - x_3 + x_4 \\ 2x_1 - 3x_2 + x_3 - x_4 \\ 5x_1 + x_2 + 2x_3 + 2x_4 \\ x_1 - x_2 - x_3 - x_4 \end{bmatrix}.$$

If AX is to equal the $m \times 1$ matrix B, it must itself be $m \times 1$, as is the case above. How is the $m \times 1$ matrix AX obtained from the $m \times n$ matrix A and the $n \times 1$ matrix X? The first entry in AX is obtained by first multiplying the corresponding entries from the first row of A with those from the first (and only) column of X, then adding up the results. Thus,

$$AX = \begin{bmatrix} 1 & 2 & -1 & 1 \\ 2 & -3 & 1 & -1 \\ 5 & 1 & 2 & 2 \\ 1 & -1 & -1 & -1 \end{bmatrix} \cdot \begin{bmatrix} x_1 \\ x_2 \\ x_3 \\ x_4 \end{bmatrix} = \begin{bmatrix} x_1 + 2x_2 - x_3 + x_4 \\ \cdot \\ \cdot \\ \cdot \end{bmatrix}.$$

The second entry in AX will be the sum of products of corresponding entries in the second row of A and those of the first column of X, and so on. Now, matrix multiplication is useful in other contexts than this one. We shall see several in this book. In particular, in Chapter 5 we shall see how matrix multiplication is related to composition of certain mappings. The definition of matrix multiplication that covers all such applications is the following:

Let A and B be two matrices

$$
A = \begin{bmatrix} a_{11} & a_{12} & \cdots & a_{1n} \\ a_{21} & a_{22} & \cdots & a_{2n} \\ \vdots & \vdots & & \vdots \\ a_{m1} & a_{m2} & \cdots & a_{mn} \end{bmatrix}, \quad B = \begin{bmatrix} b_{11} & b_{12} & \cdots & b_{1k} \\ b_{21} & b_{22} & \cdots & b_{2k} \\ \vdots & \vdots & & \vdots \\ b_{n1} & b_{n2} & \cdots & b_{nk} \end{bmatrix},
$$

where A is $m \times n$ and B is $n \times k$. Then the **product matrix** AB is the $m \times k$ matrix.

$$
AB = \begin{bmatrix} c_{11} & c_{12} & \cdots & c_{1k} \\ c_{21} & c_{22} & \cdots & c_{2k} \\ \vdots & \vdots & & \vdots \\ c_{m1} & c_{m2} & \cdots & c_{mk} \end{bmatrix},
$$

where the entry in row i and column j is the sum of the products of corresponding entries from row i of A with entries in column j of B. Thus,

$$
c_{ij} = a_{i1}b_{1j} + a_{i2}b_{2j} + \ldots + a_{in}b_{nj}. \tag{1.34}
$$

By making use of the summation notation Σ, we can write Eq. (1.34) more compactly as

$$
c_{ij} = \sum_{r=1}^{n} a_{ir}b_{rj}
$$

for $i = 1, 2, \ldots, m$ and $j = 1, 2, \ldots, k$.

If you are unfamiliar with the notation Σ, you should consult a college algebra or a calculus text. Some of the basic properties are reviewed in Exercises 48–52. A little later we shall return to the system of equations in (1.32) and the question of an inverse for a matrix. Let us now concentrate on the definition of matrix multiplication which it motivated.

Example 5 Let A and B be the matrices

$$
A = \begin{bmatrix} 1 & 0 & 1 & -1 \\ -1 & 2 & 4 & 2 \\ 3 & 2 & -1 & 0 \end{bmatrix}, \quad B = \begin{bmatrix} 1 & 3 \\ 0 & 1 \\ 2 & -1 \\ -1 & 5 \end{bmatrix}.
$$

Then, since A is 3×4, and B is 4×2, the product AB is a 3×2 matrix. To determine the entry c_{22} of the product matrix $C = AB$, for example, we fix our attention on row two of A and column two of B. Using (1.34), we multiply the corresponding entries together and add them:

$$c_{22} = (-1)(3) + (2)(1) + (4)(-1) + (2)(5) = 5.$$

Thus,

$$\begin{bmatrix} 1 & 0 & 1 & -1 \\ -1 & 2 & 4 & 2 \\ 3 & 2 & -1 & 0 \end{bmatrix} \cdot \begin{bmatrix} 1 & 3 \\ 0 & 1 \\ 2 & -1 \\ -1 & 5 \end{bmatrix} = \begin{bmatrix} 4 & -3 \\ 5 & 5 \\ 1 & 12 \end{bmatrix}.$$

The remaining entries c_{ij} of $AB = (c_{ij})$ are computed similarly. For example,

$$c_{11} = (1)(1) + (0)(0) + (1)(2) + (-1)(-1) = \quad 4,$$
$$c_{32} = (3)(3) + (2)(1) + (-1)(-1) + (0)(5) = 12,$$

and so on. In fact,

$$AB = \begin{bmatrix} 4 & -3 \\ 5 & 5 \\ 1 & 12 \end{bmatrix}.$$

Note that, if we wish to multiply two matrices, it is necessary that the number of entries in a given *row* of the first matrix-factor A must be the same as the number of entries in a given *column* of the second matrix-factor B.
Thus,

$$\text{if } A \text{ is } m \times n \quad \text{and} \quad B \text{ is } n \times k, \quad \text{then } AB \text{ is } m \times k.$$

The product BA for the matrices A and B of Example 5 is, therefore, *not* defined.

The basic properties of matrix multiplication are discussed in the next section. We conclude this section with an example showing a simple application of matrix multiplication to something other than solving a system of equations. In this example, matrix multiplication is used to model the possible spread of an infection.

Example 6 Suppose that two people have contracted a contagious disease. A second group of five people has been in possible contact with the two infected people. After questioning the second group of people carefully, we construct the 2×5 matrix A in which $a_{ij} = 1$ if the jth person in the second group has been in contact with the ith infected person, and $a_{ij} = 0$ if there has been no contact. Suppose that

$$A = \begin{bmatrix} 1 & 1 & 0 & 0 & 1 \\ 0 & 1 & 1 & 1 & 0 \end{bmatrix}.$$

Now a third group of four people has been in possible contact with the second group of five people. The contact matrix for them is B with $b_{jt} = 1$ or 0, depending on whether person t of the third group has or has not been in contact with person j of the second group. Suppose that this contact matrix is

$$B = \begin{bmatrix} 1 & 1 & 0 & 1 \\ 0 & 1 & 0 & 1 \\ 0 & 0 & 1 & 0 \\ 0 & 0 & 1 & 1 \\ 0 & 1 & 1 & 0 \end{bmatrix}.$$

If we are interested in the indirect or "second-order" contacts between the people in the third group and the two infected people, this information can be obtained from the matrix product $C = AB$. The total number of second-order contacts between a given person in the third group, say person t, and the ith infected person is the entry c_{it}. This is the sum of the contacts between person t and those persons j who have had contact with infected person i. Thus,

$$C = AB = \begin{bmatrix} 1 & 3 & 1 & 2 \\ 0 & 1 & 2 & 2 \end{bmatrix}.$$

So, for example, person number 3 in the third group has had three possible second-order contacts with an infected person, one with the first infected person and two with the second. The first person in the third group has had only one such contact.

EXERCISES (1.4)

1. Solve the matrix equation

$$\begin{bmatrix} a & b \\ c & a \end{bmatrix} = \begin{bmatrix} 1 & 2a \\ 3b & 1 \end{bmatrix}.$$

In Exercises 2–13 and 20–45, consider the matrices

$$A = \begin{bmatrix} 1 & 1 \\ -1 & 2 \\ 0 & 3 \end{bmatrix}, \quad B = \begin{bmatrix} 2 & 1 & -1 \\ 3 & 1 & 4 \end{bmatrix}, \quad C = \begin{bmatrix} 1 & 0 & -1 \\ -2 & 1 & 3 \\ 1 & 1 & 0 \end{bmatrix},$$

$$D = \begin{bmatrix} 2 & -1 \\ 4 & 1 \\ 6 & 0 \end{bmatrix}, \quad E = \begin{bmatrix} 3 & 1 & 2 \\ 4 & -1 & 7 \\ 0 & 1 & 2 \end{bmatrix}, \quad F = \begin{bmatrix} 0 & 4 \\ -2 & 0 \end{bmatrix},$$

and compute (if possible).

2. $3A$ 3. $-2B$ 4. $-6C$ 5. $\frac{1}{2}D$

6. $\frac{1}{3}E$ 7. $\frac{1}{4}F$ 8. $A + D$ 9. $C + E$

10. $A + B$ 11. $B + E$ 12. $D + F$ 13. $0 + F$

In Exercises 14–19, find the indicated product when it is defined.

14. $\begin{bmatrix} 1 & 0 & -1 \end{bmatrix} \begin{bmatrix} 2 \\ 1 \\ 5 \end{bmatrix}$

15. $\begin{bmatrix} 1 & 0 & -1 \end{bmatrix} \begin{bmatrix} 2 & 3 \\ 1 & 1 \\ 5 & -2 \end{bmatrix}$

16. $\begin{bmatrix} 1 & 0 & -1 \\ 2 & -1 & -2 \end{bmatrix} \begin{bmatrix} 2 \\ 1 \\ 5 \end{bmatrix}$

17. $\begin{bmatrix} 1 & 0 & -1 \\ 2 & -1 & -2 \end{bmatrix} \begin{bmatrix} 2 & 3 \\ 1 & 1 \\ 5 & -2 \end{bmatrix}$

18. $\begin{bmatrix} 2 & 3 \\ 1 & 1 \\ 5 & -2 \end{bmatrix} \begin{bmatrix} 1 & 0 & -1 \\ 2 & -1 & 2 \end{bmatrix}$

19. $\begin{bmatrix} 2 & 3 \\ 1 & 1 \\ 5 & -2 \end{bmatrix} \begin{bmatrix} -1 \\ 4 \end{bmatrix}$

Refer to the matrices given just before Exercise 2. Compute, where possible, the following matrix products:

20. AB 21. BA 22. BD 23. DB

24. AF 25. FB 26. CA 27. EA

28. FA 29. BF 30. CE 31. EC

Refer again to the matrices given just before Exercise 2. If M is *any* matrix, then M^2 is defined as $M^2 = MM$, also $M^3 = MM^2$, etc. Compute, if possible, the following matrix powers:

32. F^2 33. C^2 34. E^2 35. F^3

36. C^3 37. E^3 38. $(AB)^2$ 39. A^2

40. B^2 41. $(AB)^3$ 42. $(BA)^2$ 43. $(BA)^3$

44. Show that the matrix F above satisfies $F^4 + 8F^2 = 0$.

45. Let A, B, C be as above. Verify that $(AB)C = A(BC)$.

46. Show that if S is any $n \times n$ matrix in which all the entries in row i are zero, and if T is any $n \times m$ matrix, then ST also has only zeros as entries in row i.

47. Show that for any two matrices S and T whose product ST is defined, the ith row of the matrix product ST is the product of the ith row of S and the matrix T.

Remember that $\sum_{i=1}^{n} a_i$ simply means *add up the numbers* a_i when i is successively equal to 1, 2, 3, ..., n. Thus, for example, $\sum_{i=1}^{7} a_i = a_1 + a_2 + a_3 + a_4 + a_5 + a_6 + a_7$. Verify (or justify) the following properties of the summation notation:

48. $\sum_{i=1}^{n} a_i = \sum_{j=1}^{n} a_j = \sum_{k-1}^{n} a_k$, etc.

49. $\sum_{i=1}^{n} ra_i = r \sum_{i=1}^{n} a_i$ for each scalar r.

50. $\sum_{i=1}^{n} (a_i + b_i) = \sum_{i=1}^{n} a_i + \sum_{i=1}^{n} b_i$

51. $\displaystyle\sum_{i=1}^{n}\left(\sum_{j=1}^{m} a_{ij}\right) = \sum_{j=1}^{m}\left(\sum_{i=1}^{n} a_{ij}\right)$

52. $\displaystyle\sum_{k=1}^{n} a_{jk}\left(\sum_{s=1}^{m} b_{ks}c_{sj}\right) = \sum_{s=1}^{m}\left(\sum_{k=1}^{n} a_{jk}b_{ks}\right)c_{sj}$

The **transpose** A^t of $n \times m$ matrix $A = (a_{ij})$ is the $m \times n$ matrix whose entry in row i and column j is a_{ji}, the entry in row j and column i of A. Thus, the rows of A are the columns of A^t and the columns of A are the rows of A^t. Prove that

53. $(A^t)^t = A$ **54.** $(rA)^t = rA^t$ for any scalar r

55. $(A + B)^t = A^t + B^t$ **56.** $(AB)^t = B^t A^t$

57. A square matrix A is said to be **symmetric** if $A = A^t$. Show that the sum of two symmetric matrices is symmetric.

58. Show by an example that it is not true that matrix multiplication is commutative; i.e., show that in general $AB \neq BA$.

In Exercises 59–62, prove Theorem 1.3:

59. Part (i)   **60.** Part (ii)

61. Demonstrate that if $A + Z = Z + A = A$ for every $m \times n$ matrix A, then Z is the $m \times n$ zero matrix 0.

62. Show that $-A$ is unique by demonstrating that if $A + B = B + A = 0$, then $B = -A$.

In Exercises 63–65 prove Theorem 1.4:

63. Part (ii)   **64.** Part (iii)   **65.** Part (iv)

66. Show that if r is any scalar, then for 3×3 matrices A and B it is true that

$$A(rB) = r(AB).$$

1.5 ALGEBRA OF MATRICES

We saw in Theorems 1.3 and 1.4 that many of the rules of ordinary real- or complex-number algebra carry over easily to matrices since matrix addition and multiplication by a scalar involve entry-by-entry operations. However, there are also important differences between matrix algebra and real-number algebra. One of the most significant of these differences involves the commutative law of multiplication. If a and b are real (or complex) numbers, then it is always true that $ab = ba$. *This law fails for matrix multiplication.* You have probably already noticed this from the exercises of the preceding section. Even when the matrices involved are $n \times n$, or square, it is usually false that $AB = BA$.

Example 1 Let

$$A = \begin{bmatrix} 0 & 1 \\ -2 & 1 \end{bmatrix} \quad \text{and} \quad B = \begin{bmatrix} 1 & 4 \\ -2 & 1 \end{bmatrix}.$$

Then

$$AB = \begin{bmatrix} -2 & 1 \\ -4 & -7 \end{bmatrix} \quad \text{while} \quad BA = \begin{bmatrix} -8 & 5 \\ -2 & -1 \end{bmatrix}.$$

Clearly, even in this relatively simple example, $AB \neq BA$.

Although it is false that matrix multiplication is commutative, there are still several properties of ordinary multiplication of real numbers that have analogs in matrix multiplication. The following theorem summarizes the basic ones.

Theorem 1.5

Let A, B, C be matrices of appropriate sizes so that the indicated operations can be performed. Then:

i) $(AB)C = A(BC)$ *(associative law);* ✓
ii) $A(B+C) = AB + AC$ *(left distributive law);*
iii) $(A+B)C = AC + BC$ *(right distributive law);*
iv) $r(AB) = (rA)B = A(rB)$ *for any scalar r.*

The various parts of this theorem can again be proved by using the definitions. However, these proofs are somewhat more tedious than those of Theorems 1.3 and 1.4. To illustrate, let us prove part (i); the rest are left as exercises. The proof depends on Exercises 49 and 51 in the last section.

Proof of part (i): Let A be the $m \times n$ matrix (a_{ij}), with B the $n \times k$ matrix $(b_{j\sigma})$, and C the $k \times h$ matrix (c_{rs}). Then the element in row i and column t of the matrix product $(AB)C$ is the element

$$d_{it} = \sum_{f=1}^{k} \left(\sum_{j=1}^{n} a_{ij} b_{jf} \right) c_{ft}$$

$$= \sum_{f=1}^{k} \sum_{j=1}^{n} a_{ij} (b_{jf} c_{ft}) \quad \text{(by Exercise 49)}.$$

Now use Exercise 51 to interchange the two summation signs. Then factor a_{ij} using Exercise 49:

$$d_{it} = \sum_{j=1}^{n} a_{ij} \left(\sum_{f=1}^{k} b_{jf} c_{ft} \right).$$

The interchange of summation signs indicates merely a rearrangement of the terms in the finite sum and a different factoring. This last expression is, however, the element in row i and column t of the matrix product $A(BC)$. Thus, the two matrices $A(BC)$ and $(AB)C$ are equal.

Example 2 To illustrate other properties of matrix multiplication, in particular the distributive laws, consider

$$A = \begin{bmatrix} 1 & 0 \\ -1 & 2 \\ 3 & -1 \end{bmatrix}, \quad B = \begin{bmatrix} 1 & -4 \\ 2 & 0 \end{bmatrix}, \quad \text{and} \quad C = \begin{bmatrix} 0 & 3 \\ -1 & 4 \end{bmatrix}.$$

Then

$$AB = \begin{bmatrix} 1 & -4 \\ 3 & 4 \\ 1 & -12 \end{bmatrix}, \quad AC = \begin{bmatrix} 0 & 3 \\ -2 & 5 \\ 1 & 5 \end{bmatrix}, \quad AB + AC = \begin{bmatrix} 1 & -1 \\ 1 & 9 \\ 2 & -7 \end{bmatrix};$$

$$B + C = \begin{bmatrix} 1 & -1 \\ 1 & 4 \end{bmatrix}, \quad A(B+C) = \begin{bmatrix} 1 & -1 \\ 1 & 9 \\ 2 & -7 \end{bmatrix}.$$

Thus, $A(B+C) = AB + AC$.

Additional properties of matrix algebra are given in the following theorem.

Theorem 1.6

If the matrices A, B, C are of appropriate sizes to perform the indicated operations, then the following is true:

i) $-1(A) = -A$;

ii) $-(-A) = A$;

iii) $A - B = -(B - A)$;

iv) $A(B - C) = AB - AC$;

v) $(A - B)C = AC - BC$;

vi) $(r - s)A = rA - sA$, r *and* s *scalars*;

vii) $r(A - B) = rA - rB$;

viii) $0A = A0 = 0$.

The proof of Theorem 1.6 is a straightforward application of the definitions and theorems. Most of it is left as an exercise; we prove part (viii).

Proof of part (viii): Since the zero matrix 0 has only 0 entries, for any matrix $A = (a_{ij})$ of appropriate size we have

$$0A = (c_{ij}), \quad \text{where} \quad c_{ij} = \sum_{k=1}^{n} 0_{ik} a_{kj} = 0.$$

Similarly, $A0$ has only zero entries.

Any size matrix all of whose entries are zero is called a *zero matrix* and is designated by 0. When the size is important, we write $0_{m \times n}$.

Example 3   Each of the following is a zero matrix:

$$\begin{bmatrix} 0 & 0 & 0 \\ 0 & 0 & 0 \\ 0 & 0 & 0 \end{bmatrix}, \quad \begin{bmatrix} 0 \\ 0 \\ 0 \\ 0 \end{bmatrix}, \quad [0], \quad \begin{bmatrix} 0 & 0 & 0 & 0 \\ 0 & 0 & 0 & 0 \end{bmatrix}.$$

Let

$$A = \begin{bmatrix} 1 & -1 & 4 \\ 1 & 0 & 2 \\ 3 & 6 & 0 \\ 2 & -1 & 2 \end{bmatrix}, \quad \text{then} \quad 0_{2 \times 4} A = \begin{bmatrix} 0 & 0 & 0 \\ 0 & 0 & 0 \end{bmatrix} = 0_{2 \times 3}.$$

Now it is a fact of real- and complex-number algebra that if $ab = 0$, then $a = 0$ or $b = 0$. This property fails in matrix algebra, as can be seen from the following example. We say that a nonzero matrix A is a **zero divisor** if there is another nonzero matrix B such that $AB = 0$ or $BA = 0$.

Example 4   Let

$$A = \begin{bmatrix} -6 & 3 \\ 4 & -2 \end{bmatrix} \quad \text{and} \quad B = \begin{bmatrix} 1 & -2 \\ 2 & -4 \end{bmatrix}.$$

Then

$$AB = \begin{bmatrix} 0 & 0 \\ 0 & 0 \end{bmatrix},$$

while neither A nor B is a zero matrix.

Note also that the property of having zero divisors means that matrix algebra has no multiplicative cancellation law. For example, if A and B are as in Example 4, then $AB = 0$. But $A0 = 0$ and hence $AB = A0$. If it were possible to cancel the nonzero matrix A, we would have $B = 0$, which, of course, is false. Therefore, *multiplicative cancellation fails for matrices.*

Let A be a square matrix, say $n \times n$. The entries a_{ii}, whose row and column indices are the same, are said to lie on the **main diagonal** of A. For example, the main diagonal of the following matrix is shaded:

$$A = \begin{bmatrix} a_{11} & a_{12} & \cdots & a_{1n} \\ a_{21} & a_{22} & \cdots & a_{2n} \\ \vdots & \vdots & & \vdots \\ a_{n1} & a_{n2} & \cdots & a_{nn} \end{bmatrix}.$$

For each positive integer n, the $n \times n$ matrix I_n, whose main-diagonal entries are all 1 and all the rest of the entries are zero, is called the $n \times n$ **identity matrix**. This is because $I_n M = M I_n = M$ for any $n \times n$ matrix M. The verification of this is left as an exercise. We have, for example,

$$I_2 = \begin{bmatrix} 1 & 0 \\ 0 & 1 \end{bmatrix}, \quad I_3 = \begin{bmatrix} 1 & 0 & 0 \\ 0 & 1 & 0 \\ 0 & 0 & 1 \end{bmatrix}, \quad I_4 = \begin{bmatrix} 1 & 0 & 0 & 0 \\ 0 & 1 & 0 & 0 \\ 0 & 0 & 1 & 0 \\ 0 & 0 & 0 & 1 \end{bmatrix}, \quad \text{etc.}$$

Sometimes we also denote the identity matrix I_n by I.

A matrix, such as I_n, whose only nonzero entries (if any) lie on the main diagonal, is called a **diagonal matrix** and is often denoted

$$\mathrm{diag}[a_{11}, a_{22}, \ldots, a_{nn}].$$

Thus, $I_5 = \mathrm{diag}[1, 1, 1, 1, 1]$ and $4I_3 = \mathrm{diag}[4, 4, 4]$.

Example 5.

$$\begin{bmatrix} 8 & 0 & 0 & 0 & 0 \\ 0 & 7 & 0 & 0 & 0 \\ 0 & 0 & 6 & 0 & 0 \\ 0 & 0 & 0 & 5 & 0 \\ 0 & 0 & 0 & 0 & 4 \end{bmatrix} = \mathrm{diag}[8, 7, 6, 5, 4];$$

$$\mathrm{diag}[1, -1, 2, 3] = \begin{bmatrix} 1 & 0 & 0 & 0 \\ 0 & -1 & 0 & 0 \\ 0 & 0 & 2 & 0 \\ 0 & 0 & 0 & 3 \end{bmatrix}.$$

As we have noted above, the identity matrix I_n acts like a multiplicative identity for matrix multiplication. In real-number algebra, if $a \neq 0$, there is always a real number b so that $ab = 1$. This is not always the case in matrix algebra, as we shall see in the following.

Example 6 Show that there is no matrix X such that $BX = I_2$, when B is the matrix

$$\begin{bmatrix} 1 & -2 \\ 2 & -4 \end{bmatrix}$$

of Example 4.

Let us denote such a possible X by

$$\begin{bmatrix} x_{11} & x_{12} \\ x_{21} & x_{22} \end{bmatrix}.$$

Then,

$$BX = \begin{bmatrix} x_{11} - 2x_{21} & x_{12} - 2x_{22} \\ 2x_{11} - 4x_{21} & 2x_{12} - 4x_{22} \end{bmatrix} = \begin{bmatrix} 1 & 0 \\ 0 & 1 \end{bmatrix},$$

so we must solve the system of linear equations

$$\begin{aligned}
x_{11} & & -2x_{21} & & &= 1, \\
& x_{12} & & & -2x_{22} &= 0, \\
2x_{11} & & -4x_{21} & & &= 0, \\
& 2x_{12} & & & -4x_{22} &= 1.
\end{aligned}$$

The augmented matrix for this system is

$$\begin{bmatrix} 1 & 0 & -2 & 0 & 1 \\ 0 & 1 & 0 & -2 & 0 \\ 2 & 0 & -4 & 0 & 0 \\ 0 & 2 & 0 & -4 & 1 \end{bmatrix},$$

which reduces to (verify this)

$$\begin{bmatrix} 1 & 0 & -2 & 0 & 1 \\ 0 & 1 & 0 & -2 & 0 \\ 0 & 0 & 0 & 0 & 1 \\ 0 & 0 & 0 & 0 & 0 \end{bmatrix}.$$

The third row of this matrix indicates an inconsistency in this system of equations. Therefore, $BX = I_2$ has no solution.

Examples 4 and 6 tell us some important things. Note that if the equation $BX = I$ of Example 6 had a solution $X = K$, so that $BK = I$, then, since (from Example 4) $AB = 0$, by applying the rules of matrix algebra we would have the following result:

$$A = AI = A(BK) = (AB)K = 0K = 0,$$

contrary to the fact that $A \neq 0$ (see Example 4). This is a matrix-algebra proof (an alternative to the method used in Example 6) that there is no solution to $BX = I$.

In the next section we shall discuss the intimate connection between solutions to the matrix equation $AX = I$ and solutions to systems of linear equations $AX = B$. We conclude this present section by proving the following lemma that indicates one of these relationships. The proof illustrates some of the power of matrix algebra.

Lemma 1.7

Every system of linear equations has either no solutions, or exactly one solution, or infinitely many solutions.

Proof. Denote the given system of equations by the matrix equation $AX = B$. If this has no solution, the lemma is satisfied, so suppose that $AX = B$ has a solution. If it has both X_1 and X_2 as solutions, with $X_1 \neq X_2$, then both $AX_1 = B$ and $AX_2 = B$. Thus,

$$AX_1 - AX_2 = B - B = 0.$$

Then, using part (iv) of Theorem 1.6, we can factor A out on the left, so that

$$A(X_1 - X_2) = 0.$$

Set $X_0 = X_1 - X_2$, and let r be any scalar (real or complex number). Observe that $AX_0 = A(X_1 - X_2) = 0$. We claim that $X = X_1 + rX_0$ is a solution to the system $AX = B$ for every scalar r. This follows because we have (give reasons)

$$AX = A(X_1 + rX_0) = AX_1 + A(rX_0) = AX_1 + r(AX_0)$$
$$= B + r0 = B + 0 = B.$$

Therefore, if $AX = B$ has more than one solution, it has infinitely many, since r can be any real number.

EXERCISES (1.5)

Calculate each of the following matrix products:

1. $\begin{bmatrix} 1 & 0 & 0 \\ 0 & 0 & 0 \\ 0 & 0 & 0 \end{bmatrix} \cdot \begin{bmatrix} a & b & c \\ d & e & f \\ g & h & i \end{bmatrix}$

2. $\begin{bmatrix} 0 & 1 & 0 \\ 0 & 0 & 0 \\ 0 & 0 & 0 \end{bmatrix} \cdot \begin{bmatrix} a & b & c \\ d & e & f \\ g & h & i \end{bmatrix}$

3. $\begin{bmatrix} 0 & 0 & 1 \\ 0 & 0 & 0 \\ 0 & 0 & 0 \end{bmatrix} \cdot \begin{bmatrix} a & b & c \\ d & e & f \\ g & h & i \end{bmatrix}$

4. $\begin{bmatrix} 0 & 0 & 0 \\ 0 & 1 & 0 \\ 0 & 0 & 0 \end{bmatrix} \cdot \begin{bmatrix} a & b & c \\ d & e & f \\ g & h & i \end{bmatrix}$

5. $\begin{bmatrix} 1 & 0 & 0 \\ 0 & 1 & 0 \\ 0 & 0 & 0 \end{bmatrix} \cdot \begin{bmatrix} a & b & c \\ d & e & f \\ g & h & i \end{bmatrix}$

6. $\begin{bmatrix} 0 & 0 & 0 \\ 0 & 0 & 0 \\ 0 & 0 & 1 \end{bmatrix} \cdot \begin{bmatrix} a & b & c \\ d & e & f \\ g & h & i \end{bmatrix}$

7. Verify that $(LM)K = L(MK)$, where K, L, and M are the matrices given below:

$$K = \begin{bmatrix} 1 & -1 \\ 2 & 1 \end{bmatrix}, \quad L = \begin{bmatrix} 1 & 0 & 1 \\ 2 & 1 & 0 \\ 0 & 1 & 3 \end{bmatrix}, \quad M = \begin{bmatrix} 2 & -1 \\ -4 & 5 \\ 0 & 1 \end{bmatrix}.$$

8. Demonstrate the associative law for matrix multiplication for the following 2×2 matrices:

$$A = \begin{bmatrix} a_{11} & a_{12} \\ a_{21} & a_{22} \end{bmatrix}, \quad B = \begin{bmatrix} b_{11} & b_{12} \\ b_{21} & b_{22} \end{bmatrix}, \quad C = \begin{bmatrix} c_{11} & c_{12} \\ c_{21} & c_{22} \end{bmatrix}.$$

9. Show that $AB = I_2$ but $BA \neq I_3$ if

$$A = \begin{bmatrix} 1 & 2 & -1 \\ 2 & 0 & 1 \end{bmatrix}, \quad B = \begin{bmatrix} 1 & -3 \\ -1 & 5 \\ -2 & 7 \end{bmatrix}.$$

In Exercises 10–12, let

$$A = \begin{bmatrix} a_{11} & a_{12} & a_{13} & a_{14} & a_{15} \\ a_{21} & a_{22} & a_{23} & a_{24} & a_{25} \end{bmatrix}.$$

10. Compute $I_2 A$.   **11.** Does $AI_2 = A$? Why?

12. What is $A^t I_2$? (*Hint*. See Exercises 53–56 of Section 1.4.)

13. Prove that $IA = AI = A$ for any square matrix A.

14. Let A be any 3×3 matrix, and let D be any 3×3 diagonal matrix. Prove or disprove that $AD = DA$.

In Exercises 15–17, finish the proof of Theorem 1.5:

15. Part (ii)   **16.** Part (iii)   **17.** Part (iv)

In Exercises 18–24 finish the proof of Theorem 1.6:

18. Part (i)   **19.** Part (ii)   **20.** Part (iii)   **21.** Part (iv)
22. Part (v)   **23.** Part (vi)   **24.** Part (vii)

25. Suppose that three men, Tom, Dick and Harry, do piecework; that is, they are paid for each unit turned out. Suppose that they manufacture three types of product and that the amount of wage paid for each type of product is given by the following table (matrix):

Type	Wage per unit, $
I	$\begin{bmatrix} 2.50 \\ 1.75 \\ 3.15 \end{bmatrix}$
II	
III	

The output of each worker on a given day is expressed by the following table (matrix):

$$
\begin{array}{c}
\\
T \\
D \\
H
\end{array}
\begin{array}{ccc}
I & II & III
\end{array}
\begin{bmatrix}
2 & 1 & 4 \\
3 & 2 & 1 \\
5 & 1 & 4
\end{bmatrix}.
$$

Use matrix multiplication to determine how much each worker earned that day.

A matrix $A = (a_{ij})$ is called **upper triangular** if $a_{ij} = 0$ for $i > j$. It is called **lower triangular** if $a_{ij} = 0$ for $i < j$.

26. Prove that the sum of two upper-triangular matrices is upper-triangular.

27. Prove that the sum of two lower-triangular matrices is lower-triangular.

28. Prove that the product of two upper-triangular matrices is upper triangular.

29. Prove that the product of two lower-triangular matrices is lower triangular.

In Exercises 30 and 31, let A be the following upper-triangular matrix:

$$
A = \begin{bmatrix}
0 & 1 & 2 \\
0 & 0 & -1 \\
0 & 0 & 0
\end{bmatrix}.
$$

30. Show that $A^3 = 0$, but $A^2 \neq 0$.   **31.** Show that $(A^t)^3 = 0$.

A square matrix N is called **nilpotent** (of index k) if $N^k = 0$, but $N^{k-1} \neq 0$ for some positive integer $k > 1$. (The zero matrix is nilpotent of index 1.)

32. Prove that any $n \times n$ upper- or lower-triangular matrix with zeros also on the main diagonal is nilpotent.

33. Show that if N is any nonzero $n \times n$ nilpotent matrix, then there is no matrix B such that $NB = I_n$. Hint. Look at $N^k B = N^{k-1}(NB)$.

Recall now the definition of transpose A^t of the matrix A (given just before Exercise 53 in Section 1.4). Exercises 34–39 show how matrix multiplication might be applied in certain sociometric experiments to interpret some of the data. In one experiment, members of a group are asked which other members they like. Suppose the responses are collected in a choice diagram, as given in Fig. 1.7, where an arrow going from person i to person j means that person i likes person j.

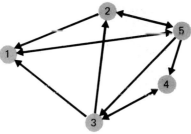

Figure 1.7

34. Convert the diagram in Fig. 1.7 to a matrix $C = (c_{ij})$, where $c_{ij} = 1$ if i likes j, and 0 otherwise. Make the diagonal elements 0. Also set up the matrix U to be $n \times 1$ and contain only ones. Note that $U^t C$ gives scores for the "popularity" of each person.

35. Using C and U of Exercise 34, interpret the matrix CU.

36. Suppose that $B = (b_{ij})$ is another matrix of choices involving a similar experiment among a group of six. Let $b_{ij} = 1$ if person i likes person j, and $b_{ij} = -1$ if person i dislikes person j, and $b_{ii} = 0$. Construct such a matrix.

37. In the experiment of Exercise 36, we also construct a matrix $P = (p_{ij})$, where $p_{ij} = 1$ if person j *believes* that person i likes him and $p_{ij} = -1$ if person j *believes* that person i dislikes him; $p_{ii} = 0$. Construct such a matrix.

38. Let $N = P^t B = (n_{ij})$; compute N. Discuss how the entries of N might be interpreted as a measure of identification; i.e., cases where person i believes that he is liked by people who in fact like person j, and where person i believes that he is disliked by those who dislike j. What would the diagonal elements of N represent?

39. Discuss whether the diagonal elements of BP^t can be interpreted as a measure of how the beliefs of person i conform to his dislikes and likes.

1.6 NONSINGULAR MATRICES AND MATRIX INVERSION

It is a fact of real- and complex-number algebra that whenever a is a nonzero number, then the equation $ax = 1$ has a unique solution $x = a^{-1} = 1/a$. The number a^{-1} is called the (multiplicative) *inverse* of the nonzero number a. By contrast, it is not always true that a given nonzero matrix A has a multiplicative inverse. In those cases where A is an $n \times n$ matrix for which there does exist an $n \times n$ matrix B such that

$$AB = BA = I_n,$$

we call A an **invertible** or **nonsingular** matrix and say that the matrix B is its **inverse**. In this event we write $B = A^{-1}$. When such a matrix B fails to exist, we say that A is **singular**.

Example 1 Let

$$B = \begin{bmatrix} 3 & 1 \\ 5 & 2 \end{bmatrix} \quad \text{and} \quad A = \begin{bmatrix} 2 & -1 \\ -5 & 3 \end{bmatrix}.$$

The matrix B is the inverse of the matrix A because

$$AB = \begin{bmatrix} 2 & -1 \\ -5 & 3 \end{bmatrix} \begin{bmatrix} 3 & 1 \\ 5 & 2 \end{bmatrix} = \begin{bmatrix} 1 & 0 \\ 0 & 1 \end{bmatrix} = I_2,$$

and

$$BA = \begin{bmatrix} 3 & 1 \\ 5 & 2 \end{bmatrix} \begin{bmatrix} 2 & -1 \\ -5 & 3 \end{bmatrix} = \begin{bmatrix} 1 & 0 \\ 0 & 1 \end{bmatrix} = I_2.$$

Note that for A^{-1} to exist, it must work on both the right and the left of A; that is,

$$AA^{-1} = A^{-1}A = I_n.$$

Exercise 9 of the preceding section is an example of a case where $AB = I$, but $BA \neq I$; try it. This is possible, since matrix multiplication is not commutative. Here is a second example of this situation.

Example 2 Let

$$A = \begin{bmatrix} 1 & -1 & 1 \\ -2 & 0 & 1 \end{bmatrix} \quad \text{and} \quad B = \begin{bmatrix} 1 & -1 \\ 2 & -2 \\ 2 & -1 \end{bmatrix}.$$

Note that

$$AB = \begin{bmatrix} 1 & -1 & 1 \\ -2 & 0 & 1 \end{bmatrix} \begin{bmatrix} 1 & -1 \\ 2 & -2 \\ 2 & -1 \end{bmatrix} = \begin{bmatrix} 1 & 0 \\ 0 & 1 \end{bmatrix} = I_2,$$

but

$$BA = \begin{bmatrix} 1 & -1 \\ 2 & -2 \\ 2 & -1 \end{bmatrix} \begin{bmatrix} 1 & -1 & 1 \\ -2 & 0 & 1 \end{bmatrix} = \begin{bmatrix} 3 & -1 & 0 \\ 6 & -2 & 0 \\ 4 & -2 & 1 \end{bmatrix} \neq I_3.$$

Therefore, $B \neq A^{-1}$. In fact, A^{-1} does not exist.

As you may have noticed, we have really defined inverses only for square matrices, so that we could not expect A^{-1} to exist for the matrix A in Example 2. However, not even all square matrices have inverses. In Example 6 of the preceding section, the matrix

$$B = \begin{bmatrix} 1 & -2 \\ 2 & -4 \end{bmatrix}$$

was shown to be singular.

It is reasonable to ask if every *invertible* matrix has just one inverse. In other words, if A^{-1} does exist, is it unique? Is the notation A^{-1} justified? We have the following theorem that provides the answer.

Theorem 1.8

    If B and C are both inverses for the matrix A, then B = C.

Proof. If $AB = BA = I$ and $CA = AC = I$, then

$$C = CI = C(AB) = (CA)B = IB = B.$$

A careful examination of the proof of Theorem 1.8 readily yields the following corollary.

Corollary

    If $AB = I$ and $CA = I$ for the $n \times n$ matrices A, B, and C, then $B = C = A^{-1}$.

The proof of this corollary is left as an exercise.

    Even more is true; for *square* matrices the situation of Example 2 cannot arise. Although the machinery for its proof is a little beyond us at this point, we have the following theorem stating that it is enough to verify that $AB = I$ or $BA = I$ (not both) to determine that A^{-1} exists and equals B.

Theorem 1.9

    If A and B are $n \times n$ matrices and $AB = I$ or $BA = I$, then A has an inverse B. (This fact considerably simplifies the necessary checking.)

    The existence of an inverse for a nonsingular (invertible) matrix A has an immediate application to solving systems of linear equations.

Example 3   Use matrix algebra and Example 1 to solve the system of equations

$$\begin{cases} 2x - y = 4, \\ -5x + 3y = -7. \end{cases}$$

Although this simple system of equations could easily be solved by other means, we write it in matrix form as

$$AX = C,$$

where

$$A = \begin{bmatrix} 2 & -1 \\ -5 & 3 \end{bmatrix}, \quad X = \begin{bmatrix} x \\ y \end{bmatrix}, \quad \text{and} \quad C = \begin{bmatrix} 4 \\ -7 \end{bmatrix}.$$

Then, since from Example 1 we know that A is invertible and

$$A^{-1} = \begin{bmatrix} 3 & 1 \\ 5 & 2 \end{bmatrix},$$

we have $A^{-1}(AX) = A^{-1}C$. But $A^{-1}(AX) = (A^{-1}A)X = IX = X$. Thus,

$$X = A^{-1}C = \begin{bmatrix} 3 & 1 \\ 5 & 2 \end{bmatrix} \begin{bmatrix} 4 \\ -7 \end{bmatrix} = \begin{bmatrix} 5 \\ 6 \end{bmatrix}$$

or $x = 5$, $y = 6$.

Theorem 1.10

If A and B are $n \times n$ nonsingular matrices, then

i) $(A^{-1})^{-1} = A$;

ii) *AB is nonsingular and* $(AB)^{-1} = B^{-1}A^{-1}$;

iii) $(rA)^{-1} = \dfrac{1}{r}A^{-1}$ *for any nonzero scalar r.*

Proof. Since $AA^{-1} = A^{-1}A = I$, part (i) follows directly from the definition and Theorem 1.8. For part (ii) note that

$$(AB)(B^{-1}A^{-1}) = A(BB^{-1})A^{-1} = AIA^{-1} = AA^{-1} = I.$$

Therefore, from Theorem 1.8 and our remarks following its corollary, we get that $B^{-1}A^{-1}$ is the unique inverse of AB. We leave part (iii) as an exercise.

These results can be extended to the product of any finite number of invertible matrices.

Let us now combine the properties of matrix multiplication (as given in Theorems 1.5 and 1.10) with the Gauss–Jordan reduction techniques for solving systems of equations to obtain an algorithm for finding the inverse A^{-1} of a given nonsingular matrix A. You recall that in Sections 1.1 and 1.2 we found that a system of n equations in n unknowns has a unique solution if the augmented matrix of the system has a reduced row-echelon form

$$\begin{bmatrix} 1 & 0 & 0 & \cdots & 0 & \vdots & c_1 \\ 0 & 1 & 0 & \cdots & 0 & \vdots & c_2 \\ 0 & 0 & 1 & \cdots & 0 & \vdots & c_3 \\ \vdots & \vdots & \vdots & & \vdots & \vdots & \vdots \\ 0 & 0 & 0 & & 1 & \vdots & c_n \end{bmatrix}.$$

That is, the coefficient matrix A of the linear system $AX = C$ will be reducible to the $n \times n$ identity matrix I_n. We note that each of the elementary row operations of Theorem 1.2 used to accomplish this, can be performed by multiplying on the left by a certain nonsingular matrix called an *elementary matrix*. We shall then note that if $E_1, E_2, \ldots, E_k$ is a sequence of these elementary matrices such that

$$E_k E_{k-1} \cdots E_2 E_1 A = I,$$

then $E_k E_{k-1} \cdots E_2 E_1 = A^{-1}$. This will lead us to the algorithm for computing the inverse of a nonsingular matrix A. Let us begin with the definition of an elementary matrix.

An $n \times n$ matrix E is called an **elementary matrix** if it can be obtained by a single elementary row operation on the identity matrix I_n.

Since there are three basic elementary row operations, there are three basic types of elementary matrices. Each, as we shall notice, is nonsingular.

Type I. Interchanging rows. The elementary matrix $E(i, j)$ is obtained by interchanging rows i and j of the identity matrix I_n. Thus

$$E(1, 3) = \begin{bmatrix} 0 & 0 & 1 & 0 \\ 0 & 1 & 0 & 0 \\ 1 & 0 & 0 & 0 \\ 0 & 0 & 0 & 1 \end{bmatrix}.$$

Note that to obtain I_n again, we need only interchange rows i and j back. You can verify that

$$(E(i, j))^{-1} = E(i, j).$$

For example, in the set of 4×4 matrices we have $E(1, 3)E(1, 3) = I_4$. It can be shown that performing a type I elementary row operation on an arbitrary matrix A is the same as multiplying A *on the left* by the appropriate elementary matrix. Thus, $E(i, j)A$ will interchange row i of A with row j of A.

Example 4   Let

$$A = \begin{bmatrix} 2 & -1 & 4 & 6 \\ 0 & 1 & 3 & 5 \\ 1 & 0 & -1 & 2 \\ 0 & 1 & 0 & 5 \end{bmatrix}.$$

Then

$$E(1, 3)A = \begin{bmatrix} 0 & 0 & 1 & 0 \\ 0 & 1 & 0 & 0 \\ 1 & 0 & 0 & 0 \\ 0 & 0 & 0 & 1 \end{bmatrix} \cdot \begin{bmatrix} 2 & -1 & 4 & 6 \\ 0 & 1 & 3 & 5 \\ 1 & 0 & -1 & 2 \\ 0 & 1 & 0 & 5 \end{bmatrix} = \begin{bmatrix} 1 & 0 & -1 & 2 \\ 0 & 1 & 3 & 5 \\ 2 & -1 & 4 & 6 \\ 0 & 1 & 0 & 5 \end{bmatrix} = B.$$

Note that B is obtained from A by interchanging rows one and three of A.

Type II. Multiplying a row by a nonzero constant c. The elementary matrix $E(ci)$ is obtained by multiplying row i of the identity matrix I_n by the nonzero constant c. Thus,

$$E(-3 \cdot 2) = \begin{bmatrix} 1 & 0 & 0 \\ 0 & -3 & 0 \\ 0 & 0 & 1 \end{bmatrix}.$$

It can be shown that, to perform this operation on a row of an arbitrary matrix A, one multiples the matrix A by the elementary matrix $E(ci)$ *on the left.*

Example 5   If

$$K = \begin{bmatrix} 2 & 1 & 0 \\ 4 & 2 & 6 \\ 1 & 3 & -1 \end{bmatrix},$$

then

$$E(\tfrac{1}{2} \cdot 2)K = \begin{bmatrix} 1 & 0 & 0 \\ 0 & \tfrac{1}{2} & 0 \\ 0 & 0 & 1 \end{bmatrix} \cdot \begin{bmatrix} 2 & 1 & 0 \\ 4 & 2 & 6 \\ 1 & 3 & -1 \end{bmatrix} = \begin{bmatrix} 2 & 1 & 0 \\ 2 & 1 & 3 \\ 1 & 3 & -1 \end{bmatrix}.$$

To find the inverse for the type II elementary matrix $E(ci)$, we note that it is only necessary to multiply row i by $1/c$ to obtain the identity matrix I_n again. It can be verified that $E(\tfrac{1}{c}i)E(ci) = I_n$, so

$$(E(ci))^{-1} = E\left(\frac{1}{c}i\right).$$

Type III. Substituting for a given row its sum with a nonzero constant multiple of another row. The elementary matrix $E(i + kj)$ is obtained from the identity matrix I_n by adding k times row j to row i and substituting this for row i. For example,

$$E(2 - 3 \cdot 1) = \begin{bmatrix} 1 & 0 & 0 & 0 \\ -3 & 1 & 0 & 0 \\ 0 & 0 & 1 & 0 \\ 0 & 0 & 0 & 1 \end{bmatrix}.$$

Again one can show that multiplying by this elementary matrix has the same effect as performing the elementary operation on A, and also that the inverse of $E(i + kj)$ is $E(i - kj)$.

Example 6   Let A be the matrix of Example 4. Then

$$E(1-2\cdot3)A = \begin{bmatrix} 1 & 0 & -2 & 0 \\ 0 & 1 & 0 & 0 \\ 0 & 0 & 1 & 0 \\ 0 & 0 & 0 & 1 \end{bmatrix} \cdot \begin{bmatrix} 2 & -1 & 4 & 6 \\ 0 & 1 & 3 & 5 \\ 1 & 0 & -1 & 2 \\ 0 & 1 & 0 & 5 \end{bmatrix} = \begin{bmatrix} 0 & -1 & 6 & 2 \\ 0 & 1 & 3 & 5 \\ 1 & 0 & -1 & 2 \\ 0 & 1 & 0 & 5 \end{bmatrix} = B.$$

Note that B is derived from A by subtracting twice row three of A from row one.

Example 7   Let us show that the matrix K of Example 5 has reduced echelon form I_3, and is nonsingular. We shall find K^{-1} as the product of the elementary matrices involved in reducing K to I_3.

From Example 5 we have:

$$E_0 K = E\left(\frac{1}{2}\cdot2\right)K = \begin{bmatrix} 2 & 1 & 0 \\ 2 & 1 & 3 \\ 1 & 3 & -1 \end{bmatrix}.$$

Then

$$E(1,3)(E_0 K) = \begin{bmatrix} 0 & 0 & 1 \\ 0 & 1 & 0 \\ 1 & 0 & 0 \end{bmatrix} \begin{bmatrix} 2 & 1 & 0 \\ 2 & 1 & 3 \\ 1 & 3 & -1 \end{bmatrix} = \begin{bmatrix} 1 & 3 & -1 \\ 2 & 1 & 3 \\ 2 & 1 & 0 \end{bmatrix} = E_1 E_0 K,$$

$$E(2-1\cdot3)(E_1 E_0 K) = \begin{bmatrix} 1 & 0 & 0 \\ 0 & 1 & -1 \\ 0 & 0 & 1 \end{bmatrix} \begin{bmatrix} 1 & 3 & -1 \\ 2 & 1 & 3 \\ 2 & 1 & 0 \end{bmatrix} = \begin{bmatrix} 1 & 3 & -1 \\ 0 & 0 & 3 \\ 2 & 1 & 0 \end{bmatrix} = E_2 E_1 E_0 K,$$

$$E\left(\frac{1}{3}\cdot2\right)(E_2 E_1 E_0 K) = \begin{bmatrix} 1 & 0 & 0 \\ 0 & \frac{1}{3} & 0 \\ 0 & 0 & 1 \end{bmatrix} \begin{bmatrix} 1 & 3 & -1 \\ 0 & 0 & 3 \\ 2 & 1 & 0 \end{bmatrix} = \begin{bmatrix} 1 & 3 & -1 \\ 0 & 0 & 1 \\ 2 & 1 & 0 \end{bmatrix} = E_3 \ldots E_0 K,$$

$$E(3-2\cdot1)(E_3 \ldots E_0 K) = \begin{bmatrix} 1 & 0 & 0 \\ 0 & 1 & 0 \\ -2 & 0 & 1 \end{bmatrix} \begin{bmatrix} 1 & 3 & -1 \\ 0 & 0 & 1 \\ 2 & 1 & 0 \end{bmatrix} = \begin{bmatrix} 1 & 3 & -1 \\ 0 & 0 & 1 \\ 0 & -5 & 2 \end{bmatrix}$$
$$= E_4 E_3 \ldots E_0 K,$$

$$E(2,3)(E_4 \ldots E_0 K) = \begin{bmatrix} 1 & 0 & 0 \\ 0 & 0 & 1 \\ 0 & 1 & 0 \end{bmatrix} \begin{bmatrix} 1 & 3 & -1 \\ 0 & 0 & 1 \\ 0 & -5 & 2 \end{bmatrix} = \begin{bmatrix} 1 & 3 & -1 \\ 0 & -5 & 2 \\ 0 & 0 & 1 \end{bmatrix}$$
$$= E_5 E_4 \ldots E_0 K,$$

$$E(2-2\cdot3)(E_5 \ldots E_0 K) = \begin{bmatrix} 1 & 0 & 0 \\ 0 & 1 & -2 \\ 0 & 0 & 1 \end{bmatrix} \begin{bmatrix} 1 & 3 & -1 \\ 0 & -5 & 2 \\ 0 & 0 & 1 \end{bmatrix} = \begin{bmatrix} 1 & 3 & -1 \\ 0 & -5 & 0 \\ 0 & 0 & 1 \end{bmatrix}$$

$$= E_6 E_5 \ldots E_0 K,$$

$$E(-\tfrac{1}{5}\cdot2)(E_6 \ldots E_0 K) = \begin{bmatrix} 1 & 0 & 0 \\ 0 & -\tfrac{1}{5} & 0 \\ 0 & 0 & 1 \end{bmatrix} \begin{bmatrix} 1 & 3 & -1 \\ 0 & -5 & 0 \\ 0 & 0 & 1 \end{bmatrix} = \begin{bmatrix} 1 & 3 & -1 \\ 0 & 1 & 0 \\ 0 & 0 & 1 \end{bmatrix}$$

$$= E_7 \ldots E_0 K,$$

$$E(1+1\cdot3)(E_7 \ldots E_0 K) = \begin{bmatrix} 1 & 3 & 0 \\ 0 & 1 & 0 \\ 0 & 0 & 1 \end{bmatrix} = E_8 E_7 \ldots E_0 K,$$

$$E(1-3\cdot2)(E_8 \ldots E_0 K) = \begin{bmatrix} 1 & 0 & 0 \\ 0 & 1 & 0 \\ 0 & 0 & 1 \end{bmatrix} = I_3 = E_9 E_8 \ldots E_1 E_0 K.$$

Therefore,

$$(E_9 E_8 E_7 \ldots E_1 E_0)K = I_3,$$

so (by Theorem 1.9) K is indeed a nonsingular matrix and the inverse of K is the product of the elementary matrices used in the reduction:

$$K^{-1} = E_9 E_8 E_7 \ldots E_2 E_1 E_0.$$

You can perform the required multiplication and obtain

$$K^{-1} = \begin{bmatrix} \tfrac{2}{3} & -\tfrac{1}{30} & -\tfrac{1}{5} \\ -\tfrac{1}{3} & \tfrac{1}{15} & \tfrac{2}{5} \\ -\tfrac{1}{3} & \tfrac{1}{6} & 0 \end{bmatrix}.$$

Example 7 and the remarks preceding it give an indication of the proof of the following theorem.

Theorem 1.11

If A is an $n \times n$ matrix, then A is nonsingular if and only if A is row equivalent to the identity matrix I_n.

Rather than actually computing each elementary matrix in turn, collecting them, and multiplying them together at the end to find A^{-1}, it is usually easier to perform row operations directly. This gives the following algorithm for computing the inverse of a matrix, when it has one.

Matrix Inversion Algorithm

1. Adjoin the identity matrix I_n to the left of the given matrix A, forming $n \times 2n$ matrix denoted by

$$[I_n : A] \tag{1.35}$$

2. Apply row operations to the matrix $[I_n : A]$ so as to present the matrix A in its reduced row-echelon form.

If A is nonsingular, its reduced row-echelon form will be I_n, so that the final result will have the form

$$[A^{-1} : I_n] \tag{1.36}$$

This is true because, at each stage of the process of row reducing A and simultaneously the matrix of (1.35), the product of the elementary matrices involved appears in the left half of the large matrix and their product with A in the right half of the large matrix. That is, at each intermediate stage the large matrix has the form

$$[E_k E_{k-1} \ldots E_1 E_0 : E_k E_{k-1} \ldots E_0 A]$$

At the last stage the product on the right will be I_n and the product on the left will be A^{-1}. A simplified flowchart of this procedure is depicted in Chart 2 of the Appendix.

Example 8 Find A^{-1}, if it exists, for the matrix

$$A = \begin{bmatrix} 1 & -1 & 2 \\ 0 & 2 & -1 \\ 3 & -1 & 4 \end{bmatrix}.$$

Step 1. Form the matrix

$$[I_3 : A] = \begin{bmatrix} 1 & 0 & 0 & 1 & -1 & 2 \\ 0 & 1 & 0 & 0 & 2 & -1 \\ 0 & 0 & 1 & 3 & -1 & 4 \end{bmatrix}.$$

Step 2. Row-reduce A to I_3; if A is nonsingular, I_3 will become A^{-1}.
a) add (-3) times row one to row three:

$$\begin{bmatrix} 1 & 0 & 0 & 1 & -1 & 2 \\ 0 & 1 & 0 & 0 & 2 & -1 \\ -3 & 0 & 1 & 0 & 2 & -2 \end{bmatrix};$$

b) add (-1) times row two to row three:

$$\begin{bmatrix} 1 & 0 & 0 & 1 & -1 & 2 \\ 0 & 1 & 0 & 0 & 2 & -1 \\ -3 & -1 & 1 & 0 & 0 & -1 \end{bmatrix};$$

c) multiply row three by (-1):

$$\begin{bmatrix} 1 & 0 & 0 & 1 & -1 & 2 \\ 0 & 1 & 0 & 0 & 2 & -1 \\ 3 & 1 & -1 & 0 & 0 & 1 \end{bmatrix};$$

d) add row three to row two, and then add (-2) times row three to row one:

$$\begin{bmatrix} -5 & -2 & 2 & 1 & -1 & 0 \\ 3 & 2 & -1 & 0 & 2 & 0 \\ 3 & 1 & -1 & 0 & 0 & 1 \end{bmatrix};$$

e) multiply row two by $\frac{1}{2}$:

$$\begin{bmatrix} -5 & -2 & 2 & 1 & -1 & 0 \\ \frac{3}{2} & 1 & -\frac{1}{2} & 0 & 1 & 0 \\ 3 & 1 & -1 & 0 & 0 & 1 \end{bmatrix};$$

f) add row two to row one:

$$\begin{bmatrix} -\frac{7}{2} & -1 & \frac{3}{2} & 1 & 0 & 0 \\ \frac{3}{2} & 1 & -\frac{1}{2} & 0 & 1 & 0 \\ 3 & 1 & -1 & 0 & 0 & 1 \end{bmatrix}.$$

Stage (f) is of the desired form (1.36). You can quickly check by multiplication that with

$$A^{-1} = \begin{bmatrix} -\frac{7}{2} & -1 & \frac{3}{2} \\ \frac{3}{2} & 1 & -\frac{1}{2} \\ 3 & 1 & -1 \end{bmatrix};$$

$AA^{-1} = I$ so that A is indeed nonsingular.

Even if we do not know in advance whether a given matrix A is singular or nonsingular, we generally proceed with the inversion algorithm anyway. Because of Theorem 1.11, we will be unable to reduce A to I_n if A is singular. Thus, at some point in the process, we shall obtain a row of zeros in the right side of the large matrix obtained from $[I_n : A]$.

Example 9 Consider the matrix

$$B = \begin{bmatrix} 2 & 1 & 3 \\ 1 & 0 & -4 \\ 1 & -1 & 7 \end{bmatrix}.$$

Applying the matrix inversion algorithm, we proceed as follows:

$$\begin{bmatrix} 1 & 0 & 0 & 2 & -1 & 3 \\ 0 & 1 & 0 & 1 & 0 & -4; \\ 0 & 0 & 1 & 1 & -1 & 7 \end{bmatrix};$$

interchange rows one and two:

$$\begin{bmatrix} 0 & 1 & 0 & | & 1 & 0 & -4 \\ 1 & 0 & 0 & | & 2 & -1 & 3 \\ 0 & 0 & 1 & | & 1 & -1 & 7 \end{bmatrix};$$

add (-2) times row one to row two, and (-1) times row one to row three:

$$\begin{bmatrix} 0 & 1 & 0 & | & 1 & 0 & -4 \\ 1 & -2 & 0 & | & 0 & -1 & 11 \\ 0 & -1 & 1 & | & 0 & -1 & 11 \end{bmatrix};$$

subtract row two from row three:

$$\begin{bmatrix} 0 & 1 & 0 & | & 1 & 0 & -4 \\ 1 & -2 & 0 & | & 0 & -1 & 11 \\ -1 & 1 & 1 & | & 0 & 0 & 0 \end{bmatrix}.$$

The last stage shows a row of zeros in the right-hand side; therefore, B cannot be row reduced to I_3. Thus, B is a singular matrix.

Example 10 Suppose that the U.S. Government determines corporate taxes by taking a fixed percentage of the corporation's profits. The Giget Corporation does business in both the U.S. and Japan. The tax rate for the U.S. is r_{ss} for profits earned in the U.S. and r_{sj} for profits earned in Japan. Similarly, the Japanese government taxes the Giget Corporation on its profits. The rate for Japanese tax on profits earned in the U.S. is r_{js}, while its rate for profits earned in Japan is r_{jj}. We can arrange these tax rates in a matrix:

$$R = \begin{bmatrix} r_{ss} & r_{sj} \\ r_{js} & r_{jj} \end{bmatrix}.$$

We can also arrange the taxes paid by Giget Corporation and its profits in the two matrices:

$$T = \begin{bmatrix} t_s \\ t_j \end{bmatrix} \quad \text{and} \quad P = \begin{bmatrix} p_s \\ p_j \end{bmatrix}.$$

Then, clearly, $T = RP$, since

$$\text{U.S. taxes} = t_s = r_{ss}p_s + r_{sj}p_j$$

and

$$\text{Japanese taxes} = t_j = r_{js}p_s + r_{jj}p_j.$$

Suppose that for 1979 Giget paid 50 thousand dollars in U.S. taxes and 35 thousand dollars in Japanese taxes. Find the 1979 profits of the Giget Corporation if the rate matrix is

$$\begin{bmatrix} 0.03 & 0.05 \\ 0.07 & 0.02 \end{bmatrix}.$$

If R is nonsingular, we can find $P = R^{-1} T$ by simple matrix algebra, since $T = RP$. To actually compute R^{-1} (or see if it exists), we use the matrix inversion algorithm

$$[I_2 : R] = \begin{bmatrix} 1 & 0 & \vdots & 0.03 & 0.05 \\ 0 & 1 & \vdots & 0.07 & 0.02 \end{bmatrix}.$$

Therefore, $[I_2 : R]$ is row-equivalent to each of the following:

$$\begin{bmatrix} 100 & 0 & \vdots & 3 & 5 \\ 0 & 100 & \vdots & 7 & 2 \end{bmatrix} \rightarrow \begin{bmatrix} 100 & 0 & \vdots & 3 & 5 \\ -200 & 100 & \vdots & 1 & -8 \end{bmatrix} \rightarrow \begin{bmatrix} -200 & 100 & \vdots & 1 & -8 \\ 100 & 0 & \vdots & 3 & 5 \end{bmatrix} \rightarrow$$

$$\begin{bmatrix} -200 & 100 & \vdots & 1 & -8 \\ 700 & -300 & \vdots & 0 & 29 \end{bmatrix} \rightarrow \begin{bmatrix} -200 & 100 & \vdots & 1 & -8 \\ \frac{700}{29} & -\frac{300}{29} & \vdots & 0 & 1 \end{bmatrix} \rightarrow \begin{bmatrix} -\frac{200}{29} & \frac{500}{29} & \vdots & 1 & 0 \\ \frac{700}{29} & -\frac{300}{29} & \vdots & 0 & 1 \end{bmatrix}.$$

Since R^{-1} exists, we can compute the profits matrix P:

$$P = R^{-1} T = \frac{1}{29}\begin{bmatrix} -200 & 500 \\ 700 & -300 \end{bmatrix}\begin{bmatrix} 50 \\ 35 \end{bmatrix} = \frac{1}{29}\begin{bmatrix} 7500 \\ 24500 \end{bmatrix},$$

so the profits are 7500/29 thousand in U.S. and 24500/29 thousand in Japan, i.e., \$258,621 in U.S. and \$844,828 in Japan.

EXERCISES (1.6)

Find the inverse of each of the following elementary matrices:

1. $\begin{bmatrix} 0 & 1 \\ 1 & 0 \end{bmatrix}$ 2. $\begin{bmatrix} 1 & 0 \\ 3 & 1 \end{bmatrix}$ 3. $\begin{bmatrix} 1 & 0 \\ 0 & -5 \end{bmatrix}$ 4. $\begin{bmatrix} 0 & 1 & 0 \\ 1 & 0 & 0 \\ 0 & 0 & 1 \end{bmatrix}$

5. $\begin{bmatrix} 1 & 0 & 0 \\ 0 & 7 & 0 \\ 0 & 0 & 1 \end{bmatrix}$ 6. $\begin{bmatrix} 1 & 0 & 0 \\ 0 & 1 & 0 \\ -\frac{1}{5} & 0 & 1 \end{bmatrix}$ 7. $\begin{bmatrix} 0 & 0 & 1 & 0 \\ 0 & 1 & 0 & 0 \\ 1 & 0 & 0 & 0 \\ 0 & 0 & 0 & 1 \end{bmatrix}$ 8. $\begin{bmatrix} 1 & 0 & 0 & 0 \\ 0 & 1 & 0 & 0 \\ 0 & 0 & 1 & 0 \\ 0 & 5 & 0 & 1 \end{bmatrix}$

Determine which of the following matrices are nonsingular. Find the inverse for each of the nonsingular matrices.

9. $\begin{bmatrix} 7 & 0 & 0 \\ 0 & -3 & 0 \\ 0 & 0 & 4 \end{bmatrix}$ **10.** $\begin{bmatrix} 2 & -1 & 3 \\ 0 & 1 & -4 \\ 0 & 0 & -5 \end{bmatrix}$ **11.** $\begin{bmatrix} 4 & 0 & 0 \\ -2 & 3 & 0 \\ 6 & -1 & 5 \end{bmatrix}$

12. $\begin{bmatrix} 1 & 0 & -1 & 2 \\ 0 & 3 & -5 & 9 \\ 0 & 0 & 7 & 1 \\ 0 & 0 & 0 & -2 \end{bmatrix}$ **13.** $\begin{bmatrix} 1 & 0 & 0 & 1 \\ 0 & 1 & 0 & 1 \\ 1 & 0 & 1 & 0 \\ 1 & 1 & 0 & 1 \end{bmatrix}$ **14.** $\begin{bmatrix} 1 & 0 & 1 & 0 \\ 0 & 1 & 0 & 1 \\ -2 & 3 & -2 & 3 \\ 1 & 1 & 1 & 1 \end{bmatrix}$

Write the following systems of equations as matrix equations $AX = B$ and solve by finding $A^{-1}B$:

15. $\begin{aligned} 2x_1 - x_2 + 3x_3 &= 2 \\ x_2 - 4x_3 &= 5 \\ 2x_1 - x_2 - 2x_3 &= 7 \end{aligned}$ **16.** $\begin{aligned} x_1 - x_2 + x_3 &= 5 \\ x_1 + x_2 - x_3 &= -1 \\ 4x_1 - 3x_2 + 2x_3 &= -3 \end{aligned}$

17. $\begin{aligned} x_1 + 2x_2 - x_3 &= 4 \\ 2x_1 - 3x_2 + x_3 &= -1 \\ 5x_1 + 7x_2 + 2x_3 &= -1 \end{aligned}$ **18.** $\begin{aligned} x_1 + 2x_2 + x_3 - 2x_4 &= 4 \\ x_1 - x_2 - x_3 - 3x_4 &= 4 \\ 2x_1 + 2x_2 + 3x_3 - 3x_4 &= 4 \\ 3x_1 + 5x_2 + 5x_3 - x_4 &= 4 \end{aligned}$

Find the inverse for each of the given matrices, if it exists:

19. $\begin{bmatrix} 1 & 0 & 1 & 0 \\ 1 & -1 & 1 & 3 \\ 5 & 2 & 1 & 1 \\ 2 & 0 & -3 & 9 \end{bmatrix}$ **20.** $\begin{bmatrix} 1 & -1 & -1 & 1 \\ 3 & 1 & 1 & 1 \\ 2 & -1 & -1 & 1 \\ 1 & 2 & 3 & 1 \end{bmatrix}$

21. $\begin{bmatrix} 1 & 1 & 1 & 1 \\ 1 & 2 & -1 & 2 \\ 1 & -1 & 2 & 1 \\ 1 & 3 & 3 & 2 \end{bmatrix}$ **22.** $\begin{bmatrix} 1 & 1 & 2 & 1 \\ 0 & -2 & 0 & 0 \\ 1 & 2 & 1 & -2 \\ 0 & 3 & 2 & 1 \end{bmatrix}$

23. Prove the Corollary to Theorem 1.8.

24. Prove part (iii) of Theorem 1.10.

25. Prove that A is a nonsingular matrix if and only if the homogeneous system of linear equations $AX = 0$ has only the trivial solution $X = 0$.

26. Prove that if A is an $n \times n$ nonsingular matrix, then for each positive integer k, A^k is nonsingular and $(A^k)^{-1} = (A^{-1})^k$.

27. Prove that an $n \times n$ nilpotent matrix is singular (see definition on p. 50).

28. Prove that if A is nonsingular, then so is its transpose A^t and $(A^t)^{-1} = (A^{-1})^t$ (see Exercises 53–56 of Section 1.4).

29. Show that if A is a 3×3 nonsingular matrix, then the columns of A^{-1} are the three solutions to the three systems of equations

$$A \begin{bmatrix} x_{11} \\ x_{21} \\ x_{31} \end{bmatrix} = \begin{bmatrix} 1 \\ 0 \\ 0 \end{bmatrix}, \quad A \begin{bmatrix} x_{12} \\ x_{22} \\ x_{32} \end{bmatrix} = \begin{bmatrix} 0 \\ 1 \\ 0 \end{bmatrix}, \quad \text{and} \quad A \begin{bmatrix} x_{13} \\ x_{23} \\ x_{33} \end{bmatrix} = \begin{bmatrix} 0 \\ 0 \\ 1 \end{bmatrix}$$

30. Use the results of Exercise 29 to suggest an alternative justification for the matrix-inversion algorithm. Sometimes the matrix (1.35) is written in the alternative form $[A : I_n]$ and is row reduced to $[I_n : A^{-1}]$.

31. Prove or disprove the following: If A and B are nonsingular matrices, then so is $(A + B)$.

32. Show that the reduced echelon form of the matrix A of Example 4 is indeed I_4 and find all of the elementary matrices necessary to perform the row reduction.

33. Show that a 2×2 matrix

$$A = \begin{bmatrix} a_{11} & a_{12} \\ a_{21} & -a_{22} \end{bmatrix}$$

is nonsingular if and only if $d = a_{11}a_{22} - a_{12}a_{21} \neq 0$, in which case

$$A^{-1} = \frac{1}{d} \begin{bmatrix} a_{22} & -a_{12} \\ -a_{21} & a_{11} \end{bmatrix}.$$

In Exercises 34 and 35, suppose that the Macht Corporation does business in the U.S., West Germany, and France. Each country taxes the corporation profits according to the following matrix, where a_{ij} represents the tax by country i on the profits earned in country j:

	U.S.	W.G.	F.
U.S.	0.09	0.11	0.15
W.G.	0.11	0.05	0.22
F.	0.15	0.23	0.04

34. Find the amount of tax owed if the profits for 1979 are given in thousands of dollars by the matrix $[150, 210, 187]^t$.

35. How much were the profits if the taxes paid in 1978 are given in thousands of dollars by the matrix $[7, 9, 5]^t$ (see Example 10)?

Prove that for arbitrary $n \times n$ elementary matrices the following is true:

36. $(E_n(i, j))^{-1} = E_n(i, j)$ **37.** $(E_n(ci))^{-1} = E_n\left(\frac{1}{c}i\right), \quad (c \neq 0)$

38. $(F_n(i + kj))^{-1} = F_n(i - kj)$

DETERMINANTS

2

In this chapter we introduce the concept of a determinant. We shall also discuss another method for solving certain systems of equations that makes use of determinants. This determinant method, known as *Cramer's rule*, is very efficient for small and consistent systems of equations. Its value diminishes rapidly, however, as the number of variables increases.

2.1 DETERMINANT FUNCTION AND CRAMER'S RULE

The general form of a system of two linear equations in the two variables x_1 and x_2 is

$$\begin{cases} a_{11}x_1 + a_{12}x_2 = k_1, \\ a_{21}x_1 + a_{22}x_2 = k_2. \end{cases} \tag{2.1}$$

When this system is solved by the methods of Chapter 1, the augmented matrix has the following reduced row-echelon form (assuming that the denominators are not zero):

$$\begin{bmatrix} 1 & 0 & \dfrac{k_1 a_{22} - k_2 a_{12}}{a_{11} a_{22} - a_{12} a_{21}} \\ 0 & 1 & \dfrac{a_{11} k_2 - a_{21} k_1}{a_{11} a_{22} - a_{12} a_{21}} \end{bmatrix}. \tag{2.2}$$

Thus,

$$x_1 = \frac{k_1 a_{22} - k_2 a_{12}}{a_{11} a_{22} - a_{12} a_{21}} \tag{2.3}$$

and

$$x_2 = \frac{a_{11} k_2 - a_{21} k_1}{a_{11} a_{22} - a_{12} a_{21}}. \tag{2.4}$$

You should verify that these two values for x_1 and x_2 do indeed satisfy the system (2.1) provided $a_{11} a_{22} - a_{12} a_{21} \neq 0$. This number involves the entries in the coefficient matrix of the system (2.1) and leads us to the idea of a determinant of a square matrix.

If A is the 2×2 matrix

$$A = \begin{bmatrix} a_{11} & a_{12} \\ a_{21} & a_{22} \end{bmatrix},$$

the **determinant** of matrix A (denoted by det A and also by $|A|$) is the number $a_{11} a_{22} - a_{12} a_{21}$. Note that this number can be computed by the following scheme:

$$\det A = \det \begin{bmatrix} a_{11} & a_{12} \\ a_{21} & a_{22} \end{bmatrix} = a_{11} a_{22} - a_{12} a_{21}. \tag{2.5}$$

Consider again the formulas (2.3) and (2.4). Both denominators of the fractions are equal to the determinant of the coefficient matrix of the system (2.1), i.e., to

$$\Delta = \det \begin{bmatrix} a_{11} & a_{12} \\ a_{21} & a_{22} \end{bmatrix}.$$

We observe that the numerators of the fractions in (2.3) and (2.4) can also be considered to be determinants of certain 2×2 matrices. That is,

$$\det \begin{bmatrix} k_1 & a_{12} \\ k_2 & a_{22} \end{bmatrix} = k_1 a_{22} - a_{12} k_2 \tag{2.6}$$

and

$$\det \begin{bmatrix} a_{11} & k_1 \\ a_{21} & k_2 \end{bmatrix} = a_{11} k_2 - k_1 a_{21} \tag{2.7}$$

are the numerators of fractions (2.3) and (2.4), respectively. Thus, the solutions x_1, x_2 given in (2.3) and (2.4) can be cast in the following useful form known as *Cramer's rule*:

Cramer's Rule. *The solution of the system*

$$\begin{cases} a_{11}x_1 + a_{12}x_2 = k_1, \\ a_{21}x_1 + a_{22}x_2 = k_2, \end{cases}$$

where $a_{11}, a_{12}, a_{21}, a_{22}, k_1, k_2$ are known real numbers, is given by

$$x_1 = \frac{\det \begin{bmatrix} k_1 & a_{12} \\ k_2 & a_{22} \end{bmatrix}}{\det \begin{bmatrix} a_{11} & a_{12} \\ a_{21} & a_{22} \end{bmatrix}}, \qquad x_2 = \frac{\det \begin{bmatrix} a_{11} & k_1 \\ a_{21} & k_2 \end{bmatrix}}{\det \begin{bmatrix} a_{11} & a_{12} \\ a_{21} & a_{22} \end{bmatrix}}, \qquad (2.8)$$

provided that

$$\Delta = \det \begin{bmatrix} a_{11} & a_{12} \\ a_{21} & a_{22} \end{bmatrix} \neq 0.$$

Example 1   Use Cramer's rule to find the solution of the system

$$\begin{cases} 2x_1 - 3x_2 = 1, \\ 5x_1 + x_2 = 11. \end{cases}$$

Here

$$\Delta = \det \begin{bmatrix} a_{11} & a_{12} \\ a_{21} & a_{22} \end{bmatrix} = \det \begin{bmatrix} 2 & -3 \\ 5 & 1 \end{bmatrix} = (2)(1) - (-3)(5) = 17 \neq 0.$$

Thus, we may apply Cramer's rule to obtain

$$x_1 = \frac{\det \begin{bmatrix} 1 & -3 \\ 11 & 1 \end{bmatrix}}{\Delta} = \frac{(1)(1) - (-3)(11)}{17} = 2,$$

$$x_2 = \frac{\det \begin{bmatrix} 2 & 1 \\ 5 & 11 \end{bmatrix}}{\Delta} = \frac{(2)(11) - (1)(5)}{17} = 1.$$

The solution of the given system is, therefore, the pair $(2, 1)$.

If in (2.8)

$$\Delta = \det \begin{bmatrix} a_{11} & a_{12} \\ a_{21} & a_{22} \end{bmatrix} = 0,$$

then the given system will either have an *infinite* number of solutions, as in the following example:

$$\begin{cases} x_1 + x_2 = 1, \\ 2x_1 + 2x_2 = 2; \end{cases}$$

or the given system will have *no* solution at all, as in

$$\begin{cases} x_1 + x_2 = 1, \\ 2x_1 + 2x_2 = 3. \end{cases}$$

In the former case, the system is *consistent and dependent*, while in the latter case, the system is *inconsistent*. Of course, the formulas for x_1 and x_2 given in (2.8) become *meaningless* and, therefore, *cannot be used* if

$$\Delta = \det \begin{bmatrix} a_{11} & a_{12} \\ a_{21} & a_{22} \end{bmatrix} = 0.$$

With an eye on (2.8), it is natural to inquire about the solution of a system of three linear equations in three variables. Of course, we may once again use the Gaussian elimination technique to solve such a system. If we do this, the solutions for x_1, x_2, x_3 take on fractional forms that are much more complicated than the fractional forms we obtained for x_1 and x_2 in (2.3) and (2.4). Nevertheless, such solutions are made up in a similar way from determinants of 3×3 matrices defined as follows.

Let A be the matrix

$$A = \begin{bmatrix} a_{11} & a_{12} & a_{13} \\ a_{21} & a_{22} & a_{23} \\ a_{31} & a_{32} & a_{33} \end{bmatrix}. \tag{2.9}$$

The **determinant** of A, denoted by $\det A$ or $|A|$, is the number

$$\Delta = a_{11}a_{22}a_{33} + a_{12}a_{23}a_{31} + a_{13}a_{21}a_{32} - a_{31}a_{22}a_{13} - a_{32}a_{23}a_{11} - a_{33}a_{21}a_{12}. \tag{2.10}$$

This number can be computed from the following diagonalization scheme:

$$\det A = \det \begin{bmatrix} a_{11} & a_{12} & a_{13} \\ a_{21} & a_{22} & a_{23} \\ a_{31} & a_{32} & a_{33} \end{bmatrix} = \begin{bmatrix} a_{11} & a_{12} & a_{13} & a_{11} & a_{12} \\ a_{21} & a_{22} & a_{23} & a_{21} & a_{22} \\ a_{31} & a_{32} & a_{33} & a_{31} & a_{32} \end{bmatrix}. \tag{2.11}$$

Notice that we have recopied the first two columns of A at the right of this scheme. The products down the diagonals are positive, whereas those up the "sinisteral" diagonals are negative.

Example 2 Evaluate

$$\det \begin{bmatrix} 2 & -4 & -2 \\ -1 & 5 & -4 \\ 7 & 2 & -4 \end{bmatrix}.$$

Using the diagonalization scheme of (2.11), we recopy the first two columns of the matrix immediately to the right and get

Thus, the determinant is

$$(2)(5)(-4) + (-4)(-4)(7) + (-2)(-1)(2) - (7)(5)(-2)$$
$$- (2)(-4)(2) - (-4)(-1)(-4)$$
$$= -40 + 112 + 4 - (-70) - (-16) - (-16) = 178.$$

Example 3 Verify that the determinant of the 3×3 matrix A given in (2.9) can be computed in terms of three 2×2 determinants according to the following scheme:

$$\det A = a_{11} \det \begin{bmatrix} a_{22} & a_{23} \\ a_{32} & a_{33} \end{bmatrix} - a_{12} \det \begin{bmatrix} a_{21} & a_{23} \\ a_{31} & a_{33} \end{bmatrix} + a_{13} \det \begin{bmatrix} a_{21} & a_{22} \\ a_{31} & a_{32} \end{bmatrix}. \qquad (2.12)$$

A direct calculation shows that the right side of (2.12) is

$$a_{11}(a_{22}a_{33} - a_{23}a_{32}) - a_{12}(a_{21}a_{33} - a_{23}a_{31}) + a_{13}(a_{21}a_{32} - a_{22}a_{31})$$

which, when multiplied out and rearranged, is precisely the expression in (2.10) for the determinant of A.

In the next section we shall see that no simple diagonalization scheme exists for computing the determinant of a 4×4 or larger matrix, but that the method of Example 3 can be generalized to expand the determinants of $n \times n$ matrices when $n > 3$.

Knowing how to expand a 3×3 determinant allows us to extend Cramer's rule to solve systems of three linear equations in three variables.

Cramer's Rule. *For a given system*

$$\begin{cases} a_{11}x_1 + a_{12}x_2 + a_{13}x_3 = k_1, \\ a_{21}x_1 + a_{22}x_2 + a_{23}x_3 = k_2, \\ a_{31}x_1 + a_{32}x_2 + a_{33}x_3 = k_3, \end{cases} \qquad (2.13)$$

the matrix of the coefficients is

$$A = \begin{bmatrix} a_{11} & a_{12} & a_{13} \\ a_{21} & a_{22} & a_{23} \\ a_{31} & a_{32} & a_{33} \end{bmatrix}.$$

Let $\Delta = \det A$, as given in Eq. (2.10). Consider the three matrices:

$$B_1 = \begin{bmatrix} k_1 & a_{12} & a_{13} \\ k_2 & a_{22} & a_{23} \\ k_3 & a_{32} & a_{33} \end{bmatrix}, \quad B_2 = \begin{bmatrix} a_{11} & k_1 & a_{13} \\ a_{21} & k_2 & a_{23} \\ a_{31} & k_3 & a_{33} \end{bmatrix}, \quad B_3 = \begin{bmatrix} a_{11} & a_{12} & k_1 \\ a_{21} & a_{22} & k_2 \\ a_{31} & a_{32} & k_3 \end{bmatrix},$$

where in each $B_i (i = 1, 2, 3)$ the column of constants has replaced the coefficients of x_i in the matrix A. Set

$$\Delta_1 = \det B_1, \qquad \Delta_2 = \det B_2, \qquad \Delta_3 = \det B_3.$$

Then, similar to (2.8), the solution to the general 3×3 system of equations (2.13) is

$$x_1 = \frac{\Delta_1}{\Delta}, \qquad x_2 = \frac{\Delta_2}{\Delta}, \qquad x_3 = \frac{\Delta_3}{\Delta}, \tag{2.14}$$

provided $\Delta \neq 0$. These results would actually have been attained if we had augmented the matrix A with the column of constants and then used the Gauss–Jordan reduction to find an equivalent matrix in reduced row-echelon form.

Let us remind you again that, when we are computing the determinants in the numerators of the fractions in (2.14), the column of constants appears in the same position in the matrix B_i as do the coefficients of the corresponding variable x_i in the matrix A. This is similar to the case of a two-variable system (see (2.8)).

The following example illustrates the use of Cramer's rule to solve a system of three linear equations in three unknowns.

Example 4   Find the solution to the system

$$\begin{cases} 4x_2 + 3x_3 = -2, \\ -2x_1 + 5x_2 - 2x_3 = 1, \\ 3x_1 + 4x_2 + 5x_3 = 6. \end{cases} \tag{2.15}$$

Solution. Before we can apply Cramer's rule, we must first evaluate the determinant Δ of the matrix of coefficients of the variables x_1, x_2, x_3 in (2.15). Remembering that the first equation of the system is $0x_1 + 4x_2 + 3x_3 = -2$, we can write

$$\Delta = \det \begin{bmatrix} 0 & 4 & 3 \\ -2 & 5 & -2 \\ 3 & 4 & 5 \end{bmatrix}.$$

Now, by definition,

$$\Delta = 0 - 24 - 24 - 45 + 40 - 0 = -53.$$

Since $\Delta = -53 \neq 0$, Cramer's rule applies. Therefore,

$$x_1 = \frac{\det \begin{bmatrix} -2 & 4 & 3 \\ 1 & 5 & -2 \\ 6 & 4 & 5 \end{bmatrix}}{\Delta} = \frac{-50 - 48 + 12 - 90 - 20 - 16}{-53} = \frac{-212}{-53} = 4.$$

Again, by Cramer's rule,

$$x_2 = \frac{\det \begin{bmatrix} 0 & -2 & 3 \\ -2 & 1 & -2 \\ 3 & 6 & 5 \end{bmatrix}}{\Delta} = \frac{0 + 12 - 36 - 9 - 20 - 0}{-53} = \frac{12 - 65}{-53} = \frac{-53}{-53} = 1.$$

To find the value of x_3 we can either use Cramer's rule again, or else substitute the values of x_1 and x_2 already found into one of the equations of the system. If we use Cramer's rule again, we have

$$x_3 = \frac{\det \begin{bmatrix} 0 & 4 & -2 \\ -2 & 5 & 1 \\ 3 & 4 & 6 \end{bmatrix}}{\Delta} = \frac{0 + 12 + 16 - (-30) - 0 - (-48)}{-53} = \frac{106}{-53} = -2.$$

Thus,

$$\begin{aligned} x_1 &= 4, \\ x_2 &= 1, \\ x_3 &= -2. \end{aligned}$$

Therefore, the solution of system (2.15) is $(4, 1, -2)$.

You should *check* that these values of x_1, x_2, x_3 do indeed satisfy every equation in the given system of equations in (2.15).

What happens if, in Cramer's rule, the determinant of the matrix of coefficients of the variables is equal to zero? As we saw in the discussion following Example 1, here there are also two possibilities: Either the system has an *infinite* number of solutions, as in

$$\begin{cases} x_1 + x_2 + x_3 = 1, \\ 2x_1 + 2x_2 + 2x_3 = 2, \\ x_1 - x_2 + x_3 = -1, \end{cases}$$

or the system has *no* solution at all, as in

$$\begin{cases} x_1 + x_2 + x_3 = 1, \\ 2x_1 + 2x_2 + 2x_3 = 3, \\ x_1 - x_2 + x_3 = -1. \end{cases}$$

Cramer's rule for solving a system of linear equations extends in the obvious way to a system of any size. However, the determinant of an $n \times n$ matrix is a sum of $n!$ products and is difficult to compute or even to define. In fact, the computation of the determinant of a 20×20 matrix, which is a sum of $20! = 2.43 \times 10^{18}$ products, is not within the practical capability of even the fastest computer. In the next section we shall discuss a general method for finding the determinant of an $n \times n$ matrix and then we shall demonstrate through the use of several theorems a more efficient method of computation based on row reducing the matrix.

You will no doubt correctly conclude from all of this that (except for systems of two linear equations in two unknowns where Cramer's rule is highly efficient) the methods of Chapter 1 are the most efficient for solving systems of linear equations. Nevertheless, determinants are theoretically important and have numerous practical applications, as we shall see in later chapters.

EXERCISES (2.1)

Evaluate the following determinants:

1. $\det \begin{bmatrix} 1 & 2 \\ -3 & 4 \end{bmatrix}$ 2. $\det \begin{bmatrix} 3 & 1 \\ 0 & -5 \end{bmatrix}$ 3. $\det \begin{bmatrix} -1 & 0 \\ 1 & -6 \end{bmatrix}$

4. $\det \begin{bmatrix} 1 & \tan x \\ \tan x & -1 \end{bmatrix}$ 5. $\det \begin{bmatrix} a & b \\ -b & a \end{bmatrix}$ 6. $\det \begin{bmatrix} 2 & 3 & 4 \\ 1 & 5 & 3 \\ -3 & 6 & 9 \end{bmatrix}$

7. $\det \begin{bmatrix} 1 & -1 & 3 \\ 2 & 4 & 0 \\ -1 & 1 & 9 \end{bmatrix}$ 8. $\det \begin{bmatrix} 1 & 4 & -1 \\ 0 & 3 & 1 \\ 0 & 0 & -2 \end{bmatrix}$ 9. $\det \begin{bmatrix} 1 & 0 & 0 \\ -2 & -3 & 0 \\ 4 & 1 & 2 \end{bmatrix}$

In Exercises 10–12, verify that

10. $\det \begin{bmatrix} a_1 & a_2 \\ b_1 & b_2 \end{bmatrix} = \det \begin{bmatrix} a_1 & b_1 \\ a_2 & b_2 \end{bmatrix}$ 11. $\det \begin{bmatrix} a_1 & a_2 & a_3 \\ b_1 & b_2 & b_3 \\ c_1 & c_2 & c_3 \end{bmatrix} = \det \begin{bmatrix} a_1 & b_1 & c_1 \\ a_2 & b_2 & c_2 \\ a_3 & b_3 & c_3 \end{bmatrix}$

12.
$$\det \begin{bmatrix} a_1 + a_1' & a_2 + a_2' \\ b_1 & b_2 \end{bmatrix} = \det \begin{bmatrix} a_1 & a_2 \\ b_1 & b_2 \end{bmatrix} + \det \begin{bmatrix} a_1' & a_2' \\ b_1 & b_2 \end{bmatrix}$$

Use Cramer's rule to solve the following systems of equations:

13. $2x_1 - 3x_2 = 1$
$\quad\; 5x_1 + 4x_2 = -1$

14. $3x_1 + 4x_2 = 7$
$\quad\; 4x_1 + 5x_2 = 9$

15. $-4x_1 + 3x_2 \qquad = 5$
$\qquad\quad x_2 - 3x_3 = -4$
$\quad\; 2x_1 - 4x_2 + 5x_3 = 0$

16. $x_1 - x_2 + x_3 = -1$
$\quad 2x_1 + x_2 - 2x_3 = 1$
$\quad 3x_1 - 2x_2 + 3x_3 = -2$

17. $\dfrac{2}{a} - \dfrac{3}{b} + \dfrac{5}{c} = 3$

$\qquad \dfrac{2}{b} - \dfrac{1}{c} = 2$

$-\dfrac{4}{a} + \dfrac{7}{b} + \dfrac{2}{c} = 0$

18. $\quad x \cos\theta + y \sin\theta = 3$
$\qquad -x \sin\theta + y \cos\theta = 5,$
where θ is a given positive real number.

Hint. Let $x_1 = 1/a$, $x_2 = 1/b$, $x_3 = 1/c$.

19. A boy has \$3.45 consisting of nickels, dimes, and quarters. He has exactly 27 coins and the number of nickels is twice the number of dimes. How many nickels, dimes, and quarters does he have?

20. When painters A and B paint a house together, they need $60/11$ days. When painters B and C paint the house, they need $20/3$ days. Finally, when painters A and C paint the house, they need 6 days. How many days does each painter need to paint this house alone? *Hint*: Set a system of three equations and solve it using Cramer's rule.

21. A man deposits \$x at bank A that pays 6% annual rate of interest, \$y at bank B at 5% annual rate of interest, and \$z at bank C at 4% annual rate of interest. At the end of the year, his combined interest from banks A and B is \$229, from banks B and C is \$209, and from banks A and C is \$268. How much does he have in each bank and how much is his total annual interest?

22. The system

$$ax_1 - \quad 2x_2 - \quad x_3 = 0$$
$$(a+1)x_2 + \quad 4x_3 = 0$$
$$(a-1)x_3 = 0$$

has *more* than one solution; find a. *Hint.* Cramer's rule does *not* apply here; why?

23. Describe the set of all solutions of the resulting system of equations for each value of a obtained in Problem 22.

24. Show that for all *real* numbers a the only solution of the system

$$(a+1)x_1 \qquad - x_2 = 0,$$
$$2x_1 + (a-1)x_2 = 0,$$

is $x_1 = 0$, $x_2 = 0$.

25. The Plastic Products Company makes plastic plates and plastic cups. Both require time on two machines: cups require 1 hr on machine I and 2 hrs on machine II; plates require 3 hrs on machine I and 1 hr on machine II. Each machine can operate 15 hrs a day. How many of each product can be manufactured in a day under these conditions?

Exercises 26–29 refer to the following: The business analyst of Commercial Products Manufacturing Company wants to find an equation that can be used to project the sales for a relatively new cleaning product. For the years 1975–77, the amount of sales in thousands of dollars are given by the following table:

1975	1976	1977
15	64	123

26. Sketch a graph using the year 1975 as reference (0) on the horizontal axis and dividing the vertical axis into tens of thousands of dollars, so that 1977 sales appear as the point (2, 12.3).

27. Find the equation of the line $y = mx + b$ passing through the 1975 and 1976 points. Is the 1977 point on or near this line? Remember that $m = (y_2 - y_1)/(x_2 - x_1)$.

28. Find the equation of the parabola $y = ax^2 + bx + c$ passing through all three points.

29. Project the 1980 sales from these two graphs. In which prediction do you have the most confidence? Why?

30. Show that the area of a triangle ABC, where $A: (x_1, y_1)$, $B: (x_2, y_2)$, $C: (x_3, y_3)$, is equal to

$$\pm \tfrac{1}{2} \det \begin{bmatrix} x_1 & y_1 & 1 \\ x_2 & y_2 & 1 \\ x_3 & y_3 & 1 \end{bmatrix}.$$

Hint: From A, B, C drop perpendicular lines to the x-axis; then use the formula for the area of a trapezoid.

31. Show that the equation of a line L passing through the distinct points (x_1, y_1) and (x_2, y_2) can be written as the determinantal equation

$$\det \begin{bmatrix} x & y & 1 \\ x_1 & y_1 & 1 \\ x_2 & y_2 & 1 \end{bmatrix} = 0.$$

Hint: See Exercise 30.

2.2 LAPLACE EXPANSION OF DETERMINANTS

In this section we discuss some of the more important properties of determinants. These properties are often quite useful in evaluating determinants, and usually provide more efficient techniques for doing this than the definition itself.

Recall that in Section 2.1 we defined the determinant of 2×2 and 3×3 matrices. We also remarked that for any square matrix A with real-number entries the real-number det A exists. However, when $n > 3$, the definition is so complicated that we shall not even consider it here. Instead, we shall state the most important properties of determinants and discuss how some of them can be derived from others.

We start by describing a step-by-step process for computing det A from determinants of smaller matrices. Let

$$A = \begin{bmatrix} a_{11} & a_{12} & a_{13} & \cdots & a_{1n} \\ a_{21} & a_{22} & a_{23} & \cdots & a_{2n} \\ \vdots & \vdots & \vdots & \vdots & \vdots \\ a_{n1} & a_{n2} & a_{n3} & \cdots & a_{nn} \end{bmatrix}. \tag{2.16}$$

We first introduce the concepts of the minor and the cofactor of any entry in A.

The **minor** of the entry a_{ij} in row i and column j in the matrix A of (2.16) is the determinant of the submatrix obtained by deleting row i and column j from A. The **cofactor** of the entry a_{ij} in the matrix A of (2.16) is the product of the minor of a_{ij} and $(-1)^{i+j}$.

Example 1   Find the minors of each of the entries of the matrix

$$A = \begin{bmatrix} 2 & 3 & 1 \\ -1 & 0 & 4 \\ 5 & -2 & -3 \end{bmatrix}.$$

Since the entry $a_{11} = 2$ occurs in row 1 and column 1, we delete row 1 and column 1 from A, to get the submatrix

$$\begin{bmatrix} 0 & 4 \\ -2 & -3 \end{bmatrix}.$$

Hence, by definition:

$$\text{Minor of } a_{11}(= 2) = \det \begin{bmatrix} 0 & 4 \\ -2 & -3 \end{bmatrix}$$
$$= (0)(-3) - (4)(-2) = 8.$$

Similarly, we compute

$$\text{Minor of } a_{12}(= 3) = \det \begin{bmatrix} -1 & 4 \\ 5 & -3 \end{bmatrix}$$
$$= (-1)(-3) - (4)(5) = -17;$$

$$\text{Minor of } a_{13}(= 1) = \det \begin{bmatrix} -1 & 0 \\ 5 & -2 \end{bmatrix}$$
$$= (-1)(-2) - (0)(5) = 2;$$

$$\text{Minor of } a_{21}(= -1) = \det \begin{bmatrix} 3 & 1 \\ -2 & -3 \end{bmatrix}$$

$$= (3)(-3) - (1)(-2) = -7;$$

$$\text{Minor of } a_{22}(= 0) = \det \begin{bmatrix} 2 & 1 \\ 5 & -3 \end{bmatrix}$$

$$= (2)(-3) - (1)(5) = -11;$$

$$\text{Minor of } a_{23}(= 4) = \det \begin{bmatrix} 2 & 3 \\ 5 & -2 \end{bmatrix}$$

$$= (2)(-2) - (3)(5) = -19;$$

$$\text{Minor of } a_{31}(= 5) = \det \begin{bmatrix} 3 & 1 \\ 0 & 4 \end{bmatrix}$$

$$= (3)(4) - (1)(0) = 12;$$

$$\text{Minor of } a_{32}(= -2) = \det \begin{bmatrix} 2 & 1 \\ -1 & 4 \end{bmatrix}$$

$$= (2)(4) - (1)(-1) = 9;$$

$$\text{Minor of } a_{33}(= -3) = \det \begin{bmatrix} 2 & 3 \\ -1 & 0 \end{bmatrix}$$

$$= (2)(0) - (3)(-1) = 3.$$

Now denote the cofactor of a_{ij} by A_{ij}. Then the definition may be rewritten as follows:

$$A_{ij} = \text{Cofactor of } a_{ij} \doteq (-1)^{i+j} \cdot (\text{Minor of } a_{ij}). \tag{2.17}$$

Example 2 Find the cofactors of the entries of the matrix

$$A = \begin{bmatrix} 2 & 3 & 1 \\ -1 & 0 & 4 \\ 5 & -2 & -3 \end{bmatrix}.$$

Note that this is the same matrix as that given in Example 1. Hence, using the results of Example 1, we have

$$A_{11} = (-1)^{1+1} \cdot (\text{Minor of } a_{11}) = 8;$$

and

$$A_{12} = (-1)^{1+2} \cdot (\text{Minor of } a_{12}) = (-1)(-17) = 17.$$

Similarly, we verify that

$$A_{13} = 2; \quad A_{21} = 7; \quad A_{22} = -11; \quad A_{23} = 19;$$
$$A_{31} = 12; \quad A_{32} = -9; \quad A_{33} = 3.$$

We are now in a position to state the process for finding the determinant of an $n \times n$ matrix.

Let A be the $n \times n$ matrix in (2.16) and let A_{ij} denote the cofactor of a_{ij} (see (2.17)). Then the **determinant** of A (denoted by det A) is given by

$$\det A = a_{11}A_{11} + a_{12}A_{12} + a_{13}A_{13} + \ldots + a_{1n}A_{1n} = \sum_{j=1}^{n} a_{1j}A_{1j}. \quad (2.18)$$

In other words, the determinant of A is the sum of n terms obtained by multiplying each entry a_{1j} in row 1 by its corresponding cofactor A_{1j} $(j = 1, 2, 3, \ldots, n)$.

The formula in (2.18) is known as the *Laplace expansion of the determinant of A across the first row*. It can be shown, however, that we always obtain the same value of the determinant if we expand across *any* row. In fact, for each $i = 1, 2, 3, \ldots, n$,

$$\det A = a_{i1}A_{i1} + a_{i2}A_{i2} + a_{i3}A_{i3} + \ldots + a_{in}A_{in} = \sum_{j=1}^{n} a_{ij}A_{ij}. \quad (2.19)$$

Note the similarity between the expansions in (2.18) and (2.19). The formula in (2.19) is known as *Laplace expansion of the determinant of A across the ith row*.

Example 3   Illustrate (2.18) and (2.19) for the matrix

$$A = \begin{bmatrix} 2 & 3 & 1 \\ -1 & 0 & 4 \\ 5 & -2 & -3 \end{bmatrix}.$$

Again this is the same matrix as that given in Examples 1 and 2. Using the results of these examples, we see that (2.18) gives

$$\det A = a_{11}A_{11} + a_{12}A_{12} + a_{13}A_{13}$$
$$= 2(8) + 3(17) + 1(2) = 69.$$

Similarly, using (2.19) with $i = 2$, we get

$$\det A = a_{21}A_{21} + a_{22}A_{22} + a_{23}A_{23}$$
$$= (-1)(7) + 0(-11) + 4(19) = 69.$$

Finally, using (2.19) with $i = 3$, we once again get the same value:

$$\det A = a_{31}A_{31} + a_{32}A_{32} + a_{33}A_{33}$$
$$= 5(12) + (-2)(-9) + (-3)(3) = 69.$$

It can also be shown that we get the same number for the determinant of A if we expand down the jth column in the sense that

$$\det A = a_{1j}A_{1j} + a_{2j}A_{2j} + a_{3j}A_{3j} + \ldots + a_{nj}A_{nj} = \sum_{i=1}^{n} a_{ij}A_{ij}, \qquad (2.20)$$

where $j = 1, 2, 3, \ldots, n$. We illustrate this in the next example.

Example 4   Illustrate (2.20) for the matrix

$$A = \begin{bmatrix} 2 & 3 & 1 \\ -1 & 0 & 4 \\ 5 & -2 & -3 \end{bmatrix}.$$

To expand down column 1 means of course that we take $j = 1$ in (2.20) to get (see Example 2):

$$\det A = a_{11}A_{11} + a_{21}A_{21} + a_{31}A_{31}$$
$$= 2(8) + (-1)(7) + 5(12) = 69.$$

Similarly, expanding down column 2, that is, taking $j = 2$ in (2.20), we get

$$\det A = a_{12}A_{12} + a_{22}A_{22} + a_{32}A_{32}$$
$$= 3(17) + 0(-11) + (-2)(-9) = 69.$$

Finally, taking $j = 3$ in (2.20), we verify that

$$\det A = a_{13}A_{13} + a_{23}A_{23} + a_{33}A_{33}$$
$$= 1(2) + 4(19) + (-3)(3) = 69.$$

The Laplace expansion of $\det A$ across any row or down any column of the matrix A is justified by some of the basic properties of determinants that shall be considered shortly.

To begin with, we recall that in the exercises of Section 1.4 we introduced the *transpose* of a matrix. Here we restate the definition for square matrices. If $A = (a_{ij})$ is any $n \times n$ matrix, then the transpose $A^t = (b_{ij})$ of A is the $n \times n$ matrix such that $b_{ij} = a_{ji}$; that is, the entry in row i and column j of A^t is the entry in row j and column i of A, where $i, j = 1, 2, \ldots, n$. Thus the rows of A are the columns of A^t and the columns of A are the rows of A^t.

Example 5   If

$$A = \begin{bmatrix} 1 & 0 & -2 \\ 3 & 5 & 1 \\ -1 & 4 & -3 \end{bmatrix} \qquad \text{then} \quad A^t = \begin{bmatrix} 1 & 3 & -1 \\ 0 & 5 & 4 \\ -2 & 1 & -3 \end{bmatrix}.$$

The first basic property of determinants is given by the following theorem.

Theorem 2.1

For any $n \times n$ matrix A,

$$\det A = \det A^t.$$

We omit the proof here, but suggest that you check it for the 2×2 and 3×3 matrices in Exercises 31 and 32 at the end of this section.

Example 6 Let

$$A = \begin{bmatrix} 1 & 0 & -2 & -1 \\ 2 & 4 & 1 & 3 \\ 5 & -2 & 3 & -1 \\ 1 & -4 & 3 & -5 \end{bmatrix}.$$

Then its transpose is

$$A^t = \begin{bmatrix} 1 & 2 & 5 & 1 \\ 0 & 4 & -2 & -4 \\ -2 & 1 & 3 & 3 \\ -1 & 3 & -1 & -5 \end{bmatrix}.$$

Using the Laplace expansion (2.18) across the first row, we get

$$\det A = \quad (1) \det \begin{bmatrix} 4 & 1 & 3 \\ -2 & 3 & -1 \\ -4 & 3 & -5 \end{bmatrix} - (0) \det \begin{bmatrix} 2 & 1 & 3 \\ 5 & 3 & -1 \\ 1 & 3 & -5 \end{bmatrix}$$

$$+ (-2) \det \begin{bmatrix} 2 & 4 & 3 \\ 5 & -2 & -1 \\ 1 & -4 & -5 \end{bmatrix} - (-1) \det \begin{bmatrix} 2 & 4 & 1 \\ 5 & -2 & 3 \\ 1 & -4 & 3 \end{bmatrix}$$

$$= 1(-60 + 4 - 18 + 36 - 10 + 12) - 0$$
$$- 2(20 - 4 - 60 + 6 + 100 - 8) + 1(-12 + 12 - 20 + 2 - 60 + 24)$$
$$= (-36) - 2(54) + (-54) = -198.$$

Using (2.18) again we find that

$$\det A^t = \quad (1) \det \begin{bmatrix} 4 & -2 & -4 \\ 1 & 3 & 3 \\ 3 & -1 & -5 \end{bmatrix} - (2) \det \begin{bmatrix} 0 & -2 & -4 \\ -2 & 3 & 3 \\ -1 & -1 & -5 \end{bmatrix}$$

$$+ (5) \det \begin{bmatrix} 0 & 4 & -4 \\ -2 & 1 & 3 \\ -1 & 3 & -5 \end{bmatrix} - (1) \det \begin{bmatrix} 0 & 4 & -2 \\ -2 & 1 & 3 \\ -1 & 3 & -1 \end{bmatrix}$$

$$= 1(-60 - 18 + 4 + 36 + 12 - 10) - 2(0 + 6 - 8 - 12 + 0 + 20)$$
$$+ 5(0 - 12 + 24 - 4 + 0 - 40) - 1(0 - 12 + 12 - 2 + 0 - 8)$$
$$= 1(-36) - 2(6) + 5(-32) - 1(-10) = -198.$$

As you can readily infer from this example, the Laplace expansion of a determinant can be very tedious to compute. The presence of a zero in the first row of the matrix A in the above example made the computation of det A somewhat easier than the computation of det A^t. We close this section with a theorem that considerably shortens the work required to expand a determinant when it is used in connection with row-reduction techniques.

Recall from the exercises of Section 1.5 that an $n \times n$ matrix A is called upper triangular if all its entries below the main diagonal are zero. That is, the matrix $A = (a_{ij})$ is *upper triangular* if and only if $a_{ij} = 0$ whenever $j < i$. A lower-triangular matrix is defined similarly: A is *lower triangular* when $a_{ij} = 0$ for all $j > i$. For example, the matrices

$$A = \begin{bmatrix} 2 & -1 & 3 \\ 0 & 4 & 7 \\ 0 & 0 & -2 \end{bmatrix} \quad \text{and} \quad B = \begin{bmatrix} 2 & 0 & 0 \\ 1 & 3 & 0 \\ 5 & 1 & -5 \end{bmatrix}$$

are, respectively, upper- and lower-triangular. The theorem in question is the following:

Theorem 2.2

If $A = (a_{ij})$ is any $n \times n$ upper- (or lower-) triangular matrix, then

$$\det A = a_{11}a_{22}\ldots a_{nn} = \prod_{i=1}^{n} a_{ii};$$

that is, the determinant of an upper- (or lower-) triangular matrix is equal to the product of its main diagonal elements.

The proof of this theorem is a straightforward induction on the size of the matrix. It is trivial for a 1×1 matrix and, although not essential to the proof, is easy to verify for the 2×2 and 3×3 matrices by using the diagonalization schemes of (2.5) and (2.11). Indeed,

$$\det \begin{bmatrix} a_{11} & a_{12} \\ 0 & a_{22} \end{bmatrix} = a_{11}a_{22} \quad \text{and} \quad \det \begin{bmatrix} a_{11} & a_{12} & a_{13} \\ 0 & a_{22} & a_{23} \\ 0 & 0 & a_{33} \end{bmatrix} = a_{11}a_{22}a_{33}.$$

If we assume the theorem to be true for any $(n-1) \times (n-1)$ upper-triangular matrix and consider the $n \times n$ matrix

$$M = \begin{bmatrix} a_{11} & a_{12} & \cdots & a_{1n} \\ 0 & a_{22} & \cdots & a_{2n} \\ \vdots & \vdots & \vdots & \vdots \\ 0 & 0 & \cdots & a_{nn} \end{bmatrix},$$

we may use (2.20) and expand det M down the first column. This gives

$$\det M = a_{11} \det \begin{bmatrix} a_{22} & a_{23} & \cdots & a_{2n} \\ 0 & a_{33} & \cdots & a_{3n} \\ \vdots & \vdots & \vdots & \vdots \\ 0 & 0 & \cdots & a_{nn} \end{bmatrix} + 0. \qquad (2.21)$$

But the determinant on the right side of (2.21) is the determinant of an $(n-1) \times (n-1)$ upper-triangular matrix. According to our induction assumption, this determinant is equal to

$$a_{22}a_{33} \cdots a_{nn};$$

therefore,

$$\det M = a_{11}a_{22} \cdots a_{nn},$$

as desired. The result also holds for lower-triangular matrices by applying the proof given to M^t by means of Theorem 2.1.

Example 7 Find the determinant of

$$K = \begin{bmatrix} 3 & 2 & 0 & -1 & 5 \\ 0 & 1 & 4 & 1 & 3 \\ 0 & 0 & -1 & -2 & 1 \\ 0 & 0 & 0 & 2 & -1 \\ 0 & 0 & 0 & 0 & 5 \end{bmatrix}.$$

A direct application of the theorem gives us

$$\det K = (3)(1)(-1)(2)(5) = -30.$$

As another direct application of Theorem 2.2, we have the following corollaries.

Corollary 1
If $A = \text{diag}[d_1, d_2, \ldots, d_n]$, then

$$\det A = d_1 d_2 \cdots d_n.$$

The special case of the identity matrix is stated as Corollary 2.

Corollary 2
For the $n \times n$ identity matrix I_n,

$$\det I_n = 1.$$

In the next section we shall see how Theorem 2.2 can be used in connection with elementary matrices to cut down considerably on the work required to compute a determinant.

EXERCISES (2.2) ——————————————————————————————

Use the Laplace expansion across any row or column to compute the determinants of the following matrices:

1. $\begin{bmatrix} 1 & 0 & 1 \\ 2 & 1 & 0 \\ 0 & 1 & -1 \end{bmatrix}$
2. $\begin{bmatrix} -1 & 1 & 1 \\ 2 & 2 & 1 \\ 4 & 0 & -1 \end{bmatrix}$
3. $\begin{bmatrix} \sin x & \cos x \\ -\cos x & \sin x \end{bmatrix}$

4. $\begin{bmatrix} 1 & 0 & 1 & -1 \\ 0 & 1 & -1 & 2 \\ 2 & 1 & -2 & 1 \\ 0 & 1 & 0 & 3 \end{bmatrix}$
5. $\begin{bmatrix} 1 & 0 & -1 & 1 \\ 2 & 1 & -1 & 4 \\ 1 & 0 & 1 & 3 \\ 0 & 1 & -1 & 0 \end{bmatrix}$
6. $\begin{bmatrix} e^x & -\sin x \\ \sin x & e^{-x} \end{bmatrix}$

7. $\begin{bmatrix} 4 & 2 & 4 & 6 \\ 2 & 1 & 1 & 1 \\ 2 & 4 & -1 & -1 \\ 2 & 1 & 1 & 1 \end{bmatrix}$
8. $\begin{bmatrix} 1 & 2 & 0 & 4 \\ 0 & 1 & 2 & 0 \\ 1 & 0 & 1 & 2 \\ 1 & -1 & 0 & 1 \end{bmatrix}$
9. $\begin{bmatrix} 1 & 0 & 1 & 0 & 1 \\ 0 & 1 & 0 & 1 & 0 \\ 1 & 0 & 0 & 1 & 0 \\ 0 & 1 & 1 & 0 & 0 \\ 0 & 0 & 1 & 1 & 0 \end{bmatrix}$

10. Verify that det A = det A^t when

$$A = \begin{bmatrix} 1 & 0 & -2 \\ 3 & 5 & 1 \\ -1 & 4 & -3 \end{bmatrix}.$$

Use Theorem 2.2 to compute the determinants of the following matrices:

11. $\begin{bmatrix} 2 & 4 & 6 & 8 & 1 \\ 0 & 2 & 4 & 6 & 8 \\ 0 & 0 & 2 & 4 & 6 \\ 0 & 0 & 0 & 2 & 4 \\ 0 & 0 & 0 & 0 & 2 \end{bmatrix}$
12. $\begin{bmatrix} 1 & 0 & 0 & 0 & 0 & 0 \\ 3 & 1 & 0 & 0 & 0 & 0 \\ 5 & 3 & 1 & 0 & 0 & 0 \\ 7 & 5 & 3 & 1 & 0 & 0 \\ 9 & 7 & 5 & 3 & 1 & 0 \\ 1 & 9 & 7 & 5 & 3 & 1 \end{bmatrix}$

13. $5I_3$ 14. $3I_5$ 15. diag $[2, 4, 6, 8]$

Compute the determinants of the following 3×3 elementary matrices:

16. $\begin{bmatrix} 0 & 1 & 0 \\ 1 & 0 & 0 \\ 0 & 0 & 1 \end{bmatrix}$
17. $\begin{bmatrix} 1 & 0 & 0 \\ 0 & 0 & 1 \\ 0 & 1 & 0 \end{bmatrix}$
18. $\begin{bmatrix} 0 & 0 & 1 \\ 0 & 1 & 0 \\ 1 & 0 & 0 \end{bmatrix}$

19. $\begin{bmatrix} 1 & 0 & 0 \\ 0 & -3 & 0 \\ 0 & 0 & 1 \end{bmatrix}$ **20.** $\begin{bmatrix} \frac{1}{2} & 0 & 0 \\ 0 & 1 & 0 \\ 0 & 0 & 1 \end{bmatrix}$ **21.** $\begin{bmatrix} 1 & 0 & 0 \\ 0 & 1 & 0 \\ 0 & 0 & \frac{1}{6} \end{bmatrix}$

22. $\begin{bmatrix} 1 & 0 & 0 \\ 0 & 1 & 0 \\ 3 & 0 & 1 \end{bmatrix}$ **23.** $\begin{bmatrix} 1 & 0 & 0 \\ -2 & 1 & 0 \\ 0 & 0 & 1 \end{bmatrix}$ **24.** $\begin{bmatrix} 1 & -3 & 0 \\ 0 & 1 & 0 \\ 0 & 0 & 1 \end{bmatrix}$

In Exercises 25–28, let A be the following matrix:

$$A = \begin{bmatrix} 1 & 3 & 1 \\ 2 & 0 & 1 \\ 3 & -1 & 2 \end{bmatrix}.$$

25. Compute det A.

26. Find the row-echelon form M for A (upper-triangular).

27. Find the reduced row-echelon form N for A.

28. Compute det M and det N and compare with det A.

29. Use Cramer's rule to solve the following system of equations:

$$\begin{aligned} x + y + z + w &= 0, \\ x - y - z - w &= 2, \\ x \quad\;\; + z \quad\;\; &= 3, \\ y \quad\;\; - w &= 1. \end{aligned}$$

30. Let A be the matrix given before Exercise 25 and let

$$B = \begin{bmatrix} -1 & 0 & 1 \\ 1 & 2 & -1 \\ 1 & 4 & 5 \end{bmatrix}.$$

Show that $\det(AB) = (\det A)(\det B)$.

31. Let A be an arbitrary 2×2 matrix. Verify that det A = det A^t.

32. Verify that det A = det A^t for an arbitrary 3×3 matrix.

2.3 PROPERTIES OF DETERMINANTS—ROW REDUCTION

In Theorem 2.2 we learned that the determinant of an upper-triangular matrix is the product of its main-diagonal elements. In Chapter 1 we learned how to reduce a matrix to row-echelon form, which is always upper-triangular. We shall see how these two ideas can be combined to compute the determinant of a square matrix. To add a note of caution (lest your active mind race rapidly to an unwarranted conclusion), we present the following example.

Example 1 Let

$$A = \begin{bmatrix} 2 & 1 \\ 3 & 6 \end{bmatrix}.$$

Reduce A to its row-echelon form M and compare det A and det M.

First of all, by elementary row operations on A we obtain the following equivalent matrices:

a) $\begin{bmatrix} 2 & 1 \\ 1 & 2 \end{bmatrix}$, b) $\begin{bmatrix} 1 & 2 \\ 2 & 1 \end{bmatrix}$, c) $\begin{bmatrix} 1 & 2 \\ 0 & -3 \end{bmatrix}$, d) $\begin{bmatrix} 1 & 2 \\ 0 & 1 \end{bmatrix} = M.$

Now det $M = 1$ and det $A = 9$. How does one compare them? It is *not* immediately obvious that

$$\det M = \left(\frac{1}{3}\right)(-1)\left(-\frac{1}{3}\right) \det A.$$

It is our purpose to demonstrate how steps (a)–(d) determine this result. To begin with, we need the following very important theorem, whose proof is beyond us at this point. We ask you to check it in the 2×2 case as an exercise.

Theorem 2.3

If A and B are $n \times n$ matrices, then

$$\det(AB) = (\det A)(\det B). \tag{2.22}$$

In section 1.6 we learned that every elementary row operation on a matrix A can be performed by premultiplying (i.e., multiplying on left) A by an appropriate elementary matrix E. Let us compute the determinants of these types of elementary matrices and then see how this row (or column) operation will affect det A.

Type 1.   The interchange of two rows. If we interchange two rows of the identity matrix, say row i and row j, we obtain the elementary matrix E_1. By using the Laplace expansion for the determinant of this matrix, we eventually must get

$$\det E_1 = (1)(1) \ldots (1) \det \begin{bmatrix} 0 & 1 \\ 1 & 0 \end{bmatrix} = -1. \tag{2.23}$$

Then if A is any $n \times n$ matrix and B is obtained from A by interchanging rows i and j, we must have $B = E_1 A$, so by Theorem 2.3, det $B = \det E_1 \det A$ and hence

$$\det B = -\det A. \tag{2.24}$$

Because of Theorem 2.1, (2.24) is also true if columns are interchanged. We summarize these facts as Property 1 of determinants.

Property 1

If any two rows (columns) of a matrix A are interchanged, then the determinant of the resulting matrix is equal to the negative of the determinant of A.

Example 2

$$\det \begin{bmatrix} -4 & -3 \\ 5 & 9 \end{bmatrix} = -\det \begin{bmatrix} 5 & 9 \\ -4 & -3 \end{bmatrix}.$$

This becomes clear when both determinants are expanded since

$$(-4)9 - (5)(-3) = -[(5)(-3) - (-4)(9)],$$

as well as from the fact that the left-hand matrix results from interchanging rows one and two of the right-hand matrix.

Type 2. Multiplying a row by a nonzero constant. If row i of the identity matrix I_n is multiplied by the nonzero constant k, then the resulting elementary matrix E_2 is still diagonal:

$$E_2 = \operatorname{diag}(1, \ldots, 1, k, 1, \ldots, 1),$$

where k is in the ith position. Therefore, from Theorem 2.2 we have

$$\det E_2 = k. \tag{2.25}$$

Then if A is any $n \times n$ matrix and B is obtained from A by multiplying row i of A by the nonzero constant k, we have $B = E_2 A$, so by Theorem 2.3,

$$\det B = \det E_2 \det A$$

and hence

$$\det B = k \det A. \tag{2.26}$$

Because of Theorem 2.1, the same is true if a column of A is multiplied by k. Then we have the following:

Property 2

If all the elements of a row (column) in a matrix A are multiplied by k, then the determinant of the resulting matrix is equal to k times the determinant of A.

Example 3

$$\det \begin{bmatrix} 1 & 3 & 4 \\ 5 & 10 & 15 \\ 0 & 1 & 5 \end{bmatrix} = 5 \det \begin{bmatrix} 1 & 3 & 4 \\ 1 & 2 & 3 \\ 0 & 1 & 5 \end{bmatrix}.$$

The second row of the left-hand matrix is (5) times the second row of the right-hand matrix.

Type 3.   Substituting for a given row its sum with a nonzero-constant multiple of some other row. If row i of the identity matrix is replaced by its sum with (k) times row j, the resulting elementary matrix E_3 is either upper- or lower-triangular depending on whether $i < j$ or $i > j$, respectively. In any case, the diagonal elements are still all 1.

Example 4   Add k times row four to row two of the identity matrix I_4. We have the matrix

$$E_3 = \begin{bmatrix} 1 & 0 & 0 & 0 \\ 0 & 1 & 0 & k \\ 0 & 0 & 1 & 0 \\ 0 & 0 & 0 & 1 \end{bmatrix}.$$

Since a Type 3 elementary matrix is of this form, we have

$$\det E_3 = 1. \tag{2.27}$$

Therefore, if A is any $n \times n$ matrix and the matrix B is obtained from A by substituting for row i of A its sum with k times row j, we have $B = E_3 A$ so again by Theorem 2.3 we get that $\det B = \det (E_3 A) (\det E_3)(\det A)$ and hence

$$\det B = \det A. \tag{2.28}$$

The same thing will result from operating on transposes using Theorem 2.1, if a column of A is replaced by its sum with a constant multiple of any other column. Thus, we have

Property 3

If we add to a row (column) of a matrix A any multiple of another row (column) of A, then the determinant of the resulting matrix is equal to the determinant of A.

Example 5

$$\det \begin{bmatrix} 2 & 6 & 7 \\ -1 & -3 & 1 \\ 5 & 8 & 10 \end{bmatrix} = \det \begin{bmatrix} 2+2(-1) & 6+2(-3) & 7+2(1) \\ -1 & -3 & 1 \\ 5 & 8 & 10 \end{bmatrix}$$

$$= \det \begin{bmatrix} 0 & 0 & 9 \\ -1 & -3 & 1 \\ 5 & 8 & 10 \end{bmatrix} = 9 \det \begin{bmatrix} -1 & -3 \\ 5 & 8 \end{bmatrix}$$

$$= 9(-8+15) = 9(7) = 63.$$

The following additional properties of determinants are special cases, or corollaries of Properties 1, 2, and 3. You can verify them as exercises.

Property 4

If any two rows (columns) in a matrix A are identical, then the determinant of A is equal to zero.

Example 6   Verify that

$$\det \begin{bmatrix} 5 & 3 & 1 \\ 0 & 2 & 4 \\ 5 & 3 & 1 \end{bmatrix} = 0.$$

Property 5

If a row (column) in a matrix A consists entirely of zeros, then the determinant of A is equal to zero.

Example 7   Verify that

$$\det \begin{bmatrix} 4 & -5 & 2 \\ 0 & 0 & 0 \\ 1 & 3 & 7 \end{bmatrix} = 0.$$

Let us return briefly to Example 1 to justify the assertion made there about the determinant of the given matrix A and of its row-echelon form M.

Example 1   (Revisited)

$$\det \begin{bmatrix} 2 & 1 \\ 3 & 6 \end{bmatrix} = 3 \det \begin{bmatrix} 2 & 1 \\ 1 & 2 \end{bmatrix} \qquad \text{(by Property 2)}$$

$$= 3(-1) \det \begin{bmatrix} 1 & 2 \\ 2 & 1 \end{bmatrix} \qquad \text{(by Property 1)}$$

$$= 3(-1) \det \begin{bmatrix} 1 & 2 \\ 0 & -3 \end{bmatrix} \qquad \text{(by Property 3)}$$

$$= 3(-1)(1)(-3) \qquad \text{(by Theorem 2.2)}$$

$$= 9.$$

Example 8   Compute the determinant of the matrix

$$A = \begin{bmatrix} 4 & 2 & 4 & 6 \\ 2 & 1 & 1 & 1 \\ 2 & 4 & -1 & -1 \\ -2 & 1 & 1 & 1 \end{bmatrix}.$$

$$A = \begin{bmatrix} 4 & 2 & 4 & 6 \\ 2 & 1 & 1 & 1 \\ 2 & 4 & -1 & -1 \\ -2 & 1 & 1 & 1 \end{bmatrix}$$

Observe that

$$\det A = 4 \det \begin{bmatrix} 1 & 1 & 2 & 3 \\ 1 & 1 & 1 & 1 \\ 1 & 4 & -1 & -1 \\ -1 & 1 & 1 & 1 \end{bmatrix} \qquad \text{(by using Property 2 on row 1 and column 1)}$$

$$= 4 \det \begin{bmatrix} 1 & 1 & 2 & 3 \\ 0 & 0 & -1 & -2 \\ 0 & 3 & -3 & -4 \\ 0 & 2 & 2 & 2 \end{bmatrix} \qquad \text{(by using Property 3 and row reducing)}$$

$$= (-4)(2) \det \begin{bmatrix} 1 & 1 & 2 & 3 \\ 0 & 1 & 1 & 1 \\ 0 & 3 & -3 & -4 \\ 0 & 0 & -1 & -2 \end{bmatrix} \qquad \text{(by Properties 1 and 2)}$$

$$= -8 \det \begin{bmatrix} 1 & 1 & 2 & 3 \\ 0 & 1 & 1 & 1 \\ 0 & 0 & -6 & -7 \\ 0 & 0 & -1 & -2 \end{bmatrix} \qquad \text{(by Property 3)}$$

$$= 8 \det \begin{bmatrix} 1 & 1 & 2 & 3 \\ 0 & 1 & 1 & 1 \\ 0 & 0 & 1 & 2 \\ 0 & 0 & 6 & 7 \end{bmatrix} \qquad \text{(by Properties 1 and 2)}$$

$$= 8 \det \begin{bmatrix} 1 & 1 & 2 & 3 \\ 0 & 1 & 1 & 1 \\ 0 & 0 & 1 & 2 \\ 0 & 0 & 0 & -5 \end{bmatrix} \qquad \text{(by Property 3)}$$

$$= 8(-5) \qquad \text{(by Theorem 2.2)} = -40.$$

Example 9 Show that the only solution of the system

$$\begin{cases} 2x_1 - 3x_2 + x_3 = 0, \\ \qquad\quad 2x_2 + 5x_3 = 0, \\ 4x_1 - 5x_2 \qquad = 0, \end{cases} \tag{2.29}$$

is the trivial solution given by $x_1 = x_2 = x_3 = 0$.

First, we evaluate the determinant D of the coefficient matrix in (2.29). Thus

$$D = \det \begin{bmatrix} 2 & -3 & 1 \\ 0 & 2 & 5 \\ 4 & -5 & 0 \end{bmatrix} = 2 \det \begin{bmatrix} 1 & -3 & 1 \\ 0 & 2 & 5 \\ 2 & -5 & 0 \end{bmatrix}$$

$$= 2 \det \begin{bmatrix} 1 & -3 & 1 \\ 0 & 2 & 5 \\ 0 & 1 & -2 \end{bmatrix} = -18 \neq 0.$$

Thus $D \neq 0$ and Cramer's rule may be applied (see Section 2.1). Now, according to Cramer's rule:

$$x_1 = \frac{\det \begin{bmatrix} 0 & -3 & 1 \\ 0 & 2 & 5 \\ 0 & -5 & 0 \end{bmatrix}}{D} = 0 \qquad \text{(by Property 5)}.$$

Hence $x_1 = 0$. Similarly, using Cramer's rule we obtain $x_2 = 0$ and $x_3 = 0$.

Remember that a system of linear equations such as (2.29), where *all the constants on the right side are zero*, is called a *homogeneous system*. The argument in the above example can be generalized to yield the following interesting theorem:

Theorem 2.4

Suppose that the determinant of the matrix A of the coefficients of a homogeneous system of n linear equations in n variables is not equal to zero. Then the only solution this system has is the trivial solution given by

$$x_1 = 0, \qquad x_2 = 0, \qquad \ldots, \qquad x_n = 0.$$

On the other hand, if $\det A = 0$, then the system has a nontrivial solution (i.e., a solution in which not all of the variables are zero). In fact, in this latter case the system has an infinite number of solutions.

As a convenient reference, we have collected in the Appendix the five properties of determinants discussed in this Section.

EXERCISES (2.3)

In Exercises 1–7, use the properties of determinants discussed in this section to show that the following equalities are true. Do it *without computing* these determinants.

1. $\det \begin{bmatrix} 2 & 3 & 5 \\ 1 & 4 & 6 \\ 0 & 3 & 0 \end{bmatrix} = -\det \begin{bmatrix} 0 & 3 & 0 \\ 1 & 4 & 6 \\ 2 & 3 & 5 \end{bmatrix}$

2. $\det \begin{bmatrix} 1 & 5 & 4 \\ 3 & 6 & -3 \\ 2 & 4 & 7 \end{bmatrix} = 3 \det \begin{bmatrix} 1 & 5 & 4 \\ 1 & 2 & -1 \\ 2 & 4 & 7 \end{bmatrix}$

3. $\det \begin{bmatrix} 1 & 3 & 4 \\ 2 & 5 & 7 \\ 3 & 2 & 8 \end{bmatrix} = \det \begin{bmatrix} 1 & 3 & 4 \\ 2-2(1) & 5-2(3) & 7-2(4) \\ 3-3(1) & 2-3(3) & 8-3(4) \end{bmatrix}$

4. $\det \begin{bmatrix} 2 & 1 & 2 \\ 2 & 5 & 2 \\ 2 & 7 & 2 \end{bmatrix} = 0$

5. $\det \begin{bmatrix} 3 & 0 & 1 \\ 4 & 0 & 5 \\ 2 & 0 & 3 \end{bmatrix} = 0$

6.
$$\det \begin{bmatrix} 3 & 1 & 7 \\ 0 & 4 & 9 \\ 0 & -5 & 8 \end{bmatrix} = 3 \det \begin{bmatrix} 4 & 9 \\ -5 & 8 \end{bmatrix}$$

7.
$$\det \begin{bmatrix} a & b & c & d \\ 0 & e & f & g \\ 0 & 0 & h & i \\ 0 & 0 & 0 & j \end{bmatrix} = aehj$$

In Exercises 8 and 9 show that the given equalities hold:

8.
$$\det \begin{bmatrix} 1 & 1 & 1 \\ a & b & c \\ a^2 & b^2 & c^2 \end{bmatrix} = (a-b)(b-c)(c-a)$$

9.
$$\det \begin{bmatrix} 1 & x & x^2 & x^3 \\ 1 & y & y^2 & y^3 \\ 1 & z & z^2 & z^3 \\ 1 & w & w^2 & w^3 \end{bmatrix} = (x-y)(x-z)(x-w)(y-z)(y-w)(z-w)$$

In Exercises 10–14, evaluate the following:

10.
$$\det \begin{bmatrix} 1 & 5 & 7 \\ -2 & 1 & 0 \\ 4 & 1 & 3 \end{bmatrix}$$

11.
$$\det \begin{bmatrix} 1 & 0 & 0 & -1 \\ 2 & 3 & -4 & 5 \\ 4 & 0 & 3 & 0 \\ 0 & 0 & 2 & 8 \end{bmatrix}$$

12.
$$\det \begin{bmatrix} \frac{1}{2} & \frac{1}{2} & 0 \\ \frac{2}{3} & \frac{1}{3} & 1 \\ \frac{3}{5} & 1 & 1 \end{bmatrix}$$

13.
$$\det \begin{bmatrix} 1 & 0 & 0 & 0 \\ 2 & 3 & 0 & 0 \\ 4 & 5 & 6 & 0 \\ 7 & 8 & 9 & 1 \end{bmatrix}$$

14.
$$\det \begin{bmatrix} 0 & 1 & 0 & 1 & 0 \\ 1 & 0 & 0 & 1 & 1 \\ 0 & 1 & 1 & 0 & 1 \\ 1 & 1 & 0 & 1 & 0 \\ 1 & 1 & 1 & 1 & 1 \end{bmatrix}$$

Find the determinant and simplify the resulting expression:

15.
$$\det \begin{bmatrix} 1 & \tan \alpha \\ \tan \alpha & -1 \end{bmatrix}$$

16.
$$\det \begin{bmatrix} 1 & \csc \alpha \\ \csc \alpha & -1 \end{bmatrix}$$

17.
$$\det \begin{bmatrix} x & y \\ -y & x \end{bmatrix}$$

18.
$$\det \begin{bmatrix} x & y & 1 \\ 1 & 1 & 2 \\ 2 & 1 & 3 \end{bmatrix}$$

19.
$$\det \begin{bmatrix} 2 & 1 & 1 \\ 1 & 2 & 1 \\ 1 & 1 & 2 \end{bmatrix}$$

20. Write the transposes of each matrix in Exercises 10–14 and compute their determinants.

21. Use Property 1 to prove Property 4. *Hint.* Interchange the two identical rows.

22. Prove Property 5.

23. Show by an example that in general it is false that $\det(A+B) = \det A + \det B$.

24. Let A and B be two arbitrary 2×2 matrices. Verify Theorem 2.3 by proving that

$$\det(AB) = \det A \det B.$$

25. Prove that if $A = (a_{ij})$ is an $n \times n$ matrix, then for any i and j, where $i, j = 1, 2, \ldots, n$ and $i \neq j$,

$$a_{i1} A_{j1} + a_{i2} A_{j2} + \ldots + a_{in} A_{jn} = 0.$$

26. Show that for all *real* numbers a and b, the trivial solution (i.e., $x_1 = x_2 = x_3 = 0$) is the only solution of the system

$$\begin{aligned} x_1 + ax_2 + \qquad bx_3 &= 0, \\ (a+1)x_2 + \qquad 2x_3 &= 0, \\ (b^2+1)x_2 + (1-a)x_3 &= 0. \end{aligned}$$

In Exercises 27 and 28, solve for x:

27. $\det \begin{bmatrix} 3 & x+1 \\ 2 & x-1 \end{bmatrix} = 0$ 28. $\det \begin{bmatrix} 1+x & 1 & 1 \\ 1 & 1+x & 1 \\ 1 & 1 & 1+x \end{bmatrix} = 0$

29. Use Theorem 2.3 to prove that if A is a nonsingular matrix, then

$$\det A \neq 0 \text{ and } \det A^{-1} = 1/(\det A).$$

Exercises 30–33 are for students who have studied calculus.

If $f(x)$ is a function, its derivative is denoted by $f'(x)$. The *Wronskian* of two functions $f(x)$ and $g(x)$ at a point x_0 common to both their domains is defined by

$$w(f, g, x_0) = \det \begin{bmatrix} f(x_0) & g(x_0) \\ f'(x_0) & g'(x_0) \end{bmatrix}.$$

The Wronskian of more than two functions is defined analogously using higher derivatives as needed. Evaluate the following Wronskians:

30. $w(f, g, 0)$ for $f(x) = e^x$, $g(x) = e^{2x}$
31. $w(f, g, \pi/4)$ for $f(x) = \sin x$, $g(x) = \sin 2x$ $\sqrt{2}/2$
32. $w(f, g, h, 0)$ for $f(x) = e^x$, $g(x) = e^{x^2}$, $h(x) = e^{x^3}$
33. $w(f, g, h, 0)$ for $f(x) = 1$, $g(x) = \cos 2x$, $h(x) = \sin 2x$ 8

2.4 DETERMINANTS AND INVERSE OF A MATRIX

In this section we shall see how determinants can be used effectively in deciding whether or not a matrix has an inverse. At the same time, we shall demonstrate a second method for getting such an inverse, when it exists.

In Section 2.2 we introduced the concept of cofactor. We recall that if $A = (a_{ij})$ is an $n \times n$ matrix, then the cofactor of each entry a_{ij} is defined as

$$A_{ij} = \text{Cofactor of } a_{ij} = (-1)^{i+j} \cdot (\text{Minor of } a_{ij}). \qquad (2.30)$$

The **cofactor matrix** of $A = (a_{ij})$, denoted by Cof A, is defined as the $n \times n$ matrix whose entry in row i and column j is A_{ij}; that is,

$$\text{Cof } A = (A_{ij}). \qquad (2.31)$$

Example 1 Find the cofactor matrix of the matrix

$$A = \begin{bmatrix} 2 & 3 & 1 \\ -1 & 0 & 4 \\ 5 & -2 & -3 \end{bmatrix}.$$

In Example 2 of Section 2.2 we calculated A_{ij} for all $i, j = 1, 2, 3$. From these results we see that

$$\text{Cof } A = \begin{bmatrix} A_{11} & A_{12} & A_{13} \\ A_{21} & A_{22} & A_{23} \\ A_{31} & A_{32} & A_{33} \end{bmatrix} = \begin{bmatrix} 8 & 17 & 2 \\ 7 & -11 & 19 \\ 12 & -9 & 3 \end{bmatrix}.$$

Thus,

$$\text{Cof } A = \begin{bmatrix} 8 & 17 & 2 \\ 7 & -11 & 19 \\ 12 & -9 & 3 \end{bmatrix}.$$

Another useful definition is that of the **adjugate** (or **adjoint**) of A denoted by adj A, which is defined as the transpose of the cofactor matrix of A. That is,

$$\text{adj } A = (\text{Cof } A)^t. \tag{2.32}$$

Example 2 Find the adjugate of the matrix A in Example 1.
We calculated Cof A. Using this result, we get

$$\text{adj } A = (\text{Cof } A)^t = \begin{bmatrix} 8 & 17 & 2 \\ 7 & -11 & 19 \\ 12 & -9 & 3 \end{bmatrix}^t = \begin{bmatrix} 8 & 7 & 12 \\ 17 & -11 & -9 \\ 2 & 19 & 3 \end{bmatrix}.$$

The significance of the concept of the adjugate of a matrix A stems from the following important theorem.

Theorem 2.5
Let A be an $n \times n$ matrix. Then A^{-1} exists if and only if det $A \neq 0$. In fact,

$$A^{-1} = \frac{1}{\det A} \cdot (\text{adj } A).$$

The proof one way is easy (see Exercise 29 of Section 2.3). If $AA^{-1} = I$, then $(\det A)(\det A^{-1}) = 1$, so det $A \neq 0$. To prove that A^{-1} exists when det $A \neq 0$, recall the Laplace expansion of det A across row i ($i = 1, 2, \ldots, n$):

$$\det A = a_{i1}A_{i1} + a_{i2}A_{i2} + \ldots + a_{in}A_{in}. \tag{2.33}$$

Now, when $i \neq j$ we claim that

$$a_{i1}A_{j1} + a_{i2}A_{j2} + \ldots + a_{in}A_{jn} = 0. \tag{2.34}$$

To see this, note that the left-side of (2.34) is the expansion of det M, where M is an $n \times n$ matrix in which *both* rows i and j are the *same* as row i of A, while all other rows of M are exactly as the corresponding rows of A, and where this expansion of det M is across the jth row (see Exercise 25 in Section 2.3). Hence, det $M = 0$.

Now consider the product A adj $A = (k_{ij})$, where

$$A \text{ adj } A = \begin{bmatrix} a_{11} & a_{12} & \cdots & a_{1n} \\ a_{21} & a_{22} & \cdots & a_{2n} \\ \vdots & \vdots & \vdots & \vdots \\ a_{i1} & a_{i2} & \cdots & a_{in} \\ \vdots & \vdots & \vdots & \vdots \\ a_{n1} & a_{n2} & \cdots & a_{nn} \end{bmatrix} \begin{bmatrix} A_{11} & A_{21} & \cdots & A_{j1} & \cdots & A_{n1} \\ A_{12} & A_{22} & \cdots & A_{j2} & \cdots & A_{n2} \\ \vdots & \vdots & \vdots & \vdots & \vdots & \vdots \\ A_{1n} & A_{2n} & & A_{jn} & & A_{nn} \end{bmatrix}.$$

We see that the entry k_{ij} in row i and column j of the product A adj A is (as shaded above)

$$k_{ij} = a_{i1}A_{j1} + a_{i2}A_{j2} + \ldots + a_{in}A_{jn},$$

which is exactly the left member of (2.34) when $i \neq j$; so in these cases $k_{ij} = 0$. When $i = j$, we have (see 2.33)

$$k_{ij} = \det A.$$

Therefore

$$\boxed{A \text{ adj } A = (\det A)I_n.} \tag{2.35}$$

Now to complete the proof, note that since det $A \neq 0$, when we multiply both sides of (2.35) by the real number $1/(\det A)$ we get

$$A\left(\frac{1}{\det A}\right)(\text{adj } A) = I_n.$$

Hence, as desired,

$$A^{-1} = \left(\frac{1}{\det A}\right)\text{adj } A.$$

Example 3 Let

$$A = \begin{bmatrix} 2 & 3 & 1 \\ -1 & 0 & 4 \\ 5 & -2 & -3 \end{bmatrix}.$$

Does A^{-1} exist? If so, find it.

In Example 3 of Section 2.2 we saw that det $A = 69 \neq 0$. Hence A^{-1} exists according to Theorem 2.5. Moreover, we have

$$A^{-1} = \frac{1}{\det A} \cdot (\text{adj } A)$$

$$= \frac{1}{69} \cdot \begin{bmatrix} 8 & 7 & 12 \\ 17 & -11 & -9 \\ 2 & 19 & 3 \end{bmatrix} \quad \text{(by Example 2)}.$$

Therefore

$$A^{-1} = \begin{bmatrix} \frac{8}{69} & \frac{7}{69} & \frac{12}{69} \\ \frac{17}{69} & -\frac{11}{69} & -\frac{9}{69} \\ \frac{2}{69} & \frac{19}{69} & \frac{3}{69} \end{bmatrix}.$$

Theorem 2.5 gives us another method for finding A^{-1} (when it exists). Recall that in Chapter 1 we considered a different method for determining the inverse of a matrix. It would be instructive if you were to compute A^{-1} for the above matrix A by using the Matrix Inversion Algorithm described in Section 1.6 (see also the Appendix). The following example illustrates Theorem 2.5 in the event that a given matrix has no inverse.

Example 4 Let

$$A = \begin{bmatrix} 2 & 3 & 0 \\ -1 & 4 & 7 \\ 0 & 11 & 14 \end{bmatrix}.$$

Does A^{-1} exist? If so, find it.

We can verify that det $A = 0$. Hence (by Theorem 2.5), A^{-1} does *not* exist.

Example 5 Let

$$A = \begin{bmatrix} a & b \\ c & d \end{bmatrix},$$

where a, b, c, d are real numbers such that $ad - bc \neq 0$. Show that A^{-1} exist and, in fact,

$$A^{-1} = \frac{1}{ad - bc} \begin{bmatrix} d & -b \\ -c & a \end{bmatrix}.$$

Since det $A = ad - bc \neq 0$, A^{-1} exists. To find A^{-1}, we first find the adjugate of A. For this purpose, we note that for a 1×1 matrix $[a]$,

$$\det[a] = a.$$

Now, by definition of adjugate, we have

$$\operatorname{adj}\begin{bmatrix} a & b \\ c & d \end{bmatrix} = \begin{bmatrix} +d & -c \\ -b & +a \end{bmatrix}^t = \begin{bmatrix} d & -b \\ -c & a \end{bmatrix}.$$

Hence by Theorem 2.5 we get the desired result:

$$A^{-1} = \frac{1}{\det A} \cdot (\operatorname{adj} A) = \frac{1}{ad - bc}\begin{bmatrix} d & -b \\ -c & a \end{bmatrix}.$$

EXERCISES (2.4)—————————————————————————————————————

1. Find

$$\det\begin{bmatrix} 1 & 3 \\ -4 & 2 \end{bmatrix}.$$

Is the matrix nonsingular? If so, find its inverse.

2. Find $\det A$, adj A, and A^{-1} (if it exists) of the matrix

$$A = \begin{bmatrix} 1 & 3 & -1 \\ 4 & 0 & 1 \\ 2 & 1 & 3 \end{bmatrix}.$$

3. Let

$$A = \begin{bmatrix} 2 & 4 & 1 \\ -1 & 3 & 5 \\ 1 & 17 & 17 \end{bmatrix}.$$

Does A^{-1} exist? If so, find it. If not, why?

4. Let

$$A = \begin{bmatrix} 1 & 0 & 0 & 0 \\ 0 & 0 & 1 & 0 \\ 0 & 0 & 0 & 1 \\ 0 & 1 & 0 & 0 \end{bmatrix}.$$

Does A^{-1} exist? If so, find it. Also find adj A.

5. Let

$$A = \begin{bmatrix} a & b & c & d \\ 0 & e & f & g \\ 0 & 0 & h & i \\ 0 & 0 & 0 & j \end{bmatrix}.$$

Suppose that $a \neq 0$, $e \neq 0$, $h \neq 0$, $j \neq 0$. Show that A^{-1} exists.

6. Let

$$A = \begin{bmatrix} a & b & c \\ 0 & a & d \\ 0 & 0 & a \end{bmatrix}.$$

Suppose that $a \neq 0$. Show that A^{-1} exists. Also find A^{-1}.

7. Suppose that $a = 0$ in Problem 6. Show that A has *no* inverse. Also show that $A^3 = 0$.

8. Suppose that A is an $n \times n$ matrix such that $A^k = 0$, where k is a positive integer. Prove that A has *no* inverse.

9. Prove that if an $n \times n$ matrix A is nonsingular, so is A^t.

10. Suppose that A and B are nonzero $n \times n$ matrices such that $AB = 0$. Prove that both A and B are singular. Is the converse true? Give reasons.

11. Can the product of two nonsingular matrices be singular? Give reasons.

12. Can the product of two singular matrices be nonsingular? Give reasons.

13. Prove that the product of a singular matrix and a nonsingular matrix is always singular.

14. Suppose that A, B, C are $n \times n$ matrices such that $AB = AC$. Does this always imply that $B = C$? Give reasons.

15. Solve Problem 14 if we assume, in addition, that A is nonsingular.

16. Suppose that A is an $n \times n$ nonsingular matrix. Prove that

$$\det(\operatorname{adj} A) = (\det A)^{n-1}.$$

17. Prove that an $n \times n$ matrix A is nonsingular if and only if adj A is nonsingular.

18. Suppose that A is an $n \times n$ nonsingular matrix with real entries and that adj $A = A$. Prove that det $A = \pm 1$.

VECTOR SPACES

In this chapter we turn our attention away from solving systems of equations to a seemingly new idea of a vector space. It will become apparent quite early in our development, however, that we have not really diverged from the topics of the preceding chapters at all.

3.1 DEFINITION AND EXAMPLES OF VECTOR SPACES

Many physical quantities such as length, area, density, and mass, are completely described by a single real number. On the other hand, consider the plight of your college-admission officer who must compare student applicants described by several numbers: age, high-school GPA, test scores in mathematics, language, general ability, perhaps even numbers that assign priorities to such things as geography, financial need, etc. Many physical quantities need both a magnitude and a direction to describe them (force and velocity are two examples); such quantities are called vectors.

Example 1 Consider the directed line segments in the plane that are called *vectors* in mechanics. These have a direction and a magnitude: the direction is indicated by an arrowhead and the magnitude is represented by the length of the vector (see Fig. 3.1).

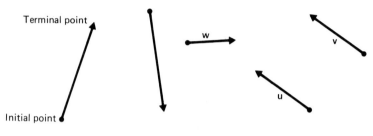

Figure 3.1

It is generally agreed in mechanics that two of these directed line segments are *equivalent vectors* if they have the same direction and the same magnitude, even if they have different initial and terminal points. Thus, the vectors **u** and **v** of Fig. 3.1 are equivalent, but neither is equivalent to **w**.

With this agreement, these *geometric vectors* may be described algebraically by an ordered pair of real numbers. To do so, we introduce a coordinate system into the plane and represent each vector in the plane by an equivalent vector whose initial point is the origin of our coordinate system. Then the terminal point of the vector is a point of the coordinate plane described by the pair (x_1, x_2). This pair, in turn, determines the vector.

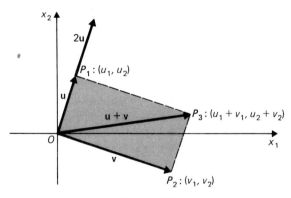

Figure 3.2

Addition of these vectors is defined by the familiar *parallelogram rule*, as illustrated by Fig. 3.2. It then turns out that the coordinates of the sum of two vectors are the sums of the coordinates of the individual vectors, as can be verified geometrically:

$$\mathbf{u} + \mathbf{v} = (u_1, u_2) + (v_1, v_2) = (u_1 + v_1, u_2 + v_2).$$

Note also that the vector $2\mathbf{u}$, whose direction is the same as that of $\mathbf{u}$ and whose length is twice that of $\mathbf{u}$, is described by the pair of numbers $(2u_1, 2u_2)$. We shall return to this example.

Example 2 Similar operations come up when we row-reduce a matrix. Let A be the following matrix:

$$A = \begin{bmatrix} 1 & 2 & -1 \\ 3 & 1 & 4 \\ 5 & 6 & -7 \end{bmatrix} \begin{matrix} \mathbf{r}, \\ \mathbf{s}, \\ \mathbf{t}. \end{matrix}$$

Let us denote the rows of A by $\mathbf{r}$, $\mathbf{s}$ and $\mathbf{t}$, respectively. Now we shall proceed to reduce A to an upper-triangular matrix by elementary row operations. To do so, we perform arithmetic with the rows of A, which are triples of real numbers. We can think of them as vectors (the *row vectors* of A):   ·

$$\begin{aligned} \mathbf{r} &= (1, 2, -1), \\ \mathbf{s} &= (3, 1, 4), \\ \mathbf{t} &= (5, 6, -7). \end{aligned}$$

Thus, to change A to the following matrix M_1, we have performed operations on the rows of A, as indicated to the right of M_1:

$$M_1 = \begin{bmatrix} 1 & 2 & -1 \\ 0 & -5 & 7 \\ 0 & -4 & -2 \end{bmatrix} \begin{matrix} \mathbf{r}, \\ \mathbf{s} - 3\mathbf{r}, \\ \mathbf{t} - 5\mathbf{r}. \end{matrix}$$

Now the matrix M_1 is row-equivalent to the matrix M_2 (again the row arithmetic is indicated to the right of M_2):

$$M_2 = \begin{bmatrix} 1 & 2 & -1 \\ 0 & -1 & 9 \\ 0 & 2 & 1 \end{bmatrix} \begin{matrix} \mathbf{r}, \\ (\mathbf{s} - 3\mathbf{r}) - (\mathbf{t} - 5\mathbf{r}) = \mathbf{s} + 2\mathbf{r} - \mathbf{t}, \\ -\tfrac{1}{2}(\mathbf{t} - 5\mathbf{r}) = \dfrac{5\mathbf{r} - \mathbf{t}}{2}. \end{matrix}$$

This matrix is row-equivalent to the following upper-triangular matrix:

$$N = \begin{bmatrix} 1 & 2 & -1 \\ 0 & 1 & -9 \\ 0 & 0 & 19 \end{bmatrix} \begin{matrix} \mathbf{r}, \\ (\mathbf{t} - 5\mathbf{r}) - (\mathbf{s} - 3\mathbf{r}) = \mathbf{t} - \mathbf{s} - 2\mathbf{r}, \\ \dfrac{5\mathbf{r} - \mathbf{t}}{2} - 2(\mathbf{t} - \mathbf{s} - 2\mathbf{r}) = \dfrac{13\mathbf{r} + 4\mathbf{s} - 5\mathbf{t}}{2}. \end{matrix}$$

The equations at the right of N indicate how its rows (row vectors) are related to the row vectors of the matrix A. Thus, the third row of N is $\frac{1}{2}(13\mathbf{r} + 4\mathbf{s} - 5\mathbf{t})$, a combination of multiples of the three rows of A. We shall also refer to this example again.

These two examples, out of many possible, serve to suggest that these aggregates called vectors may have an algebra. We have noted earlier that the algebra of matrices has similarities with and also differences from the ordinary algebra of real and complex numbers. Now let us look at the algebra of vectors. The rules for this algebra will be derived from our experience with geometric and analytic vectors and with the rows of matrices. However, we shall state the more fundamental of these rules as axioms for a vector space. From now on, a *vector* will be an *element* of a *vector space*.

Let V be the set of elements called **vectors** and let R be the set of real numbers (called **scalars**). We say that V is a (real) **vector space** if all of the following axioms hold.

Axioms for Vector Addition

Axiom V1
(*Closure law*): *If* $\mathbf{v}_1$ *and* $\mathbf{v}_2$ *are any vectors in* V, *then* $\mathbf{v}_1 + \mathbf{v}_2$ *is a unique vector in* V.

Axiom V2
(*Commutative law*): $\mathbf{v}_1 + \mathbf{v}_2 = \mathbf{v}_2 + \mathbf{v}_1$ *for all vector* $\mathbf{v}_1$, $\mathbf{v}_2$ *in* V.

Axiom V3
(*Associative law*): $(\mathbf{v}_1 + \mathbf{v}_2) + \mathbf{v}_3 = \mathbf{v}_1 + (\mathbf{v}_2 + \mathbf{v}_3)$ *for all vectors* $\mathbf{v}_1$, $\mathbf{v}_2$, $\mathbf{v}_3$ *in* V.

Axiom V4
(*Additive identity*): *There is a vector* $\mathbf{O}$, *called the zero vector, such that*

$$\mathbf{v} + \mathbf{O} = \mathbf{O} + \mathbf{v} = \mathbf{v} \qquad \textit{for all vectors } \mathbf{v} \textit{ in } V.$$

Axiom V5
(*Additive inverse*): *For every vector* $\mathbf{v}$ *in* V *there is a vector* $(-\mathbf{v})$ *in* V *such that*

$$\mathbf{v} + (-\mathbf{v}) = (-\mathbf{v}) + \mathbf{v} = \mathbf{O}.$$

This vector $-\mathbf{v}$ *is called the negative of* $\mathbf{v}$.

Axioms for Scalar Multiplication

Axiom S1
If α *is any scalar (real number) and* $\mathbf{v}$ *is a vector in* V, *then* $\alpha \cdot \mathbf{v}$ (*also written as* $\alpha\mathbf{v}$) *is a unique vector in* V.

Axiom S2

$\alpha(v_1 + v_2) = \alpha v_1 + \alpha v_2$ *for all scalars α and all vectors v_1, v_2.*

Axiom S3

$(\alpha_1 + \alpha_2)v = \alpha_1 v + \alpha_2 v$ *for all scalars α_1, α_2 and all vectors v.*

Axiom S4

$(\alpha_1 \alpha_2)v = \alpha_1 (\alpha_2 v)$ *for all scalars α_1, α_2 and all vectors v.*

Axiom S5

$1 \cdot v = v$ *for all vectors v, where the scalar 1 is the real number 1.*

Remark. When the set R of real numbers (scalars) is replaced by the set C of complex numbers in the axioms for a vector space, we say that V is a **complex-vector space**, or a **vector space over** C.

Examples of vector spaces are widespread. Let us consider some of these examples.

Example 1 (Revisited) Let us return to the set of all points in the coordinate plane; that is, let V be the set of all ordered pairs (x_1, x_2), where x_1 and x_2 are real numbers. Define vector addition and scalar multiplication as follows:

$$(x_1, x_2) + (x'_1, x'_2) = (x_1 + x'_1, x_2 + x'_2), \tag{3.1}$$

$$\alpha(x_1, x_2) = (\alpha x_1, \alpha x_2), \quad \text{where } \alpha \text{ is a scalar (a real number).} \tag{3.2}$$

It can be verified that all of the above axioms in the definition of a vector space hold. In particular, the zero vector is $(0, 0)$ and

$$-(x_1, x_2) = (-x_1, -x_2).$$

To illustrate this, let us verify Axiom V3 for this vector space. Let

$$v_1 = (x_1, x_2), \qquad v_2 = (x'_1, x'_2), \qquad v_3 = (x''_1, x''_2).$$

Then, by (3.1),

$$v_1 + v_2 = (x_1, x_2) + (x'_1, x'_2) = (x_1 + x'_1, x_2 + x'_2),$$

$$(v_1 + v_2) + v_3 = (x_1 + x'_1, x_2 + x'_2) + (x''_1, x''_2)$$
$$= ((x_1 + x'_1) + x''_1, (x_2 + x'_2) + x''_2).$$

Similarly, we see that (verify this)

$$v_1 + (v_2 + v_3) = (x_1 + (x'_1 + x''_1), x_2 + (x'_2 + x''_2)).$$

By the associative law for the real numbers, the right sides of the last two equations are equal; hence the left sides are equal also. Thus,

$$(v_1 + v_2) + v_3 = v_1 + (v_2 + v_3).$$

This verifies Axiom V3. You should have no trouble verifying that all of the other axioms in the definition of a vector space hold in this V. Thus V is a vector space.

As mentioned above, we can also interpret this example geometrically. This gives rise to the concept of *geometric vectors*. We may think of a vector $\mathbf{u} = (u_1, u_2)$ as the arrow $\overrightarrow{OP_1}$ from the origin O to the point P_1: (u_1, u_2), or as any equivalent arrow, as indicated in Fig. 3.2.

Vector addition, as defined in (3.1), now becomes the familiar *parallelogram rule* for addition of vectors.

What about scalar multiplication, as defined in (3.2), for these geometric vectors (or arrows)? This is illustrated in Fig. 3.3. For example, if

$$\overrightarrow{OP_1} = (x_1, x_2),$$

then

$$2 \cdot \overrightarrow{OP_1} = 2 \cdot (x_1, x_2) = (2x_1, 2x_2) = \overrightarrow{OP_2}.$$

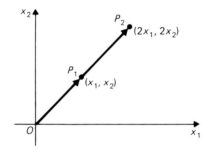

Figure 3.3

In other words, to multiply the geometric vector (or arrow) $\overrightarrow{OP_1}$ by 2 means to stretch it in the same direction to twice its original length, as indicated by $\overrightarrow{OP_2}$ in Fig. 3.3. The scalar products $\frac{1}{2} \cdot (\overrightarrow{OP_1})$ and $(-1) \cdot (\overrightarrow{OP_1})$ are illustrated in Fig. 3.4. Note that if $\overrightarrow{OP_1} = (x_1, x_2)$, then $\overrightarrow{OP_2} = \frac{1}{2}(\overrightarrow{OP_1})$ and $\overrightarrow{OP_3} = (-1)(\overrightarrow{OP_1})$.

In other words, to multiply the geometric vector (or arrow) $\overrightarrow{OP_1}$ by $\frac{1}{2}$ means to contract it in the same direction to half of its original length as indicated by $\overrightarrow{OP_2}$ in Fig. 3.4. Also, to multiply $\overrightarrow{OP_1}$ by the *negative* scalar (-1) means to extend it *in the opposite direction* to its original length, as indicated by $\overrightarrow{OP_3}$ in Fig. 3.4. You should draw other pictures illustrating other scalar products and other vector sums.

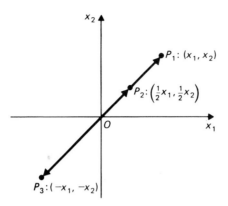

Figure 3.4

Example 3   This example generalizes Example 1 and contains Example 2 as well. Let V be the set of all points in 3-space; that is, let V be the set of all ordered triples (x_1, x_2, x_3), where x_1, x_2, x_3 are real numbers. Define vector addition and scalar multiplication as follows:

$$(x_1, x_2, x_3) + (x'_1, x'_2, x'_3) = (x_1 + x'_1, x_2 + x'_2, x_3 + x'_3);$$

$$\alpha(x_1, x_2, x_3) = (\alpha x_1, \alpha x_2, \alpha x_3), \quad \text{where } \alpha \text{ is a scalar (real number).}$$

You will have no trouble verifying that all of the axioms in the definition of a vector space hold. Indeed, the zero vector is $(0, 0, 0)$ and the negative of the vector (x_1, x_2, x_3) is $(-x_1, -x_2, -x_3)$. Thus, V is a *vector space*. Note that the row vectors of any 3×3 matrix are really vectors from this vector space.

Example 4   This example generalizes both Examples 1 and 3. Let n be any positive integer and let V be the set of all n-tuples $(x_1, x_2, x_3, \ldots, x_n)$, where $x_1, x_2, x_3, \ldots, x_n$ are real numbers.
   Define vector addition and scalar multiplication as follows:

$$(x_1, x_2, x_3, \ldots, x_n) + (x'_1, x'_2, x'_3, \ldots, x'_n) = (x_1 + x'_1, x_2 + x'_2, x_3 + x'_3, \ldots, x_n + x'_n);$$

$$\alpha(x_1, x_2, x_3, \ldots, x_n) = (\alpha x_1, \alpha x_2, \alpha x_3, \ldots, \alpha x_n), \quad \text{where } \alpha \text{ is a scalar (real number).}$$
   Again, as in Examples 1 and 3, we readily verify that V is a vector space, where $(0, 0, 0, \ldots, 0)$ is the zero vector and where

$$-(x_1, x_2, x_3, \ldots, x_n) = (-x_1, -x_2, -x_3, \ldots, -x_n).$$

This vector space is called **cartesian n-space**. We shall hereafter represent this space by $\mathbb{R}^n$. Note that the vector spaces in Examples 1 and 3 are Cartesian 2-space $\mathbb{R}^2$ and Cartesian 3-space $\mathbb{R}^3$, respectively.

Example 5   Let V be the set of all polynomials of degree n or less with real coefficients, together with the zero polynomial. Let vector (i.e., polynomial) addition and scalar multiplication be defined by the usual rules of high-school algebra. We claim that V is a vector space. In verifying this, recall first that a polynomial of degree n or less can always be expressed in the form

$$f(x) = a_0 + a_1 x + a_2 x^2 + \ldots + a_n x^n. \tag{3.3}$$

Also, if

$$g(x) = b_0 + b_1 x + b_2 x^2 + \ldots + b_n x^n,$$

then

$$f(x) + g(x) = (a_0 + b_0) + (a_1 + b_1)x + (a_2 + b_2)x^2 + \ldots + (a_n + b_n)x^n.$$

Moreover,

$$\alpha f(x) = (\alpha a_0) + (\alpha a_1)x + (\alpha a_2)x^2 + \ldots + (\alpha a_n)x^n.$$

It can be shown that all the axioms in the definition of a vector space are satisfied. Indeed, the zero vector is the zero polynomial (with all zero coefficients). Also, if $f(x)$ is as in (3.3), then

$$-f(x) = (-a_0) + (-a_1)x + (-a_2)x^2 + \ldots + (-a_n)x^n.$$

You should convince yourself that all of the axioms are indeed satisfied.

Throughout the rest of this book, this vector space (the vector space of all polynomials with real coefficients and degree at most n) will be designated P_n. In particular, P_0 is the space of all polynomials of degree zero; hence it is the same as the constant polynomials.

Example 6   Let V be the set M_n of all $n \times n$ matrices with real-number entries. Then according to the results developed in Section 1.4, M_n is a vector space. You can verify this (see Exercise 9). What is the zero vector?

This vector space differs from the space of row vectors of a matrix discussed in Example 2.

Example 7   Consider the $n \times n$ system of homogeneous linear equations

$$AX = 0. \tag{3.4}$$

For example, in addition to the trivial solution, the system

$$\begin{aligned} x_1 - x_2 - 3x_3 + 2x_4 &= 0, \\ 2x_1 + x_2 - x_3 + x_4 &= 0, \\ x_1 + 2x_2 + 2x_3 - x_4 &= 0, \\ 3x_1 + 3x_2 + x_3 \qquad\quad &= 0, \end{aligned} \tag{3.5}$$

has infinitely many nonzero solutions. Among them are the following (verify this):

$$X_1 = \begin{bmatrix} 4 \\ -5 \\ 3 \\ 0 \end{bmatrix}, \quad \text{and} \quad X_2 = \begin{bmatrix} -1 \\ 1 \\ 0 \\ 1 \end{bmatrix}.$$

Note that if X is any solution to the system (3.4) or (3.5), then so is

$$kX = \begin{bmatrix} kx_1 \\ \vdots \\ kx_n \end{bmatrix},$$

where k is any real number. This follows from the fact that, if $AX = 0$, then $A(kX) = kAX = k0 = 0$. Also if X_1 and X_2 are any solutions to (3.4), then so is the sum $X_1 + X_2$. This latter fact follows from

$$A(X_1 + X_2) = AX_1 + AX_2 = 0 + 0 = 0.$$

You should check this for the specific case of (3.5). You can also verify that the set S of *all* solutions to a given homogeneous system of equations (3.4) satisfies all of the axioms for a vector space. The space S is called the **solution space** for that homogeneous system. We usually call the solutions, which are the $n \times 1$ matrices X, *column vectors*, or the *solution vectors* to the system.

We remarked earlier that we could have chosen the complex-number system C as our set of scalars in the axioms for a vector space. In that case we would have a complex-vector space. Consider the following example.

Example 8 Let C^2 be the set of all pairs (z_1, z_2) of complex numbers. It is not difficult to show that C^2 is also a vector space, this time a *complex vector space*. The verification is based upon the laws of complex-number algebra and is almost identical with the verification made for pairs of real numbers in Example 1. You can carry this verification out for yourself.

We shall conclude this section with an additional remark and a theorem.

Remark. It can easily be seen that if V consists of the zero vector only, that is, $V = \{0\}$, then V trivially satisfies all of the axioms for a vector space (convince yourself of this). Thus $V = \{0\}$ is a vector space called the **zero vector space**. If $V \neq \{0\}$, we say that V is a *nonzero vector space*.

In view of Example 6, we might expect that the usual algebraic properties for matrix addition and scalar multiplication as contained in Theorem 1.6 will have their analogue in any vector space V. Indeed, we have the following theorem, whose proof is similar to that of Theorem 1.6 and is left to you as Exercise 25.

Theorem 3.1

If V is any real (or complex) vector space, then for all $\mathbf{u}$, $\mathbf{v}$ in V and all scalars α, β, the following is true:

i) $(-1)\mathbf{v} = -\mathbf{v}$;

ii) $-(-\mathbf{v}) = \mathbf{v}$;

iii) $\mathbf{u} - \mathbf{v} = -(\mathbf{v} - \mathbf{u})$;

iv) $0_s\mathbf{v} = 0_v$, *where* 0_s *is the zero scalar (the real number 0) and* 0_v *is the zero vector in* V;

v) $\alpha \cdot 0_v = 0_v$;

vi) *if* $\alpha\mathbf{v} = 0_v$, *then* $\alpha = 0_s$ *or* $\mathbf{v} = 0_v$;

vii) $(\alpha - \beta)\mathbf{v} = \alpha\mathbf{v} - \beta\mathbf{v}$;

viii) $\alpha(\mathbf{u} - \mathbf{v}) = \alpha\mathbf{u} - \alpha\mathbf{v}$.

A comment is in order about parts (iv) to (vi). We shall, henceforth, write simply 0 instead of 0_s or 0_v, since it is generally quite clear from the context whether the zero scalar or the zero vector is indicated.

EXERCISES (3.1)

1. Show that $0, P_1, P_2, P_3$ in Fig. 3.2 are vertices of a parallelogram. *Hint.* From P_1 and P_2 draw lines parallel to the x_2-axis and from P_3 draw a line parallel to the x_1-axis. Then show that the resulting triangles are congruent.

2. Let $\mathbf{v}_1 = (1, 2)$ and $\mathbf{v}_2 = (-1, 4)$. Find $\mathbf{v}_1 + \mathbf{v}_2$; $5\mathbf{v}_1$; $(-\frac{1}{2})\mathbf{v}_2$.

3. Sketch all the vectors in Problem 2 (including both $\mathbf{v}_1$ and $\mathbf{v}_2$).

4. Verify that all the axioms of a vector space are satisfied in Example 1.

5. Verify that all the axioms of a vector space are satisfied in Example 5.

6. Let W be the set of all ordered pairs (x_1, x_2) of real numbers that satisfy the equation $2x_1 - 5x_2 = 0$. Prove that W is a vector space.

7. Let W be the set of all ordered triples (x_1, x_2, x_3) of real numbers that satisfy the equation $3x_1 - x_2 + 3x_3 = c$. What should the real number c be for W to be a vector space? Give reasons.

8. Carry out the details to verify that C^2 of Example 8 is a complex vector space.

9. Verify that the collection M_n of all $n \times n$ matrices with real-number entries forms a real vector space (Example 6).

10. Verify that the collection G of all real-valued functions defined on the closed interval $[0, 1]$ is a real-vector space under the following definition: If f and g are two such functions, then $f + g$ is the function such that $(f + g)(x) = f(x) + g(x)$. Also, if f is any

function in G and α is any real number, then αf is the function such that $(\alpha f)(x) = \alpha(f(x))$. What is the zero vector? (See Fig. 3.5.)

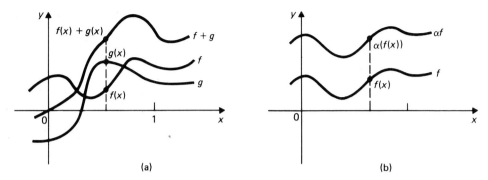

Figure 3.5

Consider the following sets and operations of addition and scalar multiplication. Determine the vector spaces among them. State which axioms fail to hold for those that are not vector spaces.

11. The set of all pairs of real numbers (x, y) with *addition* $(x, y) + (x_1, y_1) = (x + x_1, 0)$ and *scalar multiplication* $\alpha(x, y) = (\alpha x, \alpha y)$.

12. The set Q, of all rational numbers x with ordinary *addition* and *scalar multiplication* as ordinary multiplication by rational numbers.

13. The set Z of all the integers with ordinary *addition* of integers and *scalar multiplication* as multiplication by any rational number.

14. The set of all 2×2 matrices of the form

$$\begin{bmatrix} a & 1 \\ 1 & b \end{bmatrix}$$

with *addition* as matrix addition and *scalar multiplication* as multiplication by a real number.

15. The set of all 2×2 matrices of the form

$$\begin{bmatrix} a & 0 \\ 0 & b \end{bmatrix}$$

with the same operations as in Exercise 14.

16. The set of all real-valued functions f defined on the entire real line with the same operations as in Exercise 10.

17. The set of all those real-valued functions f defined on the closed interval $[0, 1]$ for which $f(1) = 0$, with the same operations as in Exercise 10.

18. The set of all those real-valued functions f defined on the closed interval $[0, 1]$ for which $f(0) = 1$, with the same operations as in Exercise 10.

19. The set C of all complex numbers $z = x + iy$ with complex addition and multiplication by real numbers $\alpha z = \alpha x + i\alpha y$ (compare with Exercise 8).

Exercises 20–22 are for those who have studied calculus. Show that each of the following sets of real-valued functions defined on the closed interval $[0, 1]$ is a real-vector space:

20. The set of all continuous functions.

21. The set of all differentiable functions.

22. The set of all integrable functions.

23. Prove that the zero vector in a vector space is unique. *Hint.* Suppose there are two zero vectors $\mathbf{0}_1$ and $\mathbf{0}_2$; what is $\mathbf{0}_1 + \mathbf{0}_2$?

24. Prove that the negative of any vector is unique.

25. Prove Theorem 3.1.

26. Verify that the solution space in Example 7 satisfies all of the axioms for a vector space.

3.2 LINEAR DEPENDENCE AND INDEPENDENCE

Let us look back at two examples in Section 3.1. In Example 2 we reduced the matrix

$$A = \begin{bmatrix} 1 & 2 & -1 \\ 3 & 1 & 4 \\ 5 & 6 & -7 \end{bmatrix} \begin{matrix} \mathbf{r}, \\ \mathbf{s}, \\ \mathbf{t}, \end{matrix}$$

with row vectors $\mathbf{r}$, $\mathbf{s}$, and $\mathbf{t}$ as indicated, to the upper-triangular matrix

$$N = \begin{bmatrix} 1 & 2 & -1 \\ 0 & 1 & -9 \\ 0 & 0 & 19 \end{bmatrix} \begin{matrix} \mathbf{u} = \mathbf{r}, \\ \mathbf{v} = \mathbf{t} - \mathbf{s} - 2\mathbf{r}, \\ \mathbf{w} = \frac{13}{2}\mathbf{r} + 2\mathbf{s} - \frac{5}{2}\mathbf{t}. \end{matrix}$$

The row vectors $\mathbf{u}$, $\mathbf{v}$, and $\mathbf{w}$ of N were derived from the row vectors of A by the equations

$$\begin{aligned} \mathbf{u} &= \mathbf{r}, \\ \mathbf{v} &= \mathbf{t} - \mathbf{s} - 2\mathbf{r}, \\ \mathbf{w} &= \tfrac{13}{2}\mathbf{r} + 2\mathbf{s} - \tfrac{5}{2}\mathbf{t}. \end{aligned} \tag{3.6}$$

In Example 7 of Section 3.1 we considered the solution space S for a homogeneous system of equations. In the example given in Eq. (3.5) we found that the system

$$\begin{cases} x_1 - x_2 - 3x_3 + 2x_4 = 0 \\ 2x_1 + x_2 - x_3 + x_4 = 0 \\ x_1 + 2x_2 + 2x_3 - x_4 = 0 \\ 3x_1 + 3x_2 + x_3 \quad\quad = 0 \end{cases} \quad (3.7)$$

had two particular solution vectors:

$$X_1 = \begin{bmatrix} 4 \\ -5 \\ 3 \\ 0 \end{bmatrix} \quad \text{and} \quad X_2 = \begin{bmatrix} -1 \\ 1 \\ 0 \\ 1 \end{bmatrix}.$$

Now let us show that, for any two real numbers s and t, the column vector

$$X = sX_1 + tX_2 \quad (3.8)$$

is also a solution. We can accomplish this most easily by matrix algebra. Indeed, we did almost the same thing in Example 7 of Section 3.1.

The coefficient matrix for the system (3.7) is the matrix K:

$$K = \begin{bmatrix} 1 & -1 & -3 & 2 \\ 2 & 1 & -1 & 1 \\ 1 & 2 & 2 & -1 \\ 3 & 3 & 1 & 0 \end{bmatrix}. \quad (3.9)$$

Therefore, using the laws of matrix algebra (see Theorem 1.5), we have

$$KX = K(sX_1 + tX_2) = s(KX_1) + t(KX_2) = 0$$

because X_1 and X_2 are both solution vectors. Thus $X = sX_1 + tX_2$ is indeed a solution vector.

Now note from these two examples that the row vectors of the matrix N were written as combinations of the row vectors of the matrix A, as indicated in Eq. (3.6). Similarly, the solution to the system of Eq. (3.7) is a combination of the two solutions X_1 and X_2, as given by Eq. (3.8). Such combinations are called *linear combinations*. In general, we have the following definition:

Let V be any vector space, $v_1, v_2, \ldots, v_n$ be any vectors from V, and $c_1, c_2, \ldots, c_n$ be any scalars (real numbers). The vector

$$\mathbf{u} = c_1 v_1 + c_2 v_2 + \ldots + c_n v_n = \sum_{i=1}^{n} c_i v_i$$

is called a **linear combination** of the vectors $v_1, v_2, \ldots, v_n$.

Clearly the vector $\mathbf{u}$ is in V. Thus, the rows of the matrix N above are *linear combinations* of the row vectors $\mathbf{r}$, $\mathbf{s}$, and $\mathbf{t}$ of the matrix A. The solution X to the system of equations $KX = 0$ of (3.7) is a *linear combination* of the particular solution vectors X_1 and X_2 from its solution space S.

Let us now take a look at the row vectors of the matrix K given in (3.9) above; call them $\mathbf{r}_1, \mathbf{r}_2, \mathbf{r}_3$, and $\mathbf{r}_4$. Although you may not have noticed it before, it is clear that

$$\mathbf{r}_1 = \mathbf{r}_2 - \mathbf{r}_3 \quad \text{and} \quad \mathbf{r}_4 = \mathbf{r}_2 + \mathbf{r}_3.$$

Of course, you did notice that the given homogeneous system (3.7) was *dependent*. Otherwise we would have had only the trivial solution. That is, the solution space S would have been the *zero vector space*.

The individual rows of the matrix K are dependent on each other; in particular, the row vectors $\mathbf{r}_1$ and $\mathbf{r}_4$ depend on the row vectors $\mathbf{r}_2$ and $\mathbf{r}_3$, as indicated. Note that

$$\mathbf{r}_1 - \mathbf{r}_2 + \mathbf{r}_3 = 0 \quad \text{and} \quad \mathbf{r}_4 - \mathbf{r}_2 - \mathbf{r}_3 = 0.$$

In generalizing these ideas, we are led to the following *definition*:

Let V be a vector space and let $S = \{\mathbf{v}_1, \mathbf{v}_2, \ldots, \mathbf{v}_n\}$ be a set of vectors from V. We say that the vectors $\mathbf{v}_1, \mathbf{v}_2, \ldots, \mathbf{v}_n$ are **linearly dependent** or that the set S is a **linearly dependent set** if there exist scalars $c_1, c_2, \ldots, c_n$, *not all zero*, such that

$$c_1\mathbf{v}_1 + c_2\mathbf{v}_2 + \ldots + c_n\mathbf{v}_n = 0; \tag{3.10}$$

otherwise the vectors $\mathbf{v}_1, \mathbf{v}_2, \ldots, \mathbf{v}_n$ (or the set S) are said to be **linearly independent**.

Thus, the row vectors $\mathbf{r}_1, \mathbf{r}_2, \mathbf{r}_3$, and $\mathbf{r}_4$ of K are linearly dependent. But the row vectors $\mathbf{r}$, $\mathbf{s}$, and $\mathbf{t}$ of the matrix A of Example 2 in Section 3.1 are linearly independent, as you can verify (see Exercise 8).

A very useful formulation of the concept of linear *independence* is given in the following lemma.

Lemma 3.2

The set $S = \{\mathbf{v}_1, \mathbf{v}_2, \ldots, \mathbf{v}_n\}$ *of vectors from* V *is a linearly independent set if, whenever any linear combination of the vectors in* S *is zero, then all of the coefficient scalars* $c_1, c_2, \ldots, c_n$ *are zero. In other words, the vectors* $\mathbf{v}_1, \ldots, \mathbf{v}_n$ *are linearly independent when the equation*

$$c_1\mathbf{v}_1 + c_2\mathbf{v}_2 + \ldots + c_n\mathbf{v}_n = 0$$

forces each and every one of the c_i *to be zero.*

This lemma follows immediately from the definition since, if there were but one of the c_i different from zero and yet $c_1\mathbf{v}_1 + c_2\mathbf{v}_2 + \ldots + c_n\mathbf{v}_n = 0$, then the vectors $\mathbf{v}_i$ would be linearly dependent.

We shall frequently use the formulation of linear independence given in this lemma.

Example 1   Are the vectors $(1, 2, -1)$, $(3, 0, 4)$, and $(1, -4, 6)$ in cartesian 3-space linearly dependent or linearly independent?

Let us suppose that we have the linear combination

$$c_1(1, 2, -1) + c_2(3, 0, 4) + c_3(1, -4, 6) = (0, 0, 0). \tag{3.11}$$

Recalling the definitions of vector addition and scalar multiplication in Example 3 of Section 3.1, we see that the above equation becomes

$$(c_1, 2c_1, -c_1) + (3c_2, 0, 4c_2) + (c_3, -4c_3, 6c_3) = (0, 0, 0),$$

or

$$(c_1 + 3c_2 + c_3, 2c_1 + 0 - 4c_3, -c_1 + 4c_2 + 6c_3) = (0, 0, 0).$$

This last equation will be satisfied if and only if the unknown scalars c_1, c_2, c_3 satisfy the following system of equations:

$$c_1 + 3c_2 + c_3 = 0,$$
$$2c_1 \qquad\quad - 4c_3 = 0,$$
$$-c_1 + 4c_2 + 6c_3 = 0.$$

Since we are searching for *any* nontrivial solution (one in which not all coefficients c_i are zero) we might try our luck by setting $c_3 = 1$ and then quickly solving the resulting system for c_1 and c_2, rather than bother with a Gaussian reduction of the augmented matrix. Were we to do so, we would obtain $c_1 = 2$, $c_2 = -1$. Thus

$$c_1 = 2, \quad c_2 = -1, \quad c_3 = 1$$

is a solution to the above system of linear equations and hence these values also satisfy Eq. (3.11), that is, the linear combination

$$2(1, 2, -1) + (-1)(3, 0, 4) + 1(1, -4, 6) = (0, 0, 0).$$

Therefore, the given vectors are *linearly dependent*.

Example 2   Is the set of vectors $\{(0, 1, 1), (1, 0, 1), (1, 1, 0)\}$ from cartesian 3-space linearly dependent or linearly independent?

Again, consider the linear combination

$$c_1(0, 1, 1) + c_2(1, 0, 1) + c_3(1, 1, 0) = (0, 0, 0). \tag{3.12}$$

Our objective is to find unknown scalars c_1, c_2, c_3 that satisfy Eq. (3.12). Simplifying the left side of (3.12) as indicated in the preceding example, we see that (3.12) yields

$$(0, c_1, c_1) + (c_2, 0, c_2) + (c_3, c_3, 0) = (0, 0, 0),$$
$$(0 + c_2 + c_3, c_1 + 0 + c_3, c_1 + c_2 + 0) = (0, 0, 0).$$

This last equation implies that

$$\begin{aligned} c_2 + c_3 &= 0, \\ c_1 \quad\; + c_3 &= 0, \\ c_1 + c_2 \quad\; &= 0. \end{aligned}$$

Solving this system of equations, we see that the only solution is the trivial one:

$$c_1 = 0, \quad c_2 = 0, \quad c_3 = 0.$$

In other words, Eq. (3.12) forces all c_1, c_2, c_3 to be zero. Hence, by Lemma 3.2, the given set of vectors is *linearly independent*.

The term "linear dependence" suggests that in any collection of linearly dependent vectors some vectors "depend" upon the others. This was the case with the row vectors of the matrix K given in (3.9). There we had, as you recall, $\mathbf{r}_1 = \mathbf{r}_2 - \mathbf{r}_3$ and $\mathbf{r}_4 = \mathbf{r}_2 + \mathbf{r}_3$. Suppose that the set

$$S = \{\mathbf{v}_1, \mathbf{v}_2, \ldots, \mathbf{v}_n\}$$

is linearly dependent. Then there exist scalars $c_1, c_2, \ldots, c_n$, not all zero, such that

$$c_1\mathbf{v}_1 + c_2\mathbf{v}_2 + \ldots + c_n\mathbf{v}_n = 0. \tag{3.13}$$

Since at least one of these c_i is not zero, let us assume (renumbering if necessary) that $c_1 \neq 0$. Then multiply both sides of (3.13) by $1/c_1$ and solve for $\mathbf{v}_1$. We have

$$\mathbf{v}_1 = \left(-\frac{c_2}{c_1}\right)\mathbf{v}_2 + \ldots + \left(-\frac{c_n}{c_1}\right)\mathbf{v}_n, \tag{3.14}$$

so $\mathbf{v}_1$ is a linear combination of the vectors $\{\mathbf{v}_2, \mathbf{v}_3, \ldots, \mathbf{v}_n\}$.

Example 3 Consider three geometric vectors $\mathbf{u}$, $\mathbf{v}$, and $\mathbf{w}$ in the plane shown in Fig. (3.6).

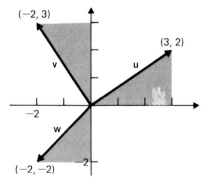

Figure 3.6

We shall see first that these three vectors are linearly dependent. To find the appropriate scalars, set

$$c_1 \mathbf{u} + c_2 \mathbf{v} + c_3 \mathbf{w} = 0$$

or

$$c_1(3, 2) + c_2(-2, 3) + c_3(-2, -2) = 0,$$

which results in

$$(3c_1 - 2c_2 - 2c_3, 2c_1 + 3c_2 - 2c_3) = (0, 0)$$

or

$$3c_1 - 2c_2 - 2c_3 = 0,$$
$$2c_1 + 3c_2 - 2c_3 = 0.$$

The general solution of this system is $c_1 = 10t/13$, $c_2 = 2t/13$, $c_3 = t$, so that

$$\frac{10}{13}\mathbf{u} + \frac{2}{13}\mathbf{v} + \mathbf{w} = 0$$

or

$$\mathbf{w} = \frac{-10}{13}\mathbf{u} - \frac{2}{13}\mathbf{v}.$$

Thus $\mathbf{u}$, $\mathbf{v}$, and $\mathbf{w}$ form a linearly dependent set of vectors. However, the vectors $\mathbf{u}$ and $\mathbf{v}$ by themselves are *linearly independent* since

$$c_1 \mathbf{u} + c_2 \mathbf{v} = 0$$

results in the system

$$3c_1 - 2c_2 = 0,$$
$$2c_1 + 3c_2 = 0,$$

whose only solution is the trivial one $c_1 = c_2 = 0$ (verify this).

Finally, if $\mathbf{x} = (x_1, x_2)$ is any vector in the plane, the vector $\mathbf{x}$ depends on $\mathbf{u}$ and $\mathbf{v}$. To see this consider the equation

$$c_1 \mathbf{u} + c_2 \mathbf{v} = \mathbf{x}.$$

Here we get

$$c_1(3, 2) + c_2(-2, 3) = (x_1, x_2)$$

or the system

$$3c_1 - 2c_2 = x_1,$$
$$2c_1 + 3c_2 = x_2.$$

The solution of this system is

$$c_1 = \frac{3x_1 + 2x_2}{13},$$

$$c_2 = -\frac{2x_1 - 3x_2}{13}.$$

Hence, the set of vectors $\{\mathbf{u}, \mathbf{v}, \mathbf{x}\}$ is dependent:

$$\mathbf{x} = \frac{3x_1 + 2x_2}{13}\mathbf{u} - \frac{2x_1 - 3x_2}{13}\mathbf{v}.$$

EXERCISES (3.2)————————————————————————————

Show that the following sets of vectors are linearly independent:

1. $\{(0, 1), (1, 0)\}$ 2. $\{(0, 0, 1), (0, 1, 0), (1, 0, 0)\}$
3. $\{(1, 0, 0, 0), (0, 1, 0, 0), (0, 0, 1, 0)\}$ 4. $\{(1, 1), (1, -1)\}$
5. $\{(1, 1, 1), (1, -1, 1)\}$ 6. $\{p_1(x) = 1, p_2(x) = x, p_3(x) = x^2\}$
7. $\{q_1(x) = 1 - x, q_2(x) = 1 + x\}$
8.

The row vectors of the matrix $A = \begin{bmatrix} 1 & 2 & -1 \\ 3 & 1 & 4 \\ 5 & 6 & -7 \end{bmatrix}$

9.

The matrices $\begin{bmatrix} 1 & 0 \\ 0 & 0 \end{bmatrix}, \begin{bmatrix} 0 & 1 \\ 0 & 0 \end{bmatrix}, \begin{bmatrix} 0 & 0 \\ 0 & 1 \end{bmatrix}$

10. The functions $\sin x$ and $\cos x$ (the zero function is zero for *all* x)

Decide which of the following sets of vectors are linearly independent and which are linearly dependent:

11. $\{(1, 1), (2, 2)\}$ 12. $\{(1, 1, 1), (1, -1, 1), (1, -3, 1)\}$
13. $\{(1, 2, 3), (-1, 2, 1), (1, 0, -1)\}$ 14. $\{1, x, 1 - x, x^2\}$
15. $\{\sin^2 x, \cos^2 x\}$ 16. $\{\sin^2 x, \tan^2 x\}$
17. $\{(0, 0), (1, 1)\}$ 18. $\{1 - x, 1 + x, 1 - x^2\}$
19. $\left\{\begin{bmatrix} 1 & 0 \\ 0 & 1 \end{bmatrix}, \begin{bmatrix} 1 & 2 \\ 0 & 1 \end{bmatrix}, \begin{bmatrix} 0 & 1 \\ 0 & 0 \end{bmatrix}\right\}$ 20. $\left\{\begin{bmatrix} 1 & 1 \\ 0 & 1 \end{bmatrix}, \begin{bmatrix} 0 & 0 \\ 0 & 0 \end{bmatrix}, \begin{bmatrix} 1 & 0 \\ 1 & 0 \end{bmatrix}\right\}$

21. Show that any collection of two vectors is linearly dependent if and only if one vector is a scalar multiple of the other.

22. Show that any set of vectors containing the zero vector is linearly dependent.

23. Show that the two vectors $\mathbf{u}$ and $\mathbf{w}$ of Example 3 are linearly independent.

24. Show that any single nonzero vector is linearly independent.

25. Show that any set of three vectors in $\mathbb{R}^2$ is linearly dependent.

26. Show that if $\{v_1, v_2, v_3\}$ is linearly independent, so are $\{v_1, v_2\}$ and $\{v_1, v_3\}$.

27. If $S = \{v_1, v_2, \ldots, v_n\}$ is a linearly independent set of vectors, show that any subset containing one or more of these vectors is also linearly independent.

Exercises 28–30 are for those who have studied calculus.

28. Let V be the vector space of all twice-differentiable real-valued functions on the unit interval $[0, 1]$. Show that three such functions $v_1(x), v_2(x), v_3(x)$ are linearly independent if their *Wronskian*

$$w(x) = \det \begin{bmatrix} v_1(x) & v_2(x) & v_3(x) \\ v_1'(x) & v_2'(x) & v_3'(x) \\ v_1''(x) & v_2''(x) & v_3''(x) \end{bmatrix}$$

is not the zero vector (the identically zero function).

29. Use the results of Exercise 28 to determine whether $v_1(x) = e^x, v_2(x) = e^{-x}, v_3(x) = e^{2x}$ are linearly independent or dependent.

30. Repeat Exercise 29 for the functions e^x, xe^x, x^2e^x.

3.3 SUBSPACES—SPANNING

As we have already noted above, it is a direct result of the axioms for a vector space that any linear combination of vectors from the space is a vector in that vector space. Thus, if $v_1, v_2, \ldots, v_n$ are vectors in the vector space V, so is

$$w = c_1v_1 + c_2v_2 + \ldots + c_nv_n.$$

In Example 3 of Section 3.2 we saw that any vector in the plane (cartesian 2-space, $\mathbb{R}^2$) was a linear combination of the two given vectors $u = (3, 2)$ and $v = (-2, 3)$ (see Fig. 3.6).

Consider also the solution space S for the homogeneous system of equations (3.7) in the preceding section. Recall that we had the system $KX = 0$, where

$$K = \begin{bmatrix} 1 & -1 & -3 & 2 \\ 2 & 1 & -1 & 1 \\ 1 & 2 & 2 & -1 \\ 3 & 3 & 1 & 0 \end{bmatrix}. \tag{3.15}$$

We have already demonstrated that any linear combination $sX_1 + tX_2$ of the two solution vectors

$$X_1 = \begin{bmatrix} 4 \\ -5 \\ 3 \\ 0 \end{bmatrix} \quad \text{and} \quad X_2 = \begin{bmatrix} -1 \\ 1 \\ 0 \\ 1 \end{bmatrix}$$

is also a solution. Let us now demonstrate that *every* solution to the system has the form

$$X = sX_1 + tX_2. \tag{3.16}$$

That is, every solution is a linear combination of these two particular solutions. Suppose that

$$X = \begin{bmatrix} x_1 \\ x_2 \\ x_3 \\ x_4 \end{bmatrix}$$

is any solution to the system $KX = 0$. The augmented matrix for the system is

$$\begin{bmatrix} 1 & -1 & -3 & 2 & 0 \\ 2 & 1 & -1 & 1 & 0 \\ 1 & 2 & 2 & -1 & 0 \\ 3 & 3 & 1 & 0 & 0 \end{bmatrix}.$$

Using the Gauss–Jordan reduction we obtain an equivalent matrix

$$\begin{bmatrix} 1 & 0 & -\frac{4}{3} & 1 & 0 \\ 0 & 1 & \frac{5}{3} & -1 & 0 \\ 0 & 0 & 0 & 0 & 0 \\ 0 & 0 & 0 & 0 & 0 \end{bmatrix}.$$

Thus, the general solution to the system must satisfy the equations

$$x_1 = \frac{4}{3}x_3 - x_4,$$

$$x_2 = -\frac{5}{3}x_3 + x_4.$$

Therefore,

$$X = \begin{bmatrix} \frac{4}{3}x_3 - x_4 \\ -\frac{5}{3}x_3 + x_4 \\ x_3 \\ x_4 \end{bmatrix} = \frac{x_3}{3} \begin{bmatrix} 4 \\ -5 \\ 3 \\ 0 \end{bmatrix} + x_4 \begin{bmatrix} -1 \\ 1 \\ 0 \\ 1 \end{bmatrix}.$$

Hence *every* vector in the solution space S is a linear combination of the two vectors X_1 and X_2. These two vectors *span* the solution space in a sense that we shall now define.

A set $\{v_1, v_2, \ldots, v_n\}$ of vectors in a vector space V is said to **span** V if every vector x in V can be written as a linear combination of the vectors in the set in the form

$$x = c_1 v_1 + c_2 v_2 + \ldots + c_n v_n, \tag{3.17}$$

where $c_1, c_2, \ldots, c_n$ are suitably chosen scalars.

Example 1   Do the vectors $(1, 0, 0)$, $(0, 1, 0)$, $(0, 0, 1)$ in cartesian 3-space $\mathbb{R}^3$ span $\mathbb{R}^3$? (See Fig. 3.7.)

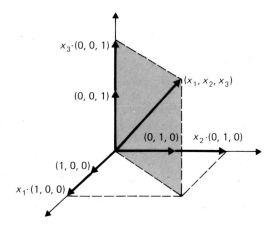

Figure 3.7

We recall that every vector in $\mathbb{R}^3$ has the form (x_1, x_2, x_3), where x_1, x_2, x_3 are real numbers. Using the definitions of vector addition and scalar multiplication given in Example 3 of Section 3.1, we see that

$$x_1(1, 0, 0) + x_2(0, 1, 0) + x_3(0, 0, 1) = (x_1, 0, 0) + (0, x_2, 0) + (0, 0, x_3)$$
$$= (x_1, x_2, x_3).$$

Hence,

$$(x_1, x_2, x_3) = x_1(1, 0, 0) + x_2(0, 1, 0) + x_3(0, 0, 1),$$

and thus the vectors $(1, 0, 0)$, $(0, 1, 0)$, $(0, 0, 1)$ span $\mathbb{R}^3$.

Example 2   Do the vectors $(1, 0, -1, 0)$, $(1, 1, 2, 0)$, $(2, -1, 0, 0)$, and $(3, 1, -1, 0)$ in cartesian 4-space $\mathbb{R}^4$ span $\mathbb{R}^4$?

As stated in Example 4 of Section 3.1, a typical vector in cartesian 4-space $\mathbb{R}^4$ has the form (x_1, x_2, x_3, x_4), where x_1, x_2, x_3, x_4 are arbitrary real numbers. Now, a glance at the four given vectors shows that the last coordinate (or entry) of each of them is zero. Moreover, in view of the way we defined vector addition and scalar multiplication in Example 4 of Section 3.1, we see that *any* vector of the form

$$c_1(1, 0, -1, 0) + c_2(1, 1, 2, 0) + c_3(2, -1, 0, 0) + c_4(3, 1, -1, 0) \qquad (3.18)$$

must have zero for its last coordinate. Hence, a vector like $(0, 0, 0, 1)$ *cannot* possibly be written in the form (3.18) since its last coordinate is 1. Thus, the given vectors do *not* span $\mathbb{R}^4$.

On the other hand, let us consider the collection W of all vectors in $\mathbb{R}^4$ that have the form

$$\mathbf{w} = (w_1, w_2, w_3, 0),$$

that is, all of those vectors in $\mathbb{R}^4$ whose fourth component is zero. You can verify that W is a real-vector space in its own right with the same operations as those in $\mathbb{R}^4$ by checking each axiom. The vector $\mathbf{w}$ in W can indeed be expressed in the form (3.18). To see this, write

$$\mathbf{w} = c_1(1, 0, -1, 0) + c_2(1, 1, 2, 0) + c_3(2, -1, 0, 0) + c_4(3, 1, -1, 0).$$

Therefore,

$$(c_1 + c_2 + 2c_3 + 3c_4, c_2 - c_3 + c_4, -c_1 + 2c_2 - c_4, 0) = (w_1, w_2, w_3, 0).$$

This gives rise to the system of equations of the form

$$\begin{aligned} c_1 + c_2 + 2c_3 + 3c_4 &= w_1, \\ c_2 - c_3 + c_4 &= w_2, \\ -c_1 + 2c_2 \qquad - c_4 &= w_3. \end{aligned}$$

We skip the details of the solution process and just give the answer. There are an infinite number of solutions given, for each t, by the equations

$$c_1 = \tfrac{1}{5}(2w_1 + 4w_2 - 3w_3 - 13t), \qquad c_2 = \tfrac{1}{5}(w_1 + 2w_2 + w_3 - 4t),$$

$$c_3 = \tfrac{1}{5}(w_1 - 3w_2 + w_3 + t), \qquad c_4 = t.$$

Therefore the vectors $(1, 0, -1, 0)$, $(1, 1, 2, 0)$, $(2, -1, 0, 0)$ and $(3, 1, -1, 0)$ *span* the vector space W. Since W is a subset of $\mathbb{R}^4$ that is also a vector space, we call it a *subspace* of $\mathbb{R}^4$. The general definition is as follows.

Let V be a vector space. A nonempty subset W of V is called a **subspace** of V if W itself is a vector space with respect to the same operations of V.

Example 3   Let

$$V = \text{set of all points } (x_1, x_2); \qquad x_1, x_2 \text{ real;}$$
$$W_1 = \text{set of all points } (x_1, 0);$$
$$W_2 = \text{set of all points } (0, x_2);$$
$$W_3 = \text{set of all points } (x_1, x_2); \qquad x_1 = x_2.$$

In other words, V is the plane, W_1 is the x_1-axis, and W_2 is the x_2-axis (see Fig. 3.8). It can be verified that W_1 is a vector space in its own right, and so are W_2 and W_3 (convince yourself that all the axioms in the definition of vector space in Section 3.1 are satisfied for W_1, W_2, and W_3). In verifying the above assertions, observe that the closure axioms for both vector addition and scalar multiplication hold in W_1, since

$$(x_1, 0) + (x'_1, 0) = (x_1 + x'_1, 0) \qquad (= \text{Element in } W_1),$$
$$k(x_1, 0) = (kx_1, 0) \qquad (= \text{Element in } W_1).$$

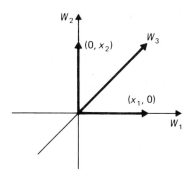

Figure 3.8

Also, $(0, 0)$ is in W_1 and the negative of any element in W_1 is again in W_1. Because all of the equational axioms (i.e., commutative, associative, distributive, etc.) are true for *all* elements in V, they are just as true if we happen to select these elements from W_1 (since every element in W_1 is also in V). Similarly, we can verify that W_2 and W_3 are subspaces of V.

It is easy to see that the subspace W_1 is spanned by the vector $\mathbf{e}_1 = (1, 0)$ since any w in W_1 is a linear combination of the form

$$x_1 \mathbf{e}_1 = (x_1, 0).$$

Similarly the vector space W_2 is spanned by the vector $\mathbf{e}_2 = (0, 1)$, while space W_3 is spanned by $\mathbf{v} = (1, 1)$.

With an eye on the above example, we are led to ask the following question: When is a nonempty subset W of a vector space V a subspace of V? The above discussion makes the following theorem quite plausible.

Theorem 3.3

Let V be a vector space and let W be a nonempty subset of V. Then W is a subspace of V if and only if the following two conditions hold:

i) if $\mathbf{w}_1$ and $\mathbf{w}_2$ are both in W, so is $\mathbf{w}_1 + \mathbf{w}_2$;
ii) if $\mathbf{w}$ is in W and k is a scalar, then $k\mathbf{w}$ is also in W.

Obviously, the two conditions of this theorem are necessary for W to be a subspace, since they are two of the axioms (VI, S1). That these two conditions are sufficient follows from the fact that W is a subset of V and so inherits many of its properties: associativity and commutativity of vector addition, etc. The zero vector is in W because $0\mathbf{w}$ is in W. Similarly, $-\mathbf{w} = (-1)\mathbf{w}$ is in W. We ask you to carry out the details of the proof as Exercise 29.

Example 4   Let V be the cartesian 3-space $\mathbb{R}^3$ and let

$$W = \text{set of all vectors } (x_1, x_2, x_3); \qquad x_1 + x_2 + x_3 = 0. \qquad (3.19)$$

Is W a subspace of V?

First, observe that $(0, 0, 0)$ is in W (Why?) and hence W is *not* empty. In view of Theorem 3.3, it suffices to verify both conditions (i) and (ii) in Theorem 3.3. Thus, suppose that

$$(x_1, x_2, x_3) \quad \text{and} \quad (x_1', x_2', x_3') \quad \text{are both in } W. \qquad (3.20)$$

Then, by definition of W, we have

$$x_1 + x_2 + x_3 = 0 \qquad \text{and} \qquad x_1' + x_2' + x_3' = 0.$$

Now, adding these two equations, we get

$$(x_1 + x_1') + (x_2 + x_2') + (x_3 + x_3') = 0.$$

By definition of W again, this last equation tells us that

$$(x_1 + x_1', x_2 + x_2', x_3 + x_3') \quad \text{is in } W,$$

and hence (Why?)

$$(x_1, x_2, x_3) + (x_1', x_2', x_3') \quad \text{is in } W. \qquad (3.21)$$

In view of (3.20) and (3.21), we see that condition (i) in Theorem 3.3 is true. Now, suppose

$$(x_1, x_2, x_3) \quad \text{is in } W \quad \text{and} \quad k \text{ is a scalar.} \qquad (3.22)$$

Then, again by definition of W, $x_1 + x_2 + x_3 = 0$ and hence

$$k(x_1 + x_2 + x_3) = k \cdot 0 = 0 \quad \text{or} \quad kx_1 + kx_2 + kx_3 = 0.$$

This equation tells us that (Why?)

$$k(x_1, x_2, x_3) \quad \text{is in } W. \tag{3.23}$$

A glance at (3.22) and (3.23) shows that condition (ii) in Theorem 3.3 is also true, hence W is a subspace of V.

It is easy to verify that W is spanned by the vectors

$$\mathbf{w}_1 = (1, -1, 0) \quad \text{and} \quad \mathbf{w}_2 = (1, 0, -1)$$

because, if $\mathbf{x} = (x_1, x_2\ x_3)$ is any vector in W, then

$$(-x_2)\mathbf{w}_1 + (-x_3)\mathbf{w}_2 = (-x_2 - x_3, x_2, x_3) = (x_1, x_2, x_3)$$

according to the defining relation (3.19). Hence, $\mathbf{x} = (-x_2)\mathbf{w}_1 + (-x_3)\mathbf{w}_2$.

If $S = \{\mathbf{v}_1, \mathbf{v}_2, \ldots, \mathbf{v}_k\}$ is any collection of vectors from the vector space V, then the set of all linear combinations

$$\mathbf{v} = \alpha_1 \mathbf{v}_1 + \alpha_2 \mathbf{v}_2 + \ldots + \alpha_k \mathbf{v}_k$$

of these vectors forms a subspace of V, we denote by $L(S)$ or $L(\mathbf{v}_1, \mathbf{v}_2, \ldots, \mathbf{v}_k)$ and call the **linear span** of the set of vectors S.

That it truly is a subspace follows from Theorem 3.3: If

$$\mathbf{v} = \alpha_1 \mathbf{v}_1 + \alpha_2 \mathbf{v}_2 + \ldots + \alpha_k \mathbf{v}_k$$

and

$$\mathbf{u} = \rho_1 \mathbf{v}_1 + \rho_2 \mathbf{v}_2 + \ldots + \rho_k \mathbf{v}_k$$

are vectors from $L(S)$, then it is clear that, for any scalar γ,

$$\gamma\mathbf{v} = \gamma\alpha_1 \mathbf{v}_1 + \gamma\alpha_2 \mathbf{v}_2 + \ldots + \gamma\alpha_k \mathbf{v}_k \quad \text{is in } L(S)$$

and

$$\mathbf{u} + \mathbf{v} = (\rho_1 + \alpha_1)\mathbf{v}_1 + \ldots + (\rho_k + \alpha_k)\mathbf{v}_k \quad \text{is in } L(S).$$

Thus, $L(\mathbf{w}_1, \mathbf{w}_2)$ in the above example is the space W.

We shall call the set of vectors S a **spanning set** for the vector space $L(S)$.

It is not necessary that a collection of vectors be linearly independent for it to span a vector space. The two ideas are distinct. Consider the following example.

Example 5 Let $V = \mathbb{R}^2$ be cartesian 2-space. We shall show that V is spanned by each of the following sets of vectors:

$$S_1 = \{(1, 1), (1, -1), (-1, 1), (0, 1)\},$$
$$S_2 = \{(1, 1), (1, 0), (0, 1)\},$$
$$S_3 = \{(1, 1), (1, -1)\}.$$

To see that S_1 is a spanning set we remember that any vector in V has the form (x_1, x_2), where x_1 and x_2 are real numbers. Then we seek certain scalars, so that

$$(x_1, x_2) = c_1(1, 1) + c_2(1, -1) + c_3(-1, 1) + c_4(0, 1)$$
$$= (c_1 + c_2 - c_3, c_1 - c_2 + c_3 + c_4).$$

There are many such scalars available to us. Any solution to the system of equations

$$c_1 + c_2 - c_3 \qquad = x_1,$$
$$c_1 - c_2 + c_3 + c_4 = x_2$$

will do, such as

$$c_1 = \tfrac{1}{2}(x_1 + x_2 - 2), \qquad c_2 = \tfrac{1}{2}(x_1 - x_2 + 2), \qquad c_3 = 0, \qquad c_4 = 2.$$

So S_1 is indeed a spanning set for V; thus $L(S_1) = \mathbb{R}^2$.

In a similar way, if $k_1 = 1, k_2 = x_1 - 1, k_3 = x_2 - 1$, we have an arbitrary vector (x_1, x_2) represented as a linear combination of the vectors in S_2 as (verify this)

$$k_1(1, 1) + k_2(1, 0) + k_3(0, 1).$$

So $\mathbb{R}^2$ is also spanned by the set S_2; thus $L(S_2) = \mathbb{R}^2$. And finally in a similar way $L(S_3) = \mathbb{R}^2$ since

$$(x_1, x_2) = \frac{x_1 + x_2}{2}(1, 1) + \frac{x_1 - x_2}{2}(1, -1).$$

Thus, each of the three sets is a spanning set for $\mathbb{R}^2$.

This example raises some interesting questions that will be answered in the next section. Does there exist a *minimal* spanning set for a vector space? That is, does there exist, among all the sets of vectors that span V, one, or more, with the least number of elements in it? Is there some significance to the fact that in Example 5 only the set S_3 is a linearly independent set? (You should verify that the vectors in S_1 and in S_2 are linearly dependent.)

Example 6 Let $V = \mathbb{R}^3$ and let the two vectors be

$$\mathbf{u} = (1, 1, 1) \quad \text{and} \quad \mathbf{v} = (1, 1, -1).$$

Geometrically, these are two three-dimensional vectors, as depicted in Fig. 3.9.

The subspace $L(\mathbf{u}, \mathbf{v})$ spanned by $\mathbf{u}$ and $\mathbf{v}$ is the collection of all vectors that have the form

$$\mathbf{x} = s\mathbf{u} + t\mathbf{v} = (s + t, s + t, s - t),$$

that is, all those vectors that lie in the plane determined by the vectors $\mathbf{u}$ and $\mathbf{v}$ (the equation of this plane is $x_1 = x_2$).

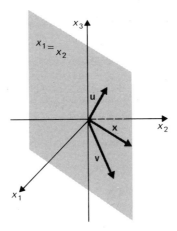

Figure 3.9

Example 7 Let $V = P_2$ be the vector space of polynomials of degree two or less. Let

$$u(x) = 1 - x, \qquad v(x) = 1 + x^2.$$

Then the subspace $L(u, v)$ is the collection of all polynomials of the form

$$p(x) = cu(x) + dv(x) = c - cx + d + dx^2$$
$$= (c + d) - cx + dx^2.$$

Note that the polynomials $f(x) = x - 1$ and $g(x) = x^2 - 2x + 3$ belong to $L(u, v)$, whereas the polynomial $x^2 + 2$ does not (why?).

EXERCISES (3.3)

Use Theorem 3.3 to determine which of the following are subspaces of the indicated vector space:

1. All vectors in $\mathbb{R}^3$ of the form $(0, 0, \alpha)$.
2. All vectors in $\mathbb{R}^3$ of the form $(1, 1, \alpha)$.
3. All vectors in $\mathbb{R}^3$ of the form (α, β, γ), where $\beta = \gamma$.
4. All vectors in $\mathbb{R}^3$ of the form (α, β, γ), where $\alpha + 1 = \beta + \gamma$.
5. All polynomials in P_2 of the form $\alpha_0 + \alpha_2 x^2$.
6. All polynomials in P_2 of the form $\alpha_0 + \alpha_1 x + \alpha_2 x^2$, where $\alpha_0 = \alpha_1 = \alpha_2$.
7. All polynomials in P_3 of the form $\alpha_0 + \alpha_1 x + \alpha_2 x^2 + \alpha_3 x^3$, where $\alpha_0 + \alpha_1 + \alpha_2 + \alpha_3 = 0$.
8. All polynomials in P_3 of the form $\alpha_0 + \alpha_1 x + \alpha_2 x^2 + \alpha_3 x^3$, whose coefficients $\alpha_0, \alpha_1, \alpha_2, \alpha_3$ are integers.

9. All 2×2 upper-triangular matrices in M_2.

10. All 2×2 matrices A in M_2 for which $A^t = A$.

11. All 2×2 matrices A in M_2 for which $\det A = 0$.

12. For those who have studied calculus: All functions $f(x)$ in the space of functions continuous on $[0, 1]$ such that $f'(x) \geqslant 0$.

13. The subset W_3 in Example 3.

In Exercises 14–24, determine whether or not the given vector $\mathbf{x}$ is in $L(S)$ for the given set of vectors S. If $\mathbf{x}$ is in $L(S)$, write it as a linear combination of the vectors of S.

14. $\mathbf{x} = (2, -1, -1)$;　　　$S = \{(1, 0, 1), (0, 1, 1)\}$

15. $\mathbf{x} = (-1, 2, 3)$;　　　$S = \{(1, 1, 0), (0, 1, 1)\}$

16. $\mathbf{x} = (3, 3, 3)$;　　　$S = \{(1, -1, 3), (2, 4, 0)\}$

17. $\mathbf{x} = (1, 5, -3)$;　　　$S = \{(1, -1, 3), (2, 4, 0)\}$

18. $\mathbf{x} = (0, 0, 0)$;　　　$S = \{(1, 3, 5), (-1, 2, 1)\}$

19. $\mathbf{x} = (1, -1, 1)$;　　　$S = \{(1, 1, -1), (-2, -2, 2)\}$

20. $\mathbf{x} = 2 - t^2$;　　　$S = \{1, t^2\}$

21. $\mathbf{x} = 3 - 2t + t^2$;　　　$S = \{1 + t, 1 - t^2\}$

22. $\mathbf{x} = 1 + t$;　　　$S = \{t - 1, t^2\}$

23. $\mathbf{x} = \begin{bmatrix} 1 & 2 \\ 0 & -1 \end{bmatrix}$;　　　$S = \left\{ \begin{bmatrix} 2 & 4 \\ 0 & 1 \end{bmatrix}, \begin{bmatrix} 1 & 2 \\ 0 & 2 \end{bmatrix} \right\}$

24. $\mathbf{x} = \begin{bmatrix} 2 & -1 \\ 1 & -2 \end{bmatrix}$;　　　$S = \left\{ \begin{bmatrix} 1 & 1 \\ 0 & 1 \end{bmatrix}, \begin{bmatrix} 1 & -1 \\ 0 & -1 \end{bmatrix} \right\}$

In Exercises 25–28, determine whether or not the given sets S of vectors span $\mathbb{R}^3$.

25. $S = \{(1, 0, 0), (0, 1, 1), (1, 0, 1)\}$

26. $S = \{1, 0, 1), (0, 1, 1), (2, -1, 1)\}$

27. $S = \{(1, 0, 1), (1, 1, 0), (0, 1, 1), (1, 1, 1)\}$

28. $S = \{(1, 2, 3), (3, 2, 1), (1, 0, -1), (2, 2, 2)\}$

29. Furnish all the details of the proof of Theorem 3.3.

30. Find an equation for the plane in $\mathbb{R}^3$ spanned by the vectors $\mathbf{u} = (1, 0, 1)$, $\mathbf{v} = (1, -1, 0)$.

31. Show that the solutions to any nonhomogeneous system of linear equations do not form a vector space.

32. Show that $\mathbb{R}^3$ is spanned by the rows of the matrix

$$A = \begin{bmatrix} 1 & 2 & -1 \\ 2 & 1 & -2 \\ 1 & 4 & 3 \end{bmatrix}.$$

33. Let C^2 be the vector space of pairs of complex numbers of Example 8 in Section 3.1. Find the subspace of C^2 spanned by $\mathbf{u} = (1, i)$ and $\mathbf{v} = (i, -1)$.

Exercises 34–36 are for those who have studied calculus. Let V be the vector space of all differentiable functions $f(x)$ on $[0, 1]$. Show that each of the following is a subspace:

34. All $f(x)$ for which $f(1) = 0$.

35. All $f(x)$ that are twice differentiable.

36. All $f(x)$ that satisfy $f''(x) + f(x) = 0$.

3.4 BASES AND DIMENSION

In the previous section we asked if there were a minimal spanning set S of vectors for a given vector space V (refer to Example 5 in Section 3.3). There we discovered that the set $S_3 = \{(1, 1), (1, -1)\}$ was such that $L(S_3) = \mathbb{R}^2$. Let us show that this is such a minimal set.

Example 1 Show that no one vector from $\mathbb{R}^2$ can span $\mathbb{R}^2$.

Let $\mathbf{u} = (u_1, u_2)$ be any vector in $\mathbb{R}^2$. Then every vector in $L(\mathbf{u})$, the subspace of $\mathbb{R}^2$ spanned by $\mathbf{u}$, has the form $k\mathbf{u} = (ku_1, ku_2)$, where k is any real number. Now, if u_1, u_2 are *nonzero* real numbers, then $\mathbf{v} = (u_1, 2u_2)$ fails to belong to $L(\mathbf{u})$ because if $\mathbf{v} = k\mathbf{u}$ then $ku_1 = u_1$, so $k = 1$. But $ku_2 = 2u_2$, so $k = 2$.

This contradiction shows that $\mathbf{v}$ is not in $L(\mathbf{u})$. If $u_1 = 0$, choose $\mathbf{v} = (1, u_2)$; if $u_2 = 0$, choose $\mathbf{v} = (u_1, 1)$.

Example 2 Show that the set $S = \{1, t\}$ is a minimal spanning set for the vector space P_1 of polynomials

$$a + bt \qquad\qquad (3.24)$$

in that no single polynomial can span P_1.

First of all, any polynomial in P_1 has the form $a + bt = a \cdot 1 + b \cdot t$ and is in $L(S)$, by definition of $L(S)$. Now, suppose that $u = a_0 + a_1 t$ in P_1 with $a_1 \neq 0$. As in Example 1, it can be shown that if $a_0 \neq 0$, then the polynomial $-a_0 + a_1 t$ is not in $L(u)$. Also, if $a_0 = 0$, then $1 + a_1 t$ is not in $L(u)$.

In fact, a spanning set will be minimal if any subset of it, consisting of fewer vectors, fails to span the space. On the other hand, as we noted in Example 5 of Section 3.3, if there are more than a minimal number of vectors in the spanning set, it is a linearly dependent set. The minimal spanning set is linearly independent (see Exercise 23). These ideas are made more useful and more formal in the concept of a *basis* for a vector space.

Let V be a vector space different from the zero vector space, that is, $V \neq \{0\}$.

Suppose that the set of vectors $S = \{v_1, v_2, \ldots, v_n\}$

i) *spans* V, i.e., $L(S) = V$ and

ii) is *linearly independent*.

Then the set S is called a **basis** for (or of) V.

Thus, a basis is a linearly independent spanning set for V. We claim that the set $S_3 = \{(1, 1), (1, -1)\}$ in Example 5 of Section 3.3 is a basis for V. We showed there that $L(S_3) = V$. That S_3 is linearly independent follows from the fact that if

$$\alpha_1(1, 1) + \alpha_2(1, -1) = (0, 0),$$

then

$$\alpha_1 + \alpha_2 = 0,$$
$$\alpha_1 - \alpha_2 = 0,$$

so $\alpha_1 = \alpha_2 = 0$.

Every vector space has a basis, finite or infinite. We say that the zero vector space has the empty set for its basis. We will accept these statements without proof.

Example 3 Do the vectors $(1, 0, 0)$, $(0, 1, 0)$, $(0, 0, 1)$ in cartesian 3-space $\mathbb{R}^3$ form a basis for $\mathbb{R}^3$?

Solution. In Example 1 of Section 3.3 we proved that the given vectors span $\mathbb{R}^3$. Now we test for linear independence. Thus, suppose that

$$c_1(1, 0, 0) + c_2(0, 1, 0) + c_3(0, 0, 1) = (0, 0, 0). \tag{3.25}$$

Computing the left side of this equation, we obtain

$$(c_1, 0, 0) + (0, c_2, 0) + (0, 0, c_3) = (0, 0, 0),$$
$$(c_1, c_2, c_3) = (0, 0, 0),$$

and hence $c_1 = 0$, $c_2 = 0$, $c_3 = 0$. We have thus shown that Eq. (3.25) forces $c_1 = 0$, $c_2 = 0$, $c_3 = 0$; and hence the vectors $(1, 0, 0)$, $(0, 1, 0)$, $(0, 0, 1)$ are linearly independent. Therefore, these vectors form a basis for $\mathbb{R}^3$.

It is a basis for a vector space that is the minimal spanning set we were looking for. However, *a basis for a vector space is by no means unique.* The set $S = \{(1, 1), (1, -1)\}$ and the set $T = \{(1, 0), (0, 1)\}$ are both bases for the vector space $\mathbb{R}^2$. The fact that they both contain *two* vectors and that no set with just *one* vector (as seen in Example 1) can be a basis, since it does not span $\mathbb{R}^2$, is crucial here. We shall make this more precise. First of all we have the following lemma.

Lemma 3.4

Let V be a vector space and let $S = \{\mathbf{v}_1, \mathbf{v}_2, \ldots, \mathbf{v}_n\}$ be a basis for V. Then every set containing more than n vectors is linearly dependent and hence cannot be a basis for V.

The proof of this lemma is an application of the machinery that we have developed to this point. We, therefore, present it even though it is a bit tedious.

Suppose that $T = \{\mathbf{w}_1, \mathbf{w}_2, \ldots, \mathbf{w}_m\}$ with $m > n$ is any collection of (more than n) vectors in V. We shall show that T is linearly dependent. Because S is a basis for V, it must span V. Every vector in V, in particular each vector in T, is a linear combination of the vectors of S. That is, for each $j = 1, 2, \ldots, m$ we have scalars a_{ij}, $i = 1, 2, \ldots, n$, so that

$$\mathbf{w}_j = a_{1j}\mathbf{v}_1 + a_{2j}\mathbf{v}_2 + \ldots + a_{nj}\mathbf{v}_n. \tag{3.26}$$

To show that the vectors $\mathbf{w}_j$ are linearly dependent, we must find scalars c_j (not all zero) such that

$$c_1\mathbf{w}_1 + c_2\mathbf{w}_2 + \ldots + c_m\mathbf{w}_m = \mathbf{0}. \tag{3.27}$$

By substituting the values of $\mathbf{w}_j$ from (3.26) into (3.27), we have

$$\sum_{j=1}^{m} c_j(a_{1j}\mathbf{v}_1 + a_{2j}\mathbf{v}_2 + \ldots + a_{nj}\mathbf{v}_n) = 0. \tag{3.28}$$

By multiplying (3.28) out and collecting the coefficients for the vectors $\mathbf{v}_1, \mathbf{v}_2, \ldots, \mathbf{v}_n$, we have

$$(c_1 a_{11} + c_2 a_{12} + \ldots + c_m a_{1m})\mathbf{v}_1 + (c_1 a_{21} + c_2 a_{22} + \ldots + c_m a_{2m})\mathbf{v}_2 + \ldots$$
$$+ (c_1 a_{n1} + c_2 a_{n2} + \ldots + c_m a_{nm})\mathbf{v}_n = \mathbf{0}.$$

But S is a basis, so the vectors $\mathbf{v}_1, \ldots, \mathbf{v}_n$ are linearly independent and hence each coefficient in the above equation is zero. This gives us the system of homogeneous linear equations

$$
\begin{aligned}
c_1 a_{11} + c_2 a_{12} + \ldots + c_m a_{1m} &= 0, \\
c_1 a_{21} + c_2 a_{22} + \ldots + c_m a_{2m} &= 0, \\
&\vdots \\
c_1 a_{n1} + c_2 a_{n2} + \ldots + c_m a_{nm} &= 0.
\end{aligned}
\tag{3.29}
$$

To see that T is indeed linearly dependent, we need only show that the system (3.29) has a *non-trivial* solution $(c_1, c_2, \ldots, c_m)$, that is, not all c_i are zero. But in this system there are fewer equations than unknowns, so such is the case (see Chapter 1). This completes the proof of the lemma.

This lemma contains the main components of the proof of the following important theorem that every finite basis for a given vector space contains the same number of vectors.

Theorem 3.5

Let $S = \{\mathbf{v}_1, \mathbf{v}_2, \ldots, \mathbf{v}_n\}$ and $T = \{\mathbf{u}_1, \mathbf{u}_2, \ldots, \mathbf{u}_m\}$ be two bases for a vector space V. Then $n = m$.

The proof follows from the lemma because $m \leqslant n$, or T is not a basis; also $n \leqslant m$, or S is not a basis. Hence, $m = n$.

Therefore the number of vectors in a basis for a vector space with a finite basis is an invariant of the vector space. We call this finite number of vectors in a basis the **dimension** of the vector space and say that V is **finite dimensional**. The dimension of the zero vector space is zero.

We have already observed in Examples 1 and 3 and subsequent remarks that the vector space $\mathbb{R}^3$ has dimension 3 and $\mathbb{R}^2$ has dimension 2. These are special cases of the following theorem.

Theorem 3.6

The dimension of cartesian n-space $\mathbb{R}^n$ is n.

Proof. Let $(x_1, x_2, \ldots, x_n)$ be any vector in $\mathbb{R}^n$. Let us single out the following n vectors in $\mathbb{R}^n$:

$$S = \{(1, 0, 0, \ldots, 0), (0, 1, 0, 0, \ldots, 0), \ldots, (0, 0, \ldots, 0, 1)\}. \qquad (3.30)$$

In other words, each vector in S is an n-tuple with all zero coordinates *except one*. The exceptional nonzero coordinate is 1 and it is placed in all possible positions as we scan the vectors in S. Note that, as in the proof in Example 3,

$$(x_1, x_2, \ldots, x_n) = x_1(1, 0, 0, \ldots, 0) + x_2(0, 1, 0, 0, \ldots, 0) + \ldots$$
$$+ x_n(0, 0, \ldots, 0, 1).$$

This last equation shows the following:

$$\text{The } n \text{ vectors in } S \text{ span } \mathbb{R}^n \quad \text{and} \quad L(S) = \mathbb{R}^n. \qquad (3.31)$$

Next, consider linear independence. The argument used in Example 3 shows that the equation

$$c_1(1, 0, 0, \ldots, 0) + c_2(0, 1, 0, 0, \ldots, 0) + \ldots + c_n(0, 0, \ldots, 0, 1) = (0, 0, \ldots, 0)$$

forces each of $c_1, c_2, \ldots, c_n$ to be zero, and hence we conclude the following:

$$\text{The } n \text{ vectors in } S \text{ are linearly independent.} \qquad (3.32)$$

Combining (3.31) and (3.32), we see that the n vectors in S form a basis for $\mathbb{R}^n$. Hence, by definition, the dimension of $\mathbb{R}^n$ is n. This proves the theorem.

Corollary

The plane (i.e., cartesian 2-space) is of dimension 2 and $\{(1, 0), (0, 1)\}$ is a basis for this vector space. Moreover, cartesian 3-space is of dimension 3 and $\{(1, 0, 0), (0, 1, 0), (0, 0, 1)\}$ is a basis for this vector space.

Each of the vectors $(1, 0, 0, \ldots, 0), (0, 1, 0, 0, \ldots, 0), \ldots, (0, 0, \ldots, 0, 1)$ in

(3.30) is called a **unit vector**. As given in (3.30), the basis S consisting of these n unit vectors is called the **standard basis** of $\mathbb{R}^n$.

Generally speaking, a vector space has many bases. As we stated earlier, what all of these bases have in common is the important property that *they all have the same number of elements*. The following example exhibits a basis of a Euclidean 3-space different from the standard basis.

Example 4   Show that the vectors $\{(0, 1, 1), (1, 0, 1), (1, 1, 0)\}$ in 3-space $\mathbb{R}^3$ form a basis for $\mathbb{R}^3$.

In Exercise 5 we will ask you to show that the given vectors are *linearly independent*. Given that fact, we have to show only that they span $\mathbb{R}^3$. To this end, suppose that $(\alpha_1, \alpha_2, \alpha_3)$ is *any* vector in $\mathbb{R}^3$. We wish to find certain scalars x_1, x_2, x_3 such that

$$x_1(0, 1, 1) + x_2(1, 0, 1) + x_3(1, 1, 0) = (\alpha_1, \alpha_2, \alpha_3). \tag{3.33}$$

Now, if we simplify the left side of (3.33), we see that it becomes

$$(0, x_1, x_1) + (x_2, 0, x_2) + (x_3, x_3, 0) = (\alpha_1, \alpha_2, \alpha_3)$$

or

$$(x_2 + x_3, x_1 + x_3, x_1 + x_2) = (\alpha_1, \alpha_2, \alpha_3).$$

This last is equivalent to the following system of linear equations:

$$\begin{aligned} x_2 + x_3 &= \alpha_1, \\ x_1 \quad\;\; + x_3 &= \alpha_2, \\ x_1 + x_2 \quad\;\; &= \alpha_3. \end{aligned}$$

Solving this system for the unknown scalars x_1, x_2, x_3, we get (verify this)

$$x_1 = \frac{-\alpha_1 + \alpha_2 + \alpha_3}{2}, \qquad x_2 = \frac{\alpha_1 - \alpha_2 + \alpha_3}{2}, \qquad x_3 = \frac{\alpha_1 + \alpha_2 - \alpha_3}{2}.$$

Hence scalars x_1, x_2, x_3 that satisfy (3.33) exist and thus $(0, 1, 1)$, $(1, 0, 1)$, $(1, 1, 0)$ span $\mathbb{R}^3$. Therefore, these vectors form a basis for $\mathbb{R}^3$.

Example 5   The "standard basis" for the vector space M_n of all $n \times n$ matrices over the real numbers consists of the n^2 matrices E_{ij} whose entry in row i and column j is 1 (where $i, j = 1, 2, \ldots, n$) with all of the other entries zero. Thus, in the space M_2 this basis consists of the four matrices

$$E_{11} = \begin{bmatrix} 1 & 0 \\ 0 & 0 \end{bmatrix}, \qquad E_{12} = \begin{bmatrix} 0 & 1 \\ 0 & 0 \end{bmatrix}, \qquad E_{21} = \begin{bmatrix} 0 & 0 \\ 1 & 0 \end{bmatrix}, \qquad E_{22} = \begin{bmatrix} 0 & 0 \\ 0 & 1 \end{bmatrix}.$$

That these matrices do indeed form a basis of M_n may be verified as follows. The matrix $A = (a_{ij})$ can be written in the form

$$A = (a_{ij}) = \sum_{i, j = 1}^{n} a_{ij} E_{ij}.$$

Also, if

$$\sum_{i, j = 1}^{n} c_{ij} E_{ij} = 0,$$

it must be true that each $c_{ij} = 0$ (why?).

Example 6 The standard basis for the vector space P_n of all real polynomials of degree $\leqslant n$ is the set of vectors (polynomials)

$$\{1, x, x^2, x^3, \ldots, x^n\}.$$

That this set is linearly independent and spans P_n is left for you to prove in Exercise 6.

Let us now consider three theorems. The proofs are left to you as exercises; however, each theorem contains some useful information regarding bases for vector spaces. The first two tell us that if a vector space V has dimension n and we have a set S of n vectors from V, we need only check if S spans V or if S is linearly independent, *not both.*

Theorem 3.7
If V is an n-dimensional vector space and $S = \{v_1, v_2, \ldots, v_n\}$ is a linearly independent set of n vectors from V, then S is a basis for V.

To prove this, show that $L(S) = V$ (see Exercise 19).

Theorem 3.8
If V is an n-dimensional vector space and $S = \{v_1, v_2, \ldots, v_n\}$ is a set of n vectors that spans V, then S is a basis for V.

To prove this show that S is linearly independent (see Exercise 20).

The final theorem tells us that every linearly independent subset of an n-dimensional vector space can be enlarged by adjoining additional linearly independent vectors to form a basis for the space. For the proof of this theorem and an example see Exercises 21 and 22.

Theorem 3.9
If $S = \{v_1, v_2, \ldots, v_k\}$ is a linearly independent set of vectors from the n-dimensional vector space V and $k < n$, then there exist vectors $v_{k+1}, v_{k+2}, \ldots, v_n$ in V such that the set

$$\{v_1, v_2, \ldots, v_k, v_{k+1}, \ldots, v_n\}$$

is a basis for V.

It is instructive to give a geometric interpretation of the result of Example 4 of Section 3.3. We saw there that the set of all points (x_1, x_2, x_3) in a cartesian 3-space V that satisfy the equation $x_1 + x_2 + x_3 = 0$ forms a subspace W of V. It is well known that the locus of all points (x_1, x_2, x_3) that satisfy the equation $x_1 + x_2 + x_3 = 0$ is a plane (in space) passing through the origin. Thus, it is not surprising that the dimension of this plane is 2. Were we to impose *another* equation, say $x_1 - x_2 - 2x_3 = 0$, we would expect the resulting subspace U of points (x_1, x_2, x_3) that satisfy *both* given equations to be of dimension 1 (why?); and this is consistent with the fact that the two planes

$$x_1 + x_2 + x_3 = 0 \qquad \text{and} \qquad x_1 - x_2 - 2x_3 = 0$$

intersect in a straight line whose dimension is, of course, 1.

We conclude this section by classifying all subspaces of the plane (i.e., the cartesian 2-space). Thus, suppose

$$V = \text{Set of all points } (x_1, x_2), \quad \text{where } x_1, x_2 \text{ are real.} \qquad (3.34)$$

In view of the result of Exercise 18 below, and because the dimension of V is 2 (why?), it follows that every subspace W of V has dimension 0, 1, or 2. It can be seen that the only subspace of dimension 0 is the vector space consisting of the zero vector only (i.e., the zero vector space). Moreover, the only subspace of V of dimension 2 is V itself. So we are left with the task of determining *all* subspaces W of V of dimension 1. Let W be any subspace of V of dimension 1 and suppose that the vector (a_1, a_2) forms a basis for W. Note that not both a_1 and a_2 are zero (why?).

Let (x_1, x_2) be *any* vector in W. Then $(x_1, x_2) = c(a_1, a_2)$ for some scalar c. This equation implies that (why?):

$$x_1 = c\,a_1, \qquad x_2 = c\,a_2$$

and hence

$$a_2\,x_1 = c\,a_1\,a_2 = a_1\,x_2;$$

that is, for all vectors (x_1, x_2) in W,

$$a_2\,x_1 - a_1\,x_2 = 0.$$

We have thus shown that W is the set of all vectors (x_1, x_2) such that

$$a_2\,x_1 - a_1\,x_2 = 0.$$

Interpreted geometrically, this says that every subspace W of dimension 1 is a straight line passing through the origin. These results are summarized in the following chart pertaining to subspace W:

Dimension	Description
0	Origin
1	A line through origin
2	Whole plane

EXERCISES (3.4)————————————————————————————

1. Do the following vectors form a basis for cartesian 3-space (give reasons): $\{(1, 0, 0),$ $(0, 1, 0), (0, 0, 1), (3, 4, -5)\}$?

2. Do the vectors in Problem 1 span cartesian 3-space? Why?

3. Let $S = \{(1, 2), (3, 4), (5, 6)\}$.
   a) Does S span the plane (i.e., cartesian 2-space)?
   b) Is S a basis for cartesian 2-space?
   c) Find all possible bases that can be selected from the vectors in S.

4. Let $S = \{(1, 2, 0), (0, -1, 3)\}$.
   a) Are the vectors in S linearly dependent? Why?
   b) Do the vectors in S span cartesian 3-space? Why?
   c) Is S a basis for cartesian 3-space? If not, can you find another vector that will produce a basis for cartesian 3-space when added to S?

5. Show that the vectors $(0, 1, 1), (1, 0, 1),$ and $(1, 1, 0)$ in $\mathbb{R}^3$ are linearly independent. Hence, conclude from Theorem 3.7 that they form a basis for $\mathbb{R}^3$ (see also Example 4).

6. Let V be the vector space P_n of polynomials described in Example 6. Show that the vectors (i.e., polynomials) $1, x, x^2, x^3, \ldots, x^n$ form a basis for this vector space. What is the dimension of P_n?

7. Let V be $\mathbb{R}^3$ and let W be the set of all vectors (x_1, x_2, x_3) that satisfy the equation $x_1 - x_2 - x_3 = 0$. Prove that W is a subspace of $\mathbb{R}^3$.

8. Find a basis for the subspace W in Problem 7. What is the dimension of W? Interpret the results geometrically.

9. Let V be cartesian 3-space $\mathbb{R}^3$ and let W be the set of all vectors (x_1, x_2, x_3) that satisfy the equations

$$x_1 - x_2 - x_3 = 0 \quad \text{and} \quad x_1 + x_2 + x_3 = 0.$$

Prove that W is a subspace of V.

10. Find a basis for the subspace W in Problem 9. What is the dimension of W? Interpret the results geometrically.

11. Determine the scalar c so that the set of all vectors (x_1, x_2, x_3) in cartesian 3-space $\mathbb{R}^3$ that satisfy the equation $2x_1 - x_2 + 3x_3 = c$ forms a subspace W of $\mathbb{R}^3$. What is the dimension of W? Give reasons.

12. Determine the scalars c and d so that the set of all vectors (x_1, x_2, x_3, x_4) in 4-space $\mathbb{R}^4$ that satisfy the equations

$$\begin{aligned} x_1 + x_2 + x_3 &= 0, \\ -x_1 + x_2 + cx_3 &= 0, \\ -x_1 + x_2 + x_3 &= d \end{aligned}$$

forms a subspace of dimension two of $\mathbb{R}^4$.

13. Show that every nonzero vector space V has at least two subspaces, namely the zero subspace (consisting of the vector 0 only) and V itself.

14. Let V be the vector space P_n of polynomials described in Example 6. Prove that the set W

of all constant polynomials forms a subspace of V. What is the dimension of W? Give reasons.

15. Suppose that a vector space V has exactly two subspaces. Prove that V is of dimension 1.

16. Is the converse of Problem 15 true? Prove your assertions.

17. What is the dimension of the subspace of the space P_n of polynomials spanned by the polynomials

$$1 - x, \quad 1 - x^2, \quad 1 + x, \quad 1 - 2x + x^2 ?$$

Give reasons.

18. Prove the following theorem: Suppose V is a vector space of dimension n and suppose W is a subspace of V. Then

i) the dimension of W does not exceed n and
ii) the dimension of W is equal to n if and only if $W = V$.

19. Prove Theorem 3.7.

20. Prove Theorem 3.8.

21. Prove Theorem 3.9.

22. Show that the vectors $(1, 1, 1)$ and $(1, -1, 1)$ are linearly independent and that they span a subspace W of $\mathbb{R}^3$ with dimension 2. Then expand the set to a basis for $\mathbb{R}^3$ by adding any vector that is not a linear combination of these two. *Hint.* Try $(0, 0, 1)$.

23. Prove that a spanning set for a vector space is minimal if and only if it is linearly independent.

3.5 ROW RANK AND COLUMN RANK

In the examples of the preceding sections we have at times been concerned with the rows of a matrix as vectors. We could equally as well have used the columns as vectors. In this section we shall focus our attention on two important vector spaces derived from the rows and columns of a matrix. These are called the *row space* and the *column space* of the given matrix, respectively.

Let A be an $m \times n$ matrix with real-number entries, say

$$A = \begin{bmatrix} a_{11} & a_{12} & \cdots & a_{1n} \\ a_{21} & a_{22} & \cdots & a_{2n} \\ \vdots & \vdots & \vdots & \vdots \\ a_{m1} & a_{m2} & \cdots & a_{mn} \end{bmatrix} ; \quad \text{all } a_{ij} \text{ real.} \qquad (3.35)$$

Let

$$\mathbf{v}_1 = (a_{11}, a_{12}, \ldots, a_{1n}),$$
$$\mathbf{v}_2 = (a_{21}, a_{22}, \ldots, a_{2n}),$$
$$\vdots \qquad \vdots$$
$$\mathbf{v}_m = (a_{m1}, a_{m2}, \ldots, a_{mn}).$$

Then $\mathbf{v}_1, \mathbf{v}_2, \ldots, \mathbf{v}_m$ are n-tuples of real numbers and are thus elements (i.e., vectors) from the cartesian n-space $\mathbb{R}^n$. They will, therefore, span some subspace of $\mathbb{R}^n$. The subspace of $\mathbb{R}^n$ spanned by the rows of the matrix A in (3.35) is called the **row space** of A. The dimension of this row space of A is called the **row rank** of A.

Example 1 Find the row space and row rank of the matrix

$$A = \begin{bmatrix} 1 & -1 & 0 \\ 2 & 3 & 1 \\ 3 & -2 & 4 \end{bmatrix}.$$

By definition, the row space of A is the subspace of $\mathbb{R}^3$ spanned by the rows of A. Thus, the row space of A is

$$\{k_1(1, -1, 0) + k_2(2, 3, 1) + k_3(3, -2, 4); \quad k_1, k_2, k_3 \text{ any real numbers}\}.$$

Moreover, since the row rank of A is the dimension of the row space, the row rank is equal to the *maximum* number of linearly independent vectors in the set $\{(1, -1, 0),$ $(2, 3, 1), (3, -2, 4)\}$. To calculate the row rank of A we might proceed as follows. Clearly the set consisting of the single vector $(1, -1, 0)$ is a linearly independent set. What about $\{(1, -1, 0), (2, 3, 1)\}$? Since neither of these two vectors is a scalar multiple of the other, they are *linearly independent* (why?). Finally, we ask: Is the set

$$\{(1, -1, 0), (2, 3, 1), (3, -2, 4)\}$$

of all three vectors linearly independent? We leave it to you to verify that this is the case. Hence, the row rank of A is 3.

The concepts of **column space** and **column rank** of a matrix A are defined in a similar way. The subspace spanned by the columns of the matrix A in (3.35) is called the column space of A. The dimension of this column space is called the column rank of A.

We can easily verify that the set of all column vectors of the type

$$\begin{bmatrix} x_1 \\ x_2 \\ \vdots \\ x_m \end{bmatrix}, \quad \text{all } x_i \text{ real,}$$

forms a vector space. This is the underlying vector space used in the definition of column space of A. We continue our practice of using matrix notation for column vectors. We illustrate this definition by the following example.

Example 2 Find the column space and column rank of the matrix

$$A = \begin{bmatrix} 1 & -1 & 0 \\ 2 & 3 & 1 \\ 3 & -2 & 4 \end{bmatrix}.$$

By definition, the column space of A is the subspace of all 3×1 column matrices (vectors) spanned by the columns of A. Thus, the column space of A is

$$\left\{ k_1 \begin{bmatrix} 1 \\ 2 \\ 3 \end{bmatrix} + k_2 \begin{bmatrix} -1 \\ 3 \\ -2 \end{bmatrix} + k_3 \begin{bmatrix} 0 \\ 1 \\ 4 \end{bmatrix}; \quad k_1, k_2, k_3 \text{ real numbers} \right\}.$$

Moreover, the column rank of A is the dimension of this subspace. Hence, the column rank of A is the *maximum* number of linearly independent vectors in the set

$$\left\{ \begin{bmatrix} 1 \\ 2 \\ 3 \end{bmatrix}, \begin{bmatrix} -1 \\ 3 \\ -2 \end{bmatrix}, \begin{bmatrix} 0 \\ 1 \\ 4 \end{bmatrix} \right\}.$$

Using the same arguments as in Example 1, we can verify that these three column vectors are *linearly independent* and hence the column rank of A is 3.

The above two examples show that for the given matrix A the row rank of A is equal to the column rank of A. Is this a coincidence? The answer is *no*. In fact, we shall shortly state an important theorem on the equality of these two ranks. But first let us see how we can more easily determine the row rank of a given matrix. We make use of the methods of Chapter 1. Indeed, by applying the Gauss–Jordan reduction techniques, we can compute the row rank of a given matrix; and for that matter by careful application we can use this method to determine a basis for any vector space spanned by a given set of row (or column) vectors. This idea is based on the following lemma and theorem.

Lemma 3.10

Elementary row operations do not change the row space of a matrix.

Proof. Suppose that the row vectors of a given matrix A are $\mathbf{r}_1, \mathbf{r}_2, \ldots, \mathbf{r}_n$. Let the matrix B be obtained from the matrix A by performing an elementary row operation. If the row operation is a row interchange, then B and A have the same row vectors and, therefore, the same row space. If the row operation is multiplication of a row by a nonzero scalar or the addition of a scalar multiple of one row to another, then the row vectors of B are linear combinations of the row vectors $\mathbf{r}_1, \mathbf{r}_2, \ldots, \mathbf{r}_n$ of A and therefore they lie in the row space of A. Since the space spanned by the row vectors of B consists entirely of linear combinations of these vectors, it consists of linear combinations of the row vectors of A. Therefore each vector in the row space of B is in the row space of A. Conversely, we can obtain the row vectors of A by inverse row operations (which are also row operations) of the rows of B. Thus the above argument with A and B interchanged shows that the row space of A is contained in that of B and the proof of the lemma is complete.

Now it follows from this lemma that reducing a matrix A to row-echelon form does not change its row space. The nonzero row vectors in the row-echelon form of A are linearly independent, as you are asked to show in Exercise 20. Therefore we have:

Theorem 3.11

The nonzero row vectors in the row-echelon form of a given matrix A are a basis for the row space of A.

Example 3 Find the row rank of the matrix

$$A = \begin{bmatrix} 1 & 0 & 1 & 2 \\ 2 & 1 & 0 & 3 \\ 1 & -1 & 3 & 3 \end{bmatrix}.$$

We reduce A to row-echelon form and obtain the matrix (verify this)

$$B = \begin{bmatrix} 1 & 0 & 1 & 2 \\ 0 & 1 & -2 & -1 \\ 0 & 0 & 0 & 0 \end{bmatrix}.$$

The nonzero row vectors $r'_1 = (1, 0, 1, 2)$ and $r'_2 = (0, 1, -2, -1)$ of B are a basis for the row space of A. Thus, the row rank of A is 2.

This method is also useful in determining a basis for the space spanned by any given collection S of vectors in $\mathbb{R}^n$, as we see from the following example.

Example 4 Find a basis for the space spanned by the set of vectors

$$S = \{(1, 3, 0), (0, 2, 4), (1, 5, 4), (1, 1, -4)\}.$$

We write these as the row vectors of a matrix A:

$$A = \begin{bmatrix} 1 & 3 & 0 \\ 0 & 2 & 4 \\ 1 & 5 & 4 \\ 1 & 1 & -4 \end{bmatrix}.$$

Then the row-echelon form of A is

$$B = \begin{bmatrix} 1 & 3 & 0 \\ 0 & 1 & 2 \\ 0 & 0 & 0 \\ 0 & 0 & 0 \end{bmatrix}.$$

Hence the vector space spanned by S is of dimension 2 and has the two vectors $(1, 3, 0)$ and $(0, 1, 2)$ as a basis.

Example 5   Find a basis for the column space of the matrix

$$A = \begin{bmatrix} 1 & 0 & -1 & 0 \\ 2 & 1 & 1 & 1 \\ -1 & 3 & 2 & 4 \end{bmatrix}.$$

If we transpose A, the column vectors of A become the row vectors of A^t. Thus the column space of A is the same as the row space of A^t. Now it can be verified that

$$A^t = \begin{bmatrix} 1 & 2 & -1 \\ 0 & 1 & 3 \\ -1 & 1 & 2 \\ 0 & 1 & 4 \end{bmatrix}$$

has row-echelon form

$$B = \begin{bmatrix} 1 & 2 & -1 \\ 0 & 1 & 3 \\ 0 & 0 & 1 \\ 0 & 0 & 0 \end{bmatrix}.$$

So the vectors $(1, 2, -1)$, $(0, 1, 3)$, and $(0, 0, 1)$ form a basis for the row space of A^t. Therefore the column vectors

$$\begin{bmatrix} 1 \\ 2 \\ -1 \end{bmatrix}, \quad \begin{bmatrix} 0 \\ 1 \\ 3 \end{bmatrix}, \quad \text{and} \quad \begin{bmatrix} 0 \\ 0 \\ 1 \end{bmatrix}$$

are a basis for the column space of A.

As this example illustrates, the process of determining the row and column ranks of a matrix is essentially the same, except for a change of notation from row to column vectors. The matrix A in Example 5 has column rank 3. Its row rank is also 3, since the row-echelon form for A is

$$C = \begin{bmatrix} 1 & 0 & -1 & 0 \\ 0 & 1 & 3 & 1 \\ 0 & 0 & 1 & -\frac{1}{8} \end{bmatrix}.$$

As we stated earlier in Examples 1 and 2, the fact that A has equal row and column ranks is not coincidental. Indeed, we have the following important theorem.

Theorem 3.12

    Let A be any $m \times n$ matrix with real-number entries. Then the row rank of A is equal to the column rank of A.

Before proving this theorem let us consider yet another example.

Example 6 Find the row and column ranks of the matrix

$$A = \begin{bmatrix} 1 & 2 & 0 & -1 \\ 3 & 1 & 2 & 5 \\ 1 & -3 & 2 & 7 \end{bmatrix}.$$

We proceed to reduce A to row-echelon form and obtain the matrix

$$B = \begin{bmatrix} 1 & 2 & 0 & -1 \\ 0 & 1 & -\frac{2}{5} & -\frac{8}{5} \\ 0 & 0 & 0 & 0 \end{bmatrix}.$$

So the row rank of A is 2. Let us now consider the column rank of A. The easiest thing to do is to compute the row rank of A^t. Note that

$$A^t = \begin{bmatrix} 1 & 3 & 1 \\ 2 & 1 & -3 \\ 0 & 2 & 2 \\ -1 & 5 & 7 \end{bmatrix}$$

can be reduced to the following row-echelon form:

$$\begin{bmatrix} 1 & 3 & 1 \\ 0 & 1 & 1 \\ 0 & 0 & 0 \\ 0 & 0 & 0 \end{bmatrix}.$$

Thus, A^t has row rank 2; therefore A has column rank 2.

The proof of Theorem 3.12 is a little tedious and is an application of the material of this chapter. Let $A = (a_{ij})$ by any $m \times n$ matrix, where $i = 1, 2, \ldots, m$ and $j = 1, 2, \ldots, n$. Denote the row vectors of A by $r_1, r_2, \ldots, r_m$ and assume that the row space $L_r = L(r_1, \ldots, r_m)$ of A has dimension k. Then L_r has a basis of k vectors, say $S = \{b_1, b_2, \ldots, b_k\}$, so $L(S) = L_r$. Suppose that for each i

$$b_i = (b_{i1}, b_{i2}, \ldots, b_{in}).$$

Since S is a basis for L_r, each row vector is expressible as a linear combination of the vectors in S. That is, for each $i = 1, 2, \ldots, m$ and appropriate scalars $c_{i1}, \ldots, c_{ik}$,

$$r_i = c_{i1} b_1 + c_{i2} b_2 + \ldots + c_{ik} b_k. \tag{3.36}$$

But two vectors in $\mathbb{R}^n$ are equal if and only if their corresponding components are equal. Therefore, the jth components on each side of (3.36) are equal for each

$i = 1, 2, \ldots, m$, and for all i and j we have

$$a_{ij} = c_{i1}b_{1j} + c_{i2}b_{2j} + \ldots + c_{ik}b_{kj}, \tag{3.37}$$

Writing out all of the columns in the system (3.37), we get the vector (matrix) equation

$$\begin{bmatrix} a_{1j} \\ a_{2j} \\ \vdots \\ a_{mj} \end{bmatrix} = b_{1j} \begin{bmatrix} c_{11} \\ c_{21} \\ \vdots \\ c_{m1} \end{bmatrix} + b_{2j} \begin{bmatrix} c_{12} \\ c_{22} \\ \vdots \\ c_{m2} \end{bmatrix} + \ldots + b_{kj} \begin{bmatrix} c_{1k} \\ c_{2k} \\ \vdots \\ c_{mk} \end{bmatrix}. \tag{3.38}$$

But the column vector on the left side of (3.38) is the jth column vector of the matrix A. Since (3.38) holds for each $j = 1, 2, \ldots, n$, we see that all column vectors of A lie in the subspace of m-dimensional column vectors spanned by the k-vectors

$$\begin{bmatrix} c_{11} \\ c_{21} \\ \vdots \\ c_{m1} \end{bmatrix}, \begin{bmatrix} c_{12} \\ c_{22} \\ \vdots \\ c_{m2} \end{bmatrix}, \ldots, \begin{bmatrix} c_{1k} \\ c_{2k} \\ \vdots \\ c_{mk} \end{bmatrix}.$$

Hence the column rank of A is at most k and thus

$$\text{Column rank of } A \leqslant k = \text{Row rank of } A. \tag{3.39}$$

Now if we do the same thing for A^t, we find that

$$\text{Column rank of } A^t \leqslant \text{Row rank of } A^t. \tag{3.40}$$

But

$$\text{Column rank of } A^t = \text{Row rank of } A,$$

and

$$\text{Row rank of } A^t = \text{Column rank of } A.$$

Therefore, (3.40) becomes

$$k = \text{Row rank of } A \leqslant \text{Column rank of } A. \tag{3.41}$$

Combining (3.39) and (3.41) we obtain the desired equality.

The common value of the row rank and the column rank of A is called the **rank** of A.

We leave it as an exercise for you to prove the following theorem for square matrices.

Theorem 3.13

If A is an n × n matrix, then A is nonsingular if and only if A has rank n.

Theorem 3.12 has some implications for the study of linear equations. Suppose that we have the linear system

$$AX = B,$$

where $A = (a_{ij})$ is $m \times n$. Then we can write out this system much as we did in the proof of Theorem 3.12. It becomes

$$x_1 \begin{bmatrix} a_{11} \\ a_{21} \\ \vdots \\ a_{m1} \end{bmatrix} + x_2 \begin{bmatrix} a_{12} \\ a_{22} \\ \vdots \\ a_{m2} \end{bmatrix} + \cdots + x_n \begin{bmatrix} a_{1n} \\ a_{2n} \\ \vdots \\ a_{mn} \end{bmatrix} = \begin{bmatrix} b_1 \\ b_2 \\ \vdots \\ b_m \end{bmatrix}. \tag{3.42}$$

Therefore to say that $AX = B$ has a solution X is to say that there exist scalars $x_1, x_2, \ldots, x_n$ (the components of X) such that (3.42) is true. But (3.42) says that the matrix column vector B belongs to the column space of the matrix A. It is a linear combination of the columns of A with scalars x_i. Therefore, the system of equations $AX = B$ will have a solution if and only if B lies in the column space of A. If we were to add the vector B to the collection of column vectors of A, we could not change the dimension of the column space, otherwise no such scalars x_i would exist. Therefore the matrix A and the augmented matrix $[A:B]$ must have the same column rank. This proves the following theorem.

Theorem 3.14

A linear system of equations $AX = B$ has a solution if and only if the rank of the augmented matrix $[A:B]$ is the same as the rank of the coefficient matrix A.

EXERCISES (3.5)———————————————————————————————

In Exercises 1–6, find the row rank and the column rank of each of the given matrices. Verify in each case that they are equal.

1. $A = \begin{bmatrix} 3 & 1 \\ 6 & 2 \end{bmatrix}$

2. $A = \begin{bmatrix} 4 & -1 & 0 \\ 3 & 1 & 2 \\ 1 & 0 & 5 \end{bmatrix}$

3. $A = \begin{bmatrix} -1 & 2 & 3 & 0 \\ 2 & 1 & 4 & 1 \\ 1 & 3 & 7 & 1 \end{bmatrix}$

4. $A = \begin{bmatrix} 1 & 2 & 3 \\ 2 & 1 & 3 \\ 3 & 0 & 3 \\ 3 & 0 & 3 \end{bmatrix}$

5. $A = \begin{bmatrix} 1 & -1 & 0 & 2 \\ 2 & 1 & 3 & 5 \\ 0 & 0 & 1 & 0 \end{bmatrix}$

6. $A = \begin{bmatrix} 1 & 0 & 0 & 0 \\ 0 & 0 & 1 & 0 \\ 0 & 1 & 0 & 0 \\ 0 & 0 & 0 & 1 \end{bmatrix}$

7–12. Find a basis for the row space of each matrix in Exercises 1 through 6, respectively.

13. Show that the rank of an $m \times n$ matrix is at most as big as the smaller of m and n.

14. Prove Theorem 3.13.

15. Can a singular $n \times n$ matrix have a rank equal to n? Give reasons.

16. Let

$$A = \begin{bmatrix} 0 & 1 & 0 & 0 \\ 0 & 0 & 1 & 0 \\ 0 & 0 & 0 & 1 \\ 0 & 0 & 0 & 0 \end{bmatrix}.$$

Find the rank of A and the rank of adj A.

17. Suppose that A is an $n \times n$ nilpotent matrix (that is, $A^k = 0$ for some positive integer k). Prove that the rank of A is less than n.

18. Find the rank of the matrix

$$A = \begin{bmatrix} 0 & 0 & 0 & 1 \\ 0 & 0 & 1 & 0 \\ 0 & 1 & 0 & 0 \\ 1 & 0 & 0 & 0 \end{bmatrix}.$$

Also, find adj A. What is the rank of adj A?

19. Let

$$A = \begin{bmatrix} 1 & 0 & 0 & 0 \\ 0 & 1 & 0 & 0 \\ 0 & 0 & 1 & 0 \\ 0 & 0 & 0 & 0 \end{bmatrix}.$$

Find the rank of A and the rank of adj A.

20. Show that the nonzero row vectors in the row-echelon form of a given matrix A are linearly independent.

21. Prove that to find a basis for the column space of a matrix A it suffices to reduce A^t to row-echelon form.

22. Use the results of Exercise 21 to find a basis for the column space of each matrix in Exercises 1–6.

23. Show that an $n \times n$ homogeneous system of linear equations $AX = 0$ has only the trivial solution if A has rank n.

24. Show that an $n \times n$ matrix A has nonzero determinant if and only if A has rank n.

25. Prove that an $n \times n$ homogeneous system $AX = 0$ of linear equations has a nontrivial solution if and only if rank $A < n$.

26. Show that an $n \times n$ matrix A has rank n if and only if A is row equivalent to the identity matrix I_n.

27. Find a basis for the subspace of $\mathbb{R}^5$ spanned by the vectors $(1, 1, 0, 1, 1)$, $(1, -1, 1, 0, 0)$, $(2, 3, 1, -1, 0)$, $(1, -2, 0, 1, -4)$.

28. Consider the space P_2 of all polynomials $ax^2 + bx + c$ of degree two or less. By writing the coefficients only, let each polynomial be represented by a row vector (a, b, c). Use the results of this section to determine a basis for the subspace of P_2 spanned by the polynomials $1 - x$, $1 + x$, $1 - x^2$, $1 + x^2$.

REAL
INNER PRODUCT
SPACES

4

In this chapter we shall discuss further the relationship between vector spaces and geometric concepts. As we mentioned at the beginning of Chapter 3, many geometric ideas can be expressed by algebraic vectors and give rise to the generalizations discussed there. In this chapter such ideas as distance and angle will be generalized to construct real inner-product spaces. We shall also generalize the usual cartesian coordinate system to develop the concept of an orthonormal basis for a vector space.

4.1 DISTANCE AND ANGLE IN 2-SPACE AND 3-SPACE

Let us begin with an ordinary cartesian coordinate system in 3-space. As usual, if the point P has coordinates (u_1, u_2, u_3) in this system, then the vector $\mathbf{u} = \overrightarrow{OP}$ will be written as the triple (u_1, u_2, u_3). Let us first derive a formula for expressing the length of $\mathbf{u}$. Refer to Fig. 4.1 sketched for the case where u_1, u_2, and u_3 are positive real numbers.

In general, the point P is located $|u_3|$ units from the $X_1 X_2$ plane, $|u_2|$ units from the $X_1 X_3$ plane and $|u_1|$ units from the $X_2 X_3$ plane. Let E be the point lying in the

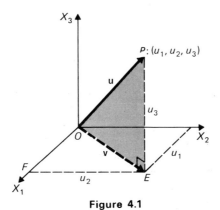

Figure 4.1

$X_1 X_2$ plane directly below the point P in Fig. 4.1 (or above, if $u_3 < 0$). Let the vector $\overrightarrow{OE}$ be denoted by $\mathbf{v}$. Now we wish to find the length of $\mathbf{u}$. We shall denote this by $||\mathbf{u}||$. Using the Pythagorean theorem we get

$$(||\mathbf{u}||)^2 = (||\mathbf{v}||)^2 + u_3^2, \tag{4.1}$$

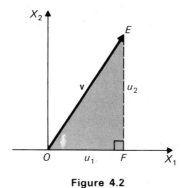

Figure 4.2

because OEP is a right triangle with the right angle at E. Thus, the problem of finding the length of the vector $\mathbf{u}$ has been reduced to the problem of finding the length of the vector $\mathbf{v}$ in the $X_1 X_2$ plane, that is, in 2-space. In Fig. 4.2 we sketch this situation oriented so that it is easier to read. Since OFE is a right triangle, we apply the Pythagorean theorem again to obtain

$$||\mathbf{v}||^2 = u_1^2 + u_2^2. \tag{4.2}$$

By substituting the value of $||\mathbf{v}||^2$ from (4.2) into (4.1), we obtain

$$||\mathbf{u}||^2 = u_1^2 + u_2^2 + u_3^2.$$

Therefore,

$$||\mathbf{u}|| = \sqrt{u_1^2 + u_2^2 + u_3^2}. \tag{4.3}$$

This relationship holds when u_1, u_2, and u_3 are not all positive, as you can verify.

Example 1   Find the length of the vector $\mathbf{w} = (1, -1, 3)$.
     From (4.3) we readily calculate:

$$||\mathbf{w}|| = \sqrt{1 + 1 + 9} = \sqrt{11}.$$

Before we consider the question of angle, let us make one or two other observations. First of all, you have probably already noticed that if $\mathbf{u}$ and $\mathbf{v}$ are any two geometric vectors, their linear span $L(\mathbf{u}, \mathbf{v})$ is either a plane, or a line, or the origin. If $\mathbf{u}$ and $\mathbf{v}$ are not collinear, they are linearly independent and, therefore, span a plane (see Fig. 4.3 where they span the plane of this page).

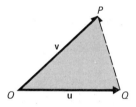

Figure 4.3

The third side of triangle OPQ formed by these vectors is the vector $\overrightarrow{QP} = \mathbf{v} - \mathbf{u}$. To see this, we use the parallelogram rule and construct $\mathbf{v} + (-\mathbf{u})$, as in Fig. 4.4. Clearly, $\overrightarrow{OR} = \overrightarrow{QP}$ since both have the same magnitude and the same direction; therefore, $\overrightarrow{QP} = \mathbf{v} - \mathbf{u}$.

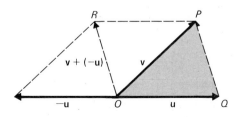

Figure 4.4

Let us make use of these ideas to derive the distance formula in 3-space. Let $\mathbf{u} = (u_1, u_2, u_3)$ and $\mathbf{v} = (v_1, v_2, v_3)$ be two vectors in 3-space; then the distance between their terminal points Q and P is the length of the vector $\mathbf{v} - \mathbf{u}$. We have

$$\mathbf{v} - \mathbf{u} = (v_1 - u_1, v_2 - u_2, v_3 - u_3),$$

so from (4.3) the distance $d(\mathbf{u}, \mathbf{v})$, is

$$\|\mathbf{v} - \mathbf{u}\| = \sqrt{(v_1 - u_1)^2 + (v_2 - u_2)^2 + (v_3 - u_3)^2}. \tag{4.4}$$

Formula (4.4) is the *distance formula* in 3-space. Its analog in the plane $\mathbb{R}^2$ is obviously

$$d(\mathbf{u}, \mathbf{v}) = \sqrt{(v_1 - u_1)^2 + (v_2 - u_2)^2}.$$

We shall see shortly that we can introduce the concept of distance into any cartesian n-space $\mathbb{R}^n$ by generalizing (4.4) to n-dimensions. Thus

$$d(\mathbf{u}, \mathbf{v}) = \sqrt{(v_1 - u_1)^2 + (v_2 - u_2)^2 + \ldots + (v_n - u_n)^2}. \tag{4.5}$$

We shall call the cartesian n-space with this distance concept **Euclidean n-space** and also denote it by $\mathbb{R}^n$.

Example 2   Let $\mathbf{u} = (1, 4, -3)$ and $\mathbf{v} = (-2, -1, 3)$ be two vectors in Euclidean 3-space. Find the distance $d(\mathbf{u}, \mathbf{v})$.

From (4.4) we have

$$d(\mathbf{u}, \mathbf{v}) = \sqrt{(1 + 2)^2 + (4 + 1)^2 + (-3 - 3)^2}$$
$$= \sqrt{9 + 25 + 36} = \sqrt{70}.$$

Let us look at additional geometric properties in 2- and 3-space. We begin with the important *Law of cosines* and this leads us to considering the angle between two vectors.

Let us focus our attention on the Euclidean 2-space. Suppose ABC is a triangle in the plane and the lengths of the sides AB, BC, CA are c, a, b, respectively, as indicated in Fig. 4.5. Suppose that we introduce a coordinate system and place the x-axis along AB with A at the origin. Let the coordinates of C be (u, v). Observe that the coordinates of B are $(c, 0)$. Moreover, by dropping the perpendicular CD indicated in Fig. 4.5, we see from the right triangle ADC that

$$\cos A = \frac{u}{b}, \qquad \sin A = \frac{v}{b},$$

and hence,

$$u = b \cos A, \qquad v = b \sin A.$$

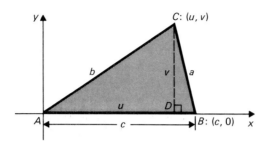

Figure 4.5

From the distance formula in the plane we know that

$$
\begin{aligned}
a = \text{Length of } BC &= \sqrt{(u-c)^2 + (v-0)^2} \\
&= \sqrt{(b\cos A - c)^2 + (b\sin A)^2} \\
&= \sqrt{b^2\cos^2 A + c^2 - 2bc\cos A + b^2\sin^2 A} \\
&= \sqrt{b^2(\cos^2 A + \sin^2 A) + c^2 - 2bc\cos A} \\
&= \sqrt{b^2 + c^2 - 2bc\cos A}.
\end{aligned}
$$

The final result is

$$
a = \sqrt{b^2 + c^2 - 2bc\cos A};
$$

and hence, by squaring both sides, we get

$$
a^2 = b^2 + c^2 - 2bc\cos A. \tag{4.6}
$$

By referring to Fig. 4.6 you can convince yourself that (4.6) is also true when A is an obtuse angle.

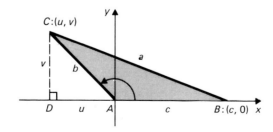

Figure 4.6

The placement of the triangle ABC on the coordinate system was highly arbitrary. We could just as well have used angle B or angle C. Using the convention that gives names to the sides and angles, as indicated in the above figures, we obtain the important *Law of cosines*:

Law of Cosines

If ABC is a triangle with sides a, b, c as indicated in Figs. 4.5 and 4.6, then

$$a^2 = b^2 + c^2 - 2bc \cos A,$$

$$b^2 = c^2 + a^2 - 2ca \cos B,$$

$$c^2 = a^2 + b^2 - 2ab \cos C.$$

Let us now apply the Law of cosines to calculate the cosine of the angle between two vectors in the plane. To this end, suppose that we have the points $P_1 : (x_1, y_1)$, $P_2 : (x_2, y_2)$, as indicated in Fig. 4.7. Let $\mathbf{u} = \overrightarrow{OP}_1$ and $\mathbf{v} = \overrightarrow{OP}_2$. Suppose that the angle $P_1 O P_2$ is θ (radians) with $0 \leqslant \theta \leqslant \pi$; such an angle θ exists. Let $\left| P_1 P_2 \right|$ denote the length of the vector $P_1 P_2 = \mathbf{v} - \mathbf{u}$ and similarly $\left| OP_1 \right|$ for $\|\mathbf{u}\|$ and $\left| OP_2 \right|$ for $\|\mathbf{v}\|$. By the Law of cosines,

$$|P_1 P_2|^2 = |OP_1|^2 + |OP_2|^2 - 2|OP_1||OP_2| \cos \theta, \qquad (4.7)$$

or, in vector notation,

$$\|\mathbf{v} - \mathbf{u}\|^2 = \|\mathbf{u}\|^2 + \|\mathbf{v}\|^2 - 2\|\mathbf{u}\|\,\|\mathbf{v}\| \cos (\mathbf{u}, \mathbf{v}).$$

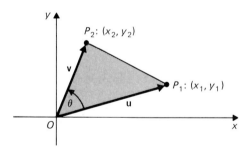

Figure 4.7

Applying the distance formula, we see that Eq. (4.7) becomes

$$(x_1 - x_2)^2 + (y_1 - y_2)^2 = (x_1^2 + y_1^2) + (x_2^2 + y_2^2) - 2\sqrt{x_1^2 + y_1^2}\,\sqrt{x_2^2 + y_2^2}\cos\theta.$$

Simplifying this equation, we get

$$-2x_1 x_2 - 2y_1 y_2 = -2\sqrt{x_1^2 + y_1^2}\,\sqrt{x_2^2 + y_2^2}\cos\theta;$$

and hence, assuming *the denominator is not zero,*

$$\cos \theta = \frac{x_1 x_2 + y_1 y_2}{\sqrt{x_1^2 + y_1^2}\ \sqrt{x_2^2 + y_2^2}}.$$ (4.8)

Note that (4.8) can also be written as follows (see Fig. 4.7):

$$\cos \theta = \frac{x_1 x_2 + y_1 y_2}{(\|\mathbf{u}\|)(\|\mathbf{v}\|)}.$$ (4.9)

If the distance formula is applied to 3-space, then

$$\cos \theta = \frac{x_1 x_2 + y_1 y_2 + z_1 z_2}{\sqrt{x_1^2 + y_1^2 + z_1^2}\ \sqrt{x_2^2 + y_2^2 + z_2^2}} = \frac{x_1 x_2 + y_1 y_2 + z_1 z_2}{\|\mathbf{u}\| \|\mathbf{v}\|},$$ (4.10)

where $P_1 : (x_1, y_1, z_1)$ and $P_2 : (x_2, y_2, z_2)$ are points in 3-space, $\overrightarrow{OP_1} = \mathbf{u}$, $\overrightarrow{OP_2} = \mathbf{v}$, and θ is the radian measure of the angle $P_1 O P_2$, $0 \leqslant \theta \leqslant \pi$ (see Fig. 4.8).

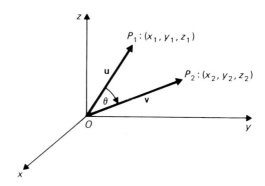

Figure 4.8

Verify this formula by repeating the derivation that led to Eqs. (4.8) and (4.9).

The numerators in formulas (4.9) and (4.10) involve a sum of products of the components of the vectors $\mathbf{u}$ and $\mathbf{v}$. This expression is not a vector but a *real number* (a scalar). It is, however, often called the *dot product* in physics and engineering; we call it the *inner product* and define it as follows:

Let $\mathbf{u} = (x_1, y_1)$ and $\mathbf{v} = (x_2, y_2)$ be two vectors in 2-space $\mathbb{R}^2$. The **inner product** $\langle \mathbf{u}, \mathbf{v} \rangle = \mathbf{u} \cdot \mathbf{v}$ of $\mathbf{u}$ and $\mathbf{v}$ is the scalar

$$\langle \mathbf{u}, \mathbf{v} \rangle = x_1 x_2 + y_1 y_2.$$ (4.11)

The 3-space definition is analogous. It states the following:

Let $\mathbf{u} = (x_1, y_1, z_1)$ and $\mathbf{v} = (x_2, y_2, z_2)$ be two vectors in 3-space $\mathbb{R}^3$. The *inner product* $\langle \mathbf{u}, \mathbf{v} \rangle = \mathbf{u} \cdot \mathbf{v}$ of $\mathbf{u}$ and $\mathbf{v}$ is the scalar

$$\langle \mathbf{u}, \mathbf{v} \rangle = x_1 x_2 + y_1 y_2 + z_1 z_2. \tag{4.12}$$

This inner product is also often called *scalar product*.

Example 3 Find the inner product of the vectors $\mathbf{u} = (1, -2)$ and $\mathbf{v} = (-3, 5)$. We have

$$\langle \mathbf{u}, \mathbf{v} \rangle = (1)(-3) + (-2)(5) = -13.$$

Example 4 Find the inner product of the vectors $\mathbf{u} = (6, -4)$ and $\mathbf{v} = (-2, -3)$. We see that

$$\langle \mathbf{u}, \mathbf{v} \rangle = (6)(-2) + (-4)(-3) = 0.$$

Nonzero vectors whose inner product is zero are perpendicular to each other in the plane since, by (4.9), $\cos \theta = 0$.

Example 5 Find the inner product of the vectors $\mathbf{u} = (-2, -3, 0)$, $\mathbf{v} = (1, -4, 2)$. By (4.12), we get

$$\langle \mathbf{u}, \mathbf{v} \rangle = (-2)(1) + (-3)(-4) + (0)(2) = 10.$$

Similarly to the situation in 2-space, vectors $\mathbf{u}$ and $\mathbf{v}$ in a Euclidean 3-space are *orthogonal* (or perpendicular) if $\langle \mathbf{u}, \mathbf{v} \rangle = 0$.

Example 6 Are the vectors $\mathbf{u} = (10, 2, 0)$ and $\mathbf{v} = (-1, 5, 4)$ orthogonal? We have

$$\langle \mathbf{u}, \mathbf{v} \rangle = (10)(-1) + (2)(5) + (0)(4) = 0$$

and hence the two given vectors are orthogonal.

It is our intention to generalize the concepts of length and angle to other vector spaces. Both of these concepts involve the idea of inner product. We, therefore, single out the basic arithmetic properties of this function and state them as Theorem 4.1.

Theorem 4.1

If $\mathbf{u}$, $\mathbf{v}$ and $\mathbf{w}$ are vectors in $\mathbb{R}^2$ or $\mathbb{R}^3$ and k_1, k_2 are any scalars (real numbers), then

i) $\langle \mathbf{u}, \mathbf{v} \rangle = \langle \mathbf{v}, \mathbf{u} \rangle$,
ii) $\langle \mathbf{u} + \mathbf{v}, \mathbf{w} \rangle = \langle \mathbf{u}, \mathbf{w} \rangle + \langle \mathbf{v}, \mathbf{w} \rangle$,
iii) $\langle k_1 \mathbf{u}, \mathbf{v} \rangle = k_1 \langle \mathbf{u}, \mathbf{v} \rangle$,
iv) $\langle k_1 \mathbf{u} + k_2 \mathbf{v}, \mathbf{w} \rangle = k_1 \langle \mathbf{u}, \mathbf{w} \rangle + k_2 \langle \mathbf{v}, \mathbf{w} \rangle$,
v) $\langle \mathbf{v}, \mathbf{v} \rangle \geqslant 0$,
vi) $\langle \mathbf{v}, \mathbf{v} \rangle = 0$ if and only if $\mathbf{v} = 0$.

We shall prove part (iv) for vectors in $\mathbb{R}^3$, the proof for $\mathbb{R}^2$ being completely analogous. The rest of the theorem is left for you to prove in the exercises.

Let $\mathbf{u} = (x_1, y_1, z_1)$, $\mathbf{v} = (x_2, y_2, z_2)$, and $\mathbf{w} = (x_3, y_3, z_3)$. Then

$$k_1\mathbf{u} + k_2\mathbf{v} = (k_1x_1 + k_2x_2, k_1y_1 + k_2y_2, k_1z_1 + k_2z_2),$$

so that

$$\begin{aligned}\langle k_1\mathbf{u} + k_2\mathbf{v}, \mathbf{w}\rangle &= (k_1x_1 + k_2x_2)x_3 + (k_1y_1 + k_2y_2)y_3 + (k_1z_1 + k_2z_2)z_3\\ &= k_1x_1x_3 + k_2x_2x_3 + k_1y_1y_3 + k_2y_2y_3 + k_1z_1z_3 + k_2z_2z_3\\ &= k_1(x_1x_3 + y_1y_3 + z_1z_3) + k_2(x_2x_3 + y_2y_3 + z_2z_3)\\ &= k_1\langle\mathbf{u}, \mathbf{w}\rangle + k_2\langle\mathbf{v}, \mathbf{w}\rangle.\end{aligned}$$

We shall also leave to you the proof of the fact that parts (ii) and (iii) together are equivalent to part (iv) (see Exercises 25 and 26).

Example 7 Let $\mathbf{u} = (1, -1, 4)$, $\mathbf{v} = (1, 2, -3)$, and $\mathbf{w} = (3, -2, -1)$. Then

$$\langle 2\mathbf{u} + 3\mathbf{v}, \mathbf{w}\rangle = \langle(5, 4, -1), (3, -2, -1)\rangle = 15 - 8 + 1 = 8$$

and

$$2\langle\mathbf{u}, \mathbf{w}\rangle + 3\langle\mathbf{v}, \mathbf{w}\rangle = 2(3 + 2 - 4) + 3(3 - 4 + 3) = 2(1) + 3(2) = 8.$$

Note that with our definition of inner product, for $\mathbf{u} = (x_1, y_1, z_1)$ and $\mathbf{v} = (x_2, y_2, z_2)$ we have

$$\|\mathbf{u}\|^2 = x_1^2 + y_1^2 + z_1^2 = \langle\mathbf{u}, \mathbf{u}\rangle. \tag{4.13}$$

Therefore, parts (v) and (vi) of Theorem 4.1 say that the square of the length of a nonzero vector in $\mathbb{R}^3$ (or in $\mathbb{R}^2$) is positive and that the only vector of zero length is the zero vector. Note also that the statement

$$\|\mathbf{v} - \mathbf{u}\|^2 = \langle\mathbf{v} - \mathbf{u}, \mathbf{v} - \mathbf{u}\rangle = (x_2 - x_1)^2 + (y_2 - y_1)^2 + (z_2 - z_1)^2 \tag{4.14}$$

is another version of the distance formula (4.4).

Using the inner-product notation in (4.10), we can write the expression for the cosine of the angle θ between two nonzero vectors $\mathbf{u}$ and $\mathbf{v}$ as

$$\cos\theta = \frac{\langle\mathbf{u}, \mathbf{v}\rangle}{\langle\mathbf{u}, \mathbf{u}\rangle^{1/2}\langle\mathbf{v}, \mathbf{v}\rangle^{1/2}}. \tag{4.15}$$

In other sections of this chapter we shall show how these geometric ideas in $\mathbb{R}^2$ and $\mathbb{R}^3$ can be extended to $\mathbb{R}^n$, P_n, and other real vector spaces. They can also be extended, in a slightly modified way, to complex vector spaces (see Exercises 39–41 of Section 4.3 and the definition preceding these exercises).

EXERCISES (4.1)

In Exercises 1–6, find the inner products $\langle\mathbf{u}, \mathbf{v}\rangle$ of the given vectors:

1. $\mathbf{u} = (1, 2)$, $\mathbf{v} = (3, 4)$ **2.** $\mathbf{u} = (0, 0)$, $\mathbf{v} = (-3, 5)$

3. $\mathbf{u} = (0, 1, 0)$, $\mathbf{v} = (1, 0, 0)$ 4. $\mathbf{u} = (-1, 1, 0)$, $\mathbf{v} = (-1, 1, 0)$

5. $\mathbf{u} = (2, 2, 2)$, $\mathbf{v} = (-2, -2, -2)$ 6. $\mathbf{u} = (1, -1, 4)$, $\mathbf{v} = (0, 0, 0)$

7. Are the vectors $(1, -1, 1)$ and $(-1, -1, 0)$ orthogonal? Why?

8. The vectors $(1, 1, 1)$ and $(x, 0, 1 - 2x)$ are orthogonal. Find x.

9. Find the lengths of the vectors in Exercise 7.

10. Find the length of the vector $\mathbf{u} = (4, -3, 1)$.

11. Find the cosine of the angle between the vectors $\mathbf{u} = (1, -4, 2)$ and $\mathbf{v} = (-2, -1, 4)$.

12. Find the distance between the points $P_1 : (1, 2, 3)$ and $P_2 : (-2, 1, 5)$ in 3-space.

13. Suppose that $\mathbf{v}$ is a vector in Euclidean 2-space such that $\langle \mathbf{v}, \mathbf{v} \rangle = 0$. What can you say about $\mathbf{v}$? Give reasons.

14. Is there a vector $\mathbf{v}$ in Euclidean 2-space such that $\langle \mathbf{v}, \mathbf{v} \rangle < 0$? Give reasons.

15. Prove that the vector $(0, 0, 0)$ is orthogonal to *every* vector in Euclidean 3-space.

16. Is there a nonzero vector $\mathbf{v}$ in Euclidean 3-space V such that $\mathbf{v}$ is orthogonal to every vector in V? Give reasons.

17. Prove directly (i.e., using the usual rules of high-school algebra) that

$$-1 \le \frac{x_1 x_2 + y_1 y_2}{\sqrt{x_1^2 + y_1^2} \, \sqrt{x_2^2 + y_2^2}} \le 1.$$

Hint. Consider the square of the fraction in the above inequalities. Compare the square of the numerator with the square of the denominator.

18. a) Prove that $\langle \mathbf{u}, \mathbf{v} \rangle = 0$ for nonzero vectors $\mathbf{u}$ and $\mathbf{v}$ in Euclidean 2-space if and only if $\mathbf{u}$ and $\mathbf{v}$ are perpendicular.
   b) Prove the same for Euclidean 3-space.

19. Derive the formula (4.10) for $\cos \theta$ in 3-space. Carry out the details.

20. Prove part (i) of Theorem 4.1 in $\mathbb{R}^2$. How does the proof go in $\mathbb{R}^3$?

21. Prove part (ii) of Theorem 4.1 in $\mathbb{R}^2$.

22. Prove part (iii) of Theorem 4.1 in $\mathbb{R}^2$.

23. Prove part (iv) of Theorem 4.1 in $\mathbb{R}^2$.

24. Prove part (v) of Theorem 4.1 in $\mathbb{R}^2$.

25. Show that in $\mathbb{R}^3$ part (iv) of Theorem 4.1 implies both parts (ii) and (iii).

26. Show that in $\mathbb{R}^3$ parts (ii) and (iii) of Theorem 4.1 imply part (iv).

27. Show that the triangle whose vertices are $P_1 : (1, -2, 3)$, $P_2 : (4, 2, 15)$, and $P_3 : (-3, 10, 0)$ is an isosceles right triangle. Use vectors.

28. Show that a rectangle in the plane is the only parallelogram whose diagonals have equal length. Use vectors.

29. Show that $\|\mathbf{u} + \mathbf{v}\| \le \|\mathbf{u}\| + \|\mathbf{v}\|$ for vectors $\mathbf{u}$ and $\mathbf{v}$ in $\mathbb{R}^3$. When does equality hold? Give reasons.

4.2 REAL INNER PRODUCTS

In this section we define the concept of a real inner product for an arbitrary real-vector space and study some of its properties.

In Section 4.1 we described inner products in Euclidean 2-space and Euclidean 3-space. With these definitions in mind, it is possible to extend this concept to an arbitrary real vector space in the following manner. Take the basic results of Theorem 4.1 for the inner product in $\mathbb{R}^2$ and $\mathbb{R}^3$ as the starting point.

Let V be any real vector space (that is, the scalars are real numbers). Suppose that to each pair $\mathbf{u}$ and $\mathbf{v}$ of vectors in V we can assign a real number $\langle \mathbf{u}, \mathbf{v} \rangle$ with the following properties: For all $\mathbf{u}$, $\mathbf{v}$, $\mathbf{w}$ in V and real numbers (scalars) k_1, k_2,

1. $\langle \mathbf{u}, \mathbf{v} \rangle = \langle \mathbf{v}, \mathbf{u} \rangle$,
2. $\langle k_1 \mathbf{u} + k_2 \mathbf{v}, \mathbf{w} \rangle = k_1 \langle \mathbf{u}, \mathbf{w} \rangle + k_2 \langle \mathbf{v}, \mathbf{w} \rangle$,
3. $\langle \mathbf{u}, \mathbf{u} \rangle \geq 0$,
4. $\langle \mathbf{u}, \mathbf{u} \rangle = 0$ if and only if $\mathbf{u} = \mathbf{0}$.

Then this function $\langle \mathbf{u}, \mathbf{v} \rangle$ is called an **inner product** in V and V is an **inner-product space** with respect to this inner product.

The fact that $\mathbb{R}^2$ and $\mathbb{R}^3$ are inner-product spaces with respect to the dot product (see Section 4.1) is the statement of Theorem 4.1 that you proved in the exercises. Our definition of a real inner product states that the inner product is a *real-valued function*. Property 1 states that the inner-product function is *symmetric*, while Property 2 asserts that the inner-product function is *linear with respect to the first argument*. This leads us to the question: Is the inner-product function also linear with respect to the second argument? The answer is yes, as the following theorem asserts.

Theorem 4.2

For vectors $\mathbf{u}$, $\mathbf{v}$, $\mathbf{w}$ in the real inner-product space V and all scalars (real numbers) a, b, it is true that

$$\langle \mathbf{u}, a\mathbf{v} + b\mathbf{w} \rangle = a \langle \mathbf{u}, \mathbf{v} \rangle + b \langle \mathbf{u}, \mathbf{w} \rangle.$$

To prove this, note that

$$\begin{aligned}
\langle \mathbf{u}, a\mathbf{v} + b\mathbf{w} \rangle &= \langle a\mathbf{v} + b\mathbf{w}, \mathbf{u} \rangle && \text{(by Property 1)} \\
&= a \langle \mathbf{v}, \mathbf{u} \rangle + b \langle \mathbf{w}, \mathbf{u} \rangle && \text{(by Property 2)} \\
&= a \langle \mathbf{u}, \mathbf{v} \rangle + b \langle \mathbf{u}, \mathbf{w} \rangle && \text{(by Property 1)}.
\end{aligned}$$

This proves the theorem.

In view of Theorem 4.2 and Property 2, we see that *the inner-product function is linear with respect to each argument*.

Let us give an example of an inner product that generalizes both definitions of

Section 4.1. Suppose V is a cartesian n-space $\mathbb{R}^n$. Suppose also that $\mathbf{v}$, $\mathbf{u}$ are any vectors in V, say,

$$\mathbf{v} = (x_1, x_2, \ldots, x_n), \qquad \mathbf{u} = (x_1', x_2', \ldots, x_n'), \tag{4.16}$$

where all x_i and all x_i' are real. Now *define* $\langle \mathbf{v}, \mathbf{u} \rangle$ by

$$\langle \mathbf{v}, \mathbf{u} \rangle = x_1 x_1' + x_2 x_2' + \ldots + x_n x_n'. \tag{4.17}$$

An argument similar to the one given to prove Theorem 4.1 shows that the following theorem is true. Verification of this we leave as an exercise for you.

Theorem 4.3
Let V be n-space $\mathbb{R}^n$ of vectors and let $\mathbf{v}$, $\mathbf{u}$ be as in (4.16); define $\langle \mathbf{v}, \mathbf{u} \rangle$ as in (4.17). Then $\langle \mathbf{v}, \mathbf{u} \rangle$ is an inner product in $\mathbb{R}^n$.

The cases $n = 2$ and $n = 3$ of this theorem recover the definitions of Section 4.1.

Thus, by Theorem 4.3, the cartesian n-space $\mathbb{R}^n$ is an inner-product space with respect to the inner-product function defined by (4.16) and (4.17). This particular inner product is called the **standard inner product** in $\mathbb{R}^n$. It is also called the **Euclidean inner product**. The vector space $\mathbb{R}^n$ with *this* inner product is then called **Euclidean n-space**. This inner product is, however, not the only possible inner product on $\mathbb{R}^n$, as you can see from the following example.

Example 1 Let $\mathbf{u} = (u_1, u_2)$ and $\mathbf{v} = (v_1, v_2)$ be vectors in cartesian 2-space $\mathbb{R}^2$. The function

$$\langle \mathbf{u}, \mathbf{v} \rangle = 2u_1 v_1 + 3u_2 v_2. \tag{4.18}$$

defines an inner product (not the standard one) on $\mathbb{R}^2$.

Let us verify that this does satisfy the definition of inner product. It is clear that $2u_1 v_1 + 3u_2 v_2$ is indeed a real number. Note that interchanging $\mathbf{u}$ and $\mathbf{v}$ in Eq. (4.18) does not alter the right-hand side, so Property 1 is satisfied. If a and b are real numbers and $\mathbf{w} = (w_1, w_2)$ is a vector in $\mathbb{R}^2$, then for Property 2 we have

$$a\mathbf{u} + b\mathbf{v} = (au_1 + bv_1, au_2 + bv_2),$$

So

$$\begin{aligned}
\langle a\mathbf{u} + b\mathbf{v}, \mathbf{w} \rangle &= 2(au_1 + bv_1)w_1 + 3(au_2 + bv_2)w_2 \\
&= 2au_1 w_1 + 2bv_1 w_1 + 3au_2 w_2 + 3bv_2 w_2 \\
&= a(2u_1 w_1 + 3u_2 w_2) + b(2v_1 w_1 + 3v_2 w_2) \\
&= a\langle \mathbf{u}, \mathbf{w} \rangle + b\langle \mathbf{v}, \mathbf{w} \rangle.
\end{aligned}$$

For Properties 3 and 4, we get $\langle \mathbf{u}, \mathbf{u} \rangle = 2u_1^2 + 3u_2^2$, which is clearly nonnegative and equals 0 if and only if $u_1 = u_2 = 0$, and thus $\mathbf{u} = \mathbf{0}$. This completes the verification.

Inner products can also be defined on vector spaces other than $\mathbb{R}^n$. Two rather interesting spaces are given in the next two examples.

Example 2 Consider the space M_n of real $n \times n$ matrices. The function

$$\langle A, B \rangle = \text{tr}(A'B)$$

is a real inner product (see Exercise 29), where the **trace** (tr) of a matrix $C = (c_{ij})$ is the sum of the main-diagonal elements of the matrix C:

$$\text{tr } C = \sum_{i=1}^{n} c_{ii}.$$

Example 3 (*for students who have studied calculus*). Let the function $\langle p(x), q(x) \rangle$ on the space P_n of real polynomials be defined by

$$\langle p, q \rangle = \int_0^1 p(t)q(t)dt. \tag{4.19}$$

This is called the *integral inner product* on P_n. To verify that it actually satisfies the definition of an inner product requires only the basic properties of integration. The integral is a real number. Moreover,

$$\langle p, p \rangle = \int_0^1 p^2(t)dt \geq 0$$

and is equal to zero if and only if $p(x)$ is the zero polynomial.
We have

$$\langle p, q \rangle = \int_0^1 p(t)q(t)dt = \int_0^1 q(t)p(t)dt = \langle q, p \rangle$$

and

$$\langle \alpha p_1 + \beta p_2, q \rangle = \int_0^1 (\alpha p_1(t) + \beta p_2(t))q(t)dt$$

$$= \int_0^1 (\alpha p_1(t)q(t) + \beta p_2(t)q(t))dt$$

$$= \alpha \int_0^1 p_1(t)q(t)dt + \beta \int_0^1 p_2(t)q(t)dt$$

$$= \alpha \langle p_1, q \rangle + \beta \langle p_2, q \rangle.$$

So this is indeed an inner product. In a particular case, if $p(x) = x^2 - 2x + 3$ and $q(x) = 3x - 4$, then

$$\langle p, q \rangle = \int_0^1 (t^2 - 2t + 3)(3t - 4)dt$$

$$= \int_0^1 (3t^3 - 10t^2 + 17t - 12)dt$$

$$= \frac{3}{4}t^4 - \frac{10}{3}t^3 + \frac{17}{2}t^2 - 12t \Big|_0^1 = -\frac{73}{12}.$$

Example 4   We can also define an inner product on P_n that resembles the Euclidean inner product in $\mathbb{R}^n$ more closely. Let

$$p(x) = a_0 + a_1 x + a_2 x^2 + \ldots + a_n x^n,$$
$$q(x) = b_0 + b_1 x + b_2 x^2 + \ldots + b_n x^n,$$

where $a_0, a_1, a_2, \ldots, a_n, b_0, b_1, b_2, \ldots, b_n$ are real numbers. Let

$$\langle p(x), q(x) \rangle = a_0 b_0 + a_1 b_1 + a_2 b_2 + \ldots + a_n b_n. \tag{4.20}$$

We claim that $\langle p(x), q(x) \rangle$ is an inner product on P_n. To see this, note first that the left member of (4.20) is clearly a real number. Furthermore, the commutative property of multiplication of real numbers says also that

$$a_0 b_0 + a_1 b_1 + \ldots + a_n b_n = b_0 a_0 + b_1 a_1 + \ldots + b_n a_n = \langle q(x), p(x) \rangle,$$

so Property 1 of our definition is satisfied by this function.

If c and d are any two real numbers, then

$$cp(x) = ca_0 + ca_1 x + ca_2 x^2 + \ldots + ca_n x^n,$$
$$dq(x) = db_0 + db_1 x + db_2 x^2 + \ldots + db_n x^n.$$

If $r(x) = g_0 + g_1 x + g_2 x^2 + \ldots + g_n x^n$, then

$$\langle cp(x) + dq(x), r(x) \rangle = (ca_0 + db_0)g_0 + (ca_1 + db_1)g_1 + (ca_2 + db_2)g_2 + \ldots$$
$$+ (ca_n + db_n)g_n$$
$$= ca_0 g_0 + db_0 g_0 + ca_1 g_1 + db_1 g_1 + ca_2 g_2 + db_2 g_2 + \ldots + ca_n g_n + db_n g_n$$
$$= c(a_0 g_0 + a_1 g_1 + \ldots + a_n g_n) + d(b_0 g_0 + b_1 g_1 + \ldots + b_n g_n)$$
$$= c \langle p(x), r(x) \rangle + d \langle q(x), r(x) \rangle.$$

Finally, $\langle p(x), p(x) \rangle = a_0^2 + a_1^2 + \ldots + a_n^2 \geqslant 0$, since it is a sum of squares of real numbers. Furthermore, it equals 0 if and only if each $a_i = 0$; that is, if $p(x)$ is the zero polynomial.

Thus $\langle p(x), q(x) \rangle$ is also an inner product in P_n. That it is different from the integral inner product is easily verified. For instance, if $p(x) = x^2 - 2x + 3$ and $q(x) = 0x^2 + 3x - 4$ as in Example 3, this inner product yields

$$\langle p(x), q(x) \rangle = 1 \cdot 0 + (-2)(3) + 3(-4) = -18.$$

Compare this with the result in Example 3.

Example 5   Let $\mathbb{R}^4$ be Euclidean 4-space and let $\mathbf{u} = (1, -1, 2, 3)$, $\mathbf{v} = (-2, -1, 1, -2)$ be two vectors in $\mathbb{R}^4$. The Euclidean inner product is

$$\langle \mathbf{u}, \mathbf{v} \rangle = 1(-2) + (-1)(-1) + 2(1) + 3(-2)$$
$$= -2 + 1 + 2 - 6 = -5.$$

In the next section we shall see how the concepts of distance, length, and angle can be defined in *any* inner-product space. We conclude this section with a minor modification of Euclidean n-space.

Example 6   Let $\overline{\mathbb{R}^n}$ be the vector space of $n \times 1$ matrices

$$X = \begin{bmatrix} x_1 \\ x_2 \\ \cdot \\ \cdot \\ \cdot \\ x_n \end{bmatrix}.$$

We define a Euclidean inner product in $\overline{\mathbb{R}^n}$ much the same as in $\mathbb{R}^n$. That is, with X as above and

$$Y = \begin{bmatrix} y_1 \\ y_2 \\ \cdot \\ \cdot \\ \cdot \\ y_n \end{bmatrix}.$$

let

$$\langle X, Y \rangle = x_1 y_1 + x_2 y_2 + \ldots + x_n y_n = \sum_{i=1}^{n} x_i y_i.$$

You can see that this is indeed a Euclidean inner product, since it is essentially the result of Theorem 4.3.

In particular, if

$$X = \begin{bmatrix} 1 \\ 2 \\ 1 \\ 5 \end{bmatrix} \quad \text{and} \quad Y = \begin{bmatrix} -1 \\ 1 \\ 0 \\ 3 \end{bmatrix},$$

then (verify this)

$$\langle X, Y \rangle = -1 + 2 + 15 = 16,$$

$$\|X\| = \sqrt{31}, \qquad \|Y\| = \sqrt{11}, \qquad \text{and} \qquad \|X - Y\| = \sqrt{10}.$$

Compare this inner product with the inner product of Example 2. Note that $\langle X, Y \rangle = X^t Y$ as matrices.

EXERCISES (4.2)

In Exercises 1–9, find the Euclidean inner products of the given vectors in $\mathbb{R}^n$.

1. $\mathbf{u} = (1, -4)$, $\mathbf{v} = (-3, 5)$
2. $\mathbf{u} = (1, 0, 1)$, $\mathbf{v} = (0, 1, 0)$

3. $\mathbf{u} = (1, 1, 1)$, $\mathbf{v} = (1, 1, 1)$
4. $\mathbf{u} = (-1, 0, 1, 2)$, $\mathbf{v} = (0, 1, 0, 0)$

5. $\mathbf{u} = (2, 1, 3, -5)$, $\mathbf{v} = (1, 4, -1, 2)$
6. $\mathbf{u} = (-1, 1, 1, 2, 3)$, $\mathbf{v} = (0, 1, 3, 5, 8)$

7. $\mathbf{u} = (2, 3, 4, -1)$, $\mathbf{v} = (0, 0, 0, 0)$
8. $\mathbf{u} = (-2, 3, 8, 0, 1, 2)$, $\mathbf{v} = (0, 0, 0, 0, 0, 1)$

9. $\mathbf{u} = (1, 0, -1, 0, 1, 2, -1)$, $\mathbf{v} = (2, 1, -1, 3, 1, 2, 2)$

In Exercises 10–14, decide which of the following functions on $\mathbb{R}^2$ are inner products and which are not. For those that are not, give an example violating one of the defining conditions of an inner product. Here, $\mathbf{u} = (u_1, u_2)$, $\mathbf{v} = (v_1, v_2)$.

10. $\langle \mathbf{u}, \mathbf{v} \rangle = 4u_1 v_1 + 4u_2 v_2 - u_1 v_2 - u_2 v_1$
11. $\langle \mathbf{u}, \mathbf{v} \rangle = u_1 v_1 u_2 v_2$.

12. $\langle \mathbf{u}, \mathbf{v} \rangle = 2u_1 v_1 - 3u_2 v_2$
13. $\langle \mathbf{u}, \mathbf{v} \rangle = u_1 v_2 - u_2 v_1$

14. $\langle \mathbf{u}, \mathbf{v} \rangle = 3u_1 v_1 - u_1 v_2 + u_2 v_1 - 3u_2 v_2$

15. Show that $\langle \mathbf{u}, \mathbf{v} \rangle = u_1 v_1 + 2u_2 v_2 + 3u_3 v_3 + 4u_4 v_4$ is an inner product in $\mathbb{R}^4$.

16. Use the inner product in Exercise 15 to find $\langle \mathbf{u}, \mathbf{v} \rangle$ for $\mathbf{u}$ and $\mathbf{v}$ of Exercise 5.

17. Use the inner product in Exercise 15 to find $\langle \mathbf{u}, \mathbf{v} \rangle$ for $\mathbf{u} = (2, -1, -2, 1)$ and $\mathbf{v} = (3, 2, -1, -1)$.

In Exercises 18–20, use the inner product of Example 2 to calculate the inner product $\langle A, B \rangle$ for the given matrices.

18. $A = \begin{bmatrix} 0 & 1 \\ -1 & -1 \end{bmatrix}$, $B = \begin{bmatrix} 2 & 3 \\ 1 & -1 \end{bmatrix}$

19. $A = \begin{bmatrix} 1 & -1 & 2 \\ 0 & 5 & -3 \\ 2 & 1 & -2 \end{bmatrix}$, $B = \begin{bmatrix} 2 & -1 & 5 \\ 4 & 3 & 1 \\ 2 & -1 & 0 \end{bmatrix}$

20. $A = \begin{bmatrix} 1 & 0 & 0 & 1 \\ 0 & 1 & 1 & 0 \\ 1 & 1 & 0 & 1 \\ 0 & 1 & 1 & 1 \end{bmatrix}$, $B = \begin{bmatrix} 1 & -1 & 1 & -1 \\ 0 & 1 & -1 & 1 \\ 0 & 0 & 1 & -1 \\ 0 & 0 & 0 & 1 \end{bmatrix}$

In Exercises 21–24 use the inner product of Example 4 in P_n to find $\langle p(x), q(x) \rangle$ for the given polynomials.

21. $p(x) = 1 - x$, $\quad q(x) = 1 + x$

22. $p(x) = x^2$, $\quad q(x) = x - 3$

23. $p(x) = 3x - 3$, $\quad q(x) = 6x - 3$

24. $p(x) = 3x^2 + 4x - 5$, $\quad q(x) = 3x + 2$

In Exercises 25–27, use the Euclidean inner product $\langle X, Y \rangle = X^t Y$ of Example 6, for the given column vectors X and Y.

25.
$$X = \begin{bmatrix} 1 \\ 0 \\ 1 \end{bmatrix}, \quad Y = \begin{bmatrix} -1 \\ 1 \\ 0 \end{bmatrix}$$

26.
$$X = \begin{bmatrix} 1 \\ -1 \\ 3 \\ 1 \end{bmatrix}, \quad Y = \begin{bmatrix} 0 \\ -2 \\ 1 \\ -2 \end{bmatrix}$$

27.
$$X = \begin{bmatrix} 1 \\ 0 \\ -1 \\ -2 \\ 1 \end{bmatrix}, \quad Y = \begin{bmatrix} 2 \\ -1 \\ 3 \\ 1 \\ 2 \end{bmatrix}$$

28. Prove Theorem 4.3.

29. Verify that the definition of $\langle A, B \rangle$ in Example 2 complies with the definition of an inner product.

30. Which of the vectors, if any, in Exercises 1–9 satisfy $\langle \mathbf{u}, \mathbf{v} \rangle = 0$?

31. Which of the vectors (polynomials), if any, in Exercises 21–24 satisfy $\langle p(x), q(x) \rangle = 0$?

32. Let $\mathbf{u} = (u_1, u_2, \ldots, u_n)$ and $\mathbf{v} = (v_1, v_2, \ldots, v_n)$ be vectors in $\mathbb{R}^n$ and let $c_1, c_2, \ldots, c_n$ be any *positive* real numbers. Show that

$$\langle \mathbf{u}, \mathbf{v} \rangle = \sum_{i=1}^{n} c_i u_i v_i = c_1 u_1 v_1 + c_2 u_2 v_2 + \ldots + c_n u_n v_n$$

is an inner product in $\mathbb{R}^n$.

33. Let V be any inner-product space. Prove that $\langle \mathbf{0}, \mathbf{v} \rangle = 0$ for all vectors $\mathbf{v}$ in V. *Hint.* Consider $\langle \mathbf{0} + \mathbf{0}, \mathbf{v} \rangle$.

34. For V as in Exercise 33, prove that $\langle \mathbf{v}, \mathbf{0} \rangle = 0$ for all vectors $\mathbf{v}$ in V.

35. For V as in Exercise 33, prove that $\langle a\mathbf{v}_1, \mathbf{v}_2 \rangle = a \langle \mathbf{v}_1, \mathbf{v}_2 \rangle$ and $\langle \mathbf{v}_1, a\mathbf{v}_2 \rangle = a \langle \mathbf{v}_1, \mathbf{v}_2 \rangle$ for all vectors $\mathbf{v}_1, \mathbf{v}_2$ and all scalars a.

36. For V as in Exercise 33, prove that $\langle a\mathbf{v}_1, b\mathbf{v}_2 \rangle = ab \langle \mathbf{v}_1, \mathbf{v}_2 \rangle$ for all vectors $\mathbf{v}_1, \mathbf{v}_2$ and all scalars a, b.

37. For V as in Exercise 33, prove that

$$\langle a_1 \mathbf{v}_1 + a_2 \mathbf{v}_2, a_1' \mathbf{v}_1' + a_2' \mathbf{v}_2' \rangle = a_1 a_1' \langle \mathbf{v}_1, \mathbf{v}_1' \rangle + a_1 a_2' \langle \mathbf{v}_1, \mathbf{v}_2' \rangle$$
$$+ a_2 a_1' \langle \mathbf{v}_2, \mathbf{v}_1' \rangle + a_2 a_2' \langle \mathbf{v}_2, \mathbf{v}_2' \rangle,$$

for all vectors $\mathbf{v}_1, \mathbf{v}_2, \mathbf{v}_1', \mathbf{v}_2'$ and all scalars a_1, a_2, a_1', a_2'.

38. With V as in Exercise 33, prove that

$$\langle \mathbf{v}_1 + \mathbf{v}_2, \mathbf{v}_1 + \mathbf{v}_2 \rangle = \langle \mathbf{v}_1, \mathbf{v}_1 \rangle + 2 \langle \mathbf{v}_1, \mathbf{v}_2 \rangle + \langle \mathbf{v}_2, \mathbf{v}_2 \rangle.$$

Hint. Recall that $1 \cdot \mathbf{v} = \mathbf{v}$ for all vectors $\mathbf{v}$.

Exercises 39–48 are for students who have studied calculus.

39. Prove that the function $\langle p(x), q(x) \rangle = \int_a^b p(t)q(t)dt$, where a and b are any real numbers.
complies with the properties defining an inner product in the space P_n of polynomials.

Use the integral inner product of Example 3 to compute $\langle p(x), q(x) \rangle$ for each of the following polynomials. Compare these results with Exercises 21–24.

40. $p(x) = 1 - x$, $q(x) = 1 + x$ **41.** $p(x) = x^2$, $q(x) = x - 3$

42. $p(x) = 3x - 3$, $q(x) = 6x - 3$ **43.** $p(x) = 3x^2 + 4x - 5$, $q(x) = 3x + 2$

44. $p(x) = x - 1$, $q(x) = 3x - 1$ **45.** $p(x) = x^2 - 2x - 1$, $q(x) = 2x - 2$

46. Define an integral inner product in the space of continuous functions on the unit interval $[0, 1]$ in the same way as in Example 3. Use this to find $\langle \sin x, \cos x \rangle$.

47. Use the integral inner product of Exercise 46 to find $\langle 1, e^x \rangle$.

48. Use the integral inner product of Exercise 46 to find $\langle x, e^{x^2} \rangle$.

4.3 LENGTH AND ANGLE IN INNER-PRODUCT SPACES

In Section 4.1 we developed the standard inner product for vectors in Euclidean 2-space and 3-space from properties of length and angle. Since we have now generalized the concept of inner product, let us see how this general concept can give rise to ideas of length and angle in any inner-product space.

Let V be any real vector space and let $\langle \mathbf{u}, \mathbf{v} \rangle$ be an inner product defined on V, that is, V is a real inner-product space. By generalizing the concept of distance in $\mathbb{R}^2$ and $\mathbb{R}^3$ let us define the **norm** (length) $\|\mathbf{v}\|$ of an arbitrary vector $\mathbf{v} \in V$ by

$$\|\mathbf{v}\| = \langle \mathbf{v}, \mathbf{v} \rangle^{1/2}. \tag{4.21}$$

Since $\langle \mathbf{v}, \mathbf{v} \rangle$ is a nonnegative real number, it does indeed have a nonnegative square root.

Example 1 Let $V = \mathbb{R}^4$ with the Euclidean inner product. Let $\mathbf{w} = (1, 2, -1, 5)$. Then

$$\|\mathbf{w}\| = \langle \mathbf{w}, \mathbf{w} \rangle^{1/2} = \sqrt{1 + 4 + 1 + 25} = \sqrt{31}.$$

Example 2 Let $V = \mathbb{R}^4$ with inner product $\langle \mathbf{u}, \mathbf{v} \rangle$ defined by

$$\langle \mathbf{u}, \mathbf{v} \rangle = 2u_1 v_1 + u_2 v_2 + 3u_3 v_3 + u_4 v_4.$$

Find the norm of the vector **w** of Example 1 with this inner product. From (4.21) we have

$$\|\mathbf{w}\| = \langle \mathbf{w}, \mathbf{w} \rangle^{1/2} = \sqrt{2(1)+4+3(1)+25} = \sqrt{34}.$$

Example 3 (for those who have studied calculus). Let P_n be the inner-product space of all polynomials of degree n or less with the integral inner product. Then the norm of $p(x) = x$ is

$$\|p\| = \langle p, p \rangle^{1/2} = \left[\int_0^1 p^2(x)dx \right]^{1/2} = \left[\int_0^1 x^2\, dx \right]^{1/2}$$

$$= \left[\frac{x^3}{3} \Big|_0^1 \right]^{1/2} = \left[\frac{1}{3} \right]^{1/2} = \frac{\sqrt{3}}{3}.$$

The norm of $q(x) = 1 - x^3$ is

$$\|1 - x^3\| = \left[\int_0^1 (1 - 2x^3 + x^6)dx \right]^{1/2}$$

$$= \left[1 - \frac{1}{2} + \frac{1}{7} \right]^{1/2} = \sqrt{9/14} = \frac{3}{\sqrt{14}}.$$

As these examples illustrate, the norm of a vector depends upon the particular inner-product function defined on the space V. Whether this function is the Euclidean inner product or some other is generally determined by factors outside of mathematics. No matter what inner product is used, the *norm* of a vector behaves much as we would expect it to — like the *length* in ordinary Euclidean geometry. Indeed, we have the following theorem.

Theorem 4.4
   Let V be a real inner-product space and let $\mathbf{u}, \mathbf{v}$ be in V. Let a be any real number. Then
   i) $\|\mathbf{v}\| \geq 0$ with $\|\mathbf{v}\| = 0$ if and only if $\mathbf{v} = \mathbf{0}$,
   ii) $\|a\mathbf{v}\| = |a|\,\|\mathbf{v}\|.$

Part (i) follows at once from Properties 3 and 4 of the definition of inner products and the definition of norm. To prove part (ii), observe that

$$\|a\mathbf{v}\|^2 = \langle a\mathbf{v}, a\mathbf{v} \rangle = a\langle \mathbf{v}, a\mathbf{v} \rangle \quad \text{(by Property 2)}$$
$$= a \cdot a \langle \mathbf{v}, \mathbf{v} \rangle \quad \text{(by Theorem 4.2)}$$
$$= a^2\|\mathbf{v}\|^2.$$

We have thus shown that

$$\|a\mathbf{v}\|^2 = a^2\|\mathbf{v}\|^2. \tag{4.22}$$

Taking the positive square roots of both sides of (4.22), we get

$$\| a\mathbf{v} \| = \sqrt{a^2} \, \| \mathbf{v} \|. \tag{4.23}$$

Recall that

$$\sqrt{a^2} = |a| = \text{(Absolute value of } a\text{)},$$

and hence (4.23) becomes

$$\| a\mathbf{v} \| = |a| \, \|\mathbf{v}\|.$$

In Equations (4.9) and (4.10) we showed that if θ is an angle between two nonzero vectors $\mathbf{u}$ and $\mathbf{v}$ in a Euclidean 2-space or 3-space, then

$$\cos\theta = \frac{\langle \mathbf{u}, \mathbf{v} \rangle}{\| \mathbf{u} \| \, \| \mathbf{v} \|}. \tag{4.24}$$

We also know that $|\cos\theta| \leqslant 1$ for all θ. Hence (4.24) implies that

$$\left| \frac{\langle \mathbf{u}, \mathbf{v} \rangle}{\| \mathbf{u} \| \, \| \mathbf{v} \|} \right| \leqslant 1; \qquad \mathbf{u} \neq \mathbf{0}, \quad \mathbf{v} \neq \mathbf{0}. \tag{4.25}$$

Multiplying both sides of the inequality (4.25) by the *positive* real number $\| \mathbf{u} \| \, \| \mathbf{v} \|$, we get

$$|\langle \mathbf{u}, \mathbf{v} \rangle| \leqslant \| \mathbf{u} \| \, \| \mathbf{v} \|. \tag{4.26}$$

In other words, the inequality (4.26) is true at least when the inner-product space under consideration is a Euclidean 2-space $\mathbb{R}^2$ or Euclidean 3-space $\mathbb{R}^3$ (with the Euclidean inner product). It is a remarkable fact that this inequality is also true in *any* inner-product space. This is the celebrated *Cauchy–Schwarz inequality*:

Theorem 4.5   Cauchy–Schwarz inequality
Let V be any inner-product space. Then for all vectors $\mathbf{u}$, $\mathbf{v}$ we have

$$|\langle \mathbf{u}, \mathbf{v} \rangle| \leqslant \| \mathbf{u} \| \, \| \mathbf{v} \|. \tag{4.27}$$

Moreover, equality in (4.27) holds if and only if $\mathbf{u}$ and $\mathbf{v}$ are linearly dependent.

Proof. Let $\mathbf{u}$ and $\mathbf{v}$ be arbitrary vectors in V. If $\mathbf{u} = \mathbf{0}$, then the equality of both sides of (4.27) is obvious (see Exercise 33 in Section 4.2). So suppose that $\mathbf{u} \neq \mathbf{0}$. Let x be a (variable) real number and consider the vector $\mathbf{x} = x\mathbf{u} + \mathbf{v}$. According to the properties of the inner product, $\langle \mathbf{x}, \mathbf{x} \rangle \geqslant 0$. Combining this fact with other properties of the inner product, we see that

$$0 \leqslant \langle x\mathbf{u} + \mathbf{v}, x\mathbf{u} + \mathbf{v} \rangle = \langle \mathbf{u}, \mathbf{u} \rangle x^2 + 2\langle \mathbf{u}, \mathbf{v} \rangle x + \langle \mathbf{v}, \mathbf{v} \rangle. \tag{4.28}$$

This is a quadratic inequality in x of the form

$$ax^2 + 2bx + c \geq 0.$$

By completing the square on the left, we have, for *every* real number x,

$$a\left(x^2 + \frac{2b}{a}x + \frac{b^2}{a^2}\right) + \left(c - \frac{b^2}{a}\right) \geq 0$$

or

$$a\left(x + \frac{b}{a}\right)^2 + \left(c - \frac{b^2}{a}\right) \geq 0. \tag{4.29}$$

In particular, this inequality holds when $x = -b/a$. Thus, setting $x = -b/a$ in (4.29), we get

$$c - \frac{b^2}{a} \geq 0. \tag{4.30}$$

Substituting the values of a, b, and c from (4.28) into (4.30), we obtain

$$\langle \mathbf{v}, \mathbf{v} \rangle \geq \frac{\langle \mathbf{u}, \mathbf{v} \rangle^2}{\langle \mathbf{u}, \mathbf{u} \rangle}.$$

But since $\langle \mathbf{u}, \mathbf{u} \rangle$ is *positive* when $\mathbf{u} \neq \mathbf{0}$, we may multiply both sides of the above inequality by $\langle \mathbf{u}, \mathbf{u} \rangle$ to get

$$\langle \mathbf{u}, \mathbf{v} \rangle^2 \leq \langle \mathbf{u}, \mathbf{u} \rangle \langle \mathbf{v}, \mathbf{v} \rangle,$$

from which (4.27) follows upon taking square roots.

Now, let us consider the case when we have equality in (4.27). In the above proof, in order for equality to hold we must have

$$\langle x\mathbf{u} + \mathbf{v}, x\mathbf{u} + \mathbf{v} \rangle = 0$$

for some real number x (see (4.28)). Hence, the two sides of (4.27) are actually equal if and only if $x\mathbf{u} + \mathbf{v} = \mathbf{0}$ for some real number x, that is, if and only if $\mathbf{u}$ and $\mathbf{v}$ are linearly dependent. This completes the proof.

As a corollary of the Cauchy–Schwarz inequality we now prove the triangle inequality.

Corollary   **Triangle inequality**
   Let $\mathbf{v}_1$, $\mathbf{v}_2$ *be any vectors in an inner-product space. Then*

$$\| \mathbf{v}_1 + \mathbf{v}_2 \| \leq \| \mathbf{v}_1 \| + \| \mathbf{v}_2 \|. \tag{4.31}$$

To prove this we use the properties in the definition of an inner product together with Theorem 4.2. We also keep in mind that $(1)(\mathbf{v}) = \mathbf{v}$ for all vectors $\mathbf{v}$. Indeed, by definition,

$$
\begin{aligned}
||\mathbf{v}_1 + \mathbf{v}_2||^2 &= \langle \mathbf{v}_1 + \mathbf{v}_2, \mathbf{v}_1 + \mathbf{v}_2 \rangle \\
&= \langle \mathbf{v}_1, \mathbf{v}_1 + \mathbf{v}_2 \rangle + \langle \mathbf{v}_2, \mathbf{v}_1 + \mathbf{v}_2 \rangle, \quad \text{(by Property 2)} \\
&= \langle \mathbf{v}_1, \mathbf{v}_1 \rangle + \langle \mathbf{v}_1, \mathbf{v}_2 \rangle + \langle \mathbf{v}_2, \mathbf{v}_1 \rangle + \langle \mathbf{v}_2, \mathbf{v}_2 \rangle \quad \text{(by Theorem 4.2)} \\
&= ||\mathbf{v}_1||^2 + 2\langle \mathbf{v}_1, \mathbf{v}_2 \rangle + ||\mathbf{v}_2||^2 \quad \text{(by Property 1 and definition of norm)}.
\end{aligned}
$$

We have thus shown that

$$
||\mathbf{v}_1 + \mathbf{v}_2||^2 = ||\mathbf{v}_1||^2 + 2\langle \mathbf{v}_1, \mathbf{v}_2 \rangle + ||\mathbf{v}_2||^2. \tag{4.32}
$$

We recall that $a \leqslant |a|$ for all real numbers a. In particular,

$$
\langle \mathbf{v}_1, \mathbf{v}_2 \rangle \leqslant |\langle \mathbf{v}_1, \mathbf{v}_2 \rangle|
$$

and hence (4.32) implies that

$$
||\mathbf{v}_1 + \mathbf{v}_2||^2 \leqslant ||\mathbf{v}_1||^2 + 2|\langle \mathbf{v}_1, \mathbf{v}_2 \rangle| + ||\mathbf{v}_2||^2. \tag{4.33}
$$

By the Cauchy–Schwarz inequality,

$$
|\langle \mathbf{v}_1, \mathbf{v}_2 \rangle| \leqslant ||\mathbf{v}_1||\, ||\mathbf{v}_2||. \tag{4.34}
$$

Combining (4.33) and (4.34), we get

$$
||\mathbf{v}_1 + \mathbf{v}_2||^2 \leqslant ||\mathbf{v}_1||^2 + 2||\mathbf{v}_1||\, ||\mathbf{v}_2|| + ||\mathbf{v}_2||^2. \tag{4.35}
$$

Note that the right side of (4.35) is equal to (verify this)

$$
(||\mathbf{v}_1|| + ||\mathbf{v}_2||)^2
$$

and hence (4.35) becomes

$$
||\mathbf{v}_1 + \mathbf{v}_2||^2 \leqslant (||\mathbf{v}_1|| + ||\mathbf{v}_2||)^2.
$$

Taking the positive square roots of both sides of this inequality, we get (4.31).

It is instructive to interpret the triangle inequality geometrically. To this end, let $\mathbf{v}_1, \mathbf{v}_2$ be vectors in Euclidean 2-space $\mathbb{R}^2$ (a plane). Then $||\mathbf{v}_1||, ||\mathbf{v}_2||, ||\mathbf{v}_1 + \mathbf{v}_2||$ denote the lengths of three sides of a triangle, as indicated in Fig. 4.9. Thus in this special case the triangle inequality reduces to the familiar fact that the length of a side of a triangle is at most as great as the sum of the lengths of the other two sides (see (4.31)). Incidentally, this also explains why this inequality is known as the triangle inequality.

Example 4 Verify that the triangle inequality and the Cauchy–Schwarz inequality are satisfied by the vectors $\mathbf{v}_1 = (1, 2), \mathbf{v}_2 = (-3, -5)$ in $\mathbb{R}^2$ with the standard inner product.

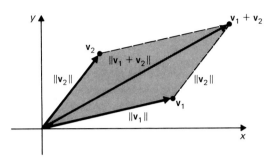

Figure 4.9

Here $\mathbf{v}_1 + \mathbf{v}_2 = (1, 2) + (-3, -5) = (-2, -3)$ and hence, by definition,

$$\| \mathbf{v}_1 + \mathbf{v}_2 \| = \sqrt{\langle \mathbf{v}_1 + \mathbf{v}_2, \mathbf{v}_1 + \mathbf{v}_2 \rangle} = \sqrt{(-2)^2 + (-3)^2} = \sqrt{13}.$$

Also,

$$\| \mathbf{v}_1 \| = \sqrt{\langle \mathbf{v}_1, \mathbf{v}_1 \rangle} = \sqrt{1^2 + 2^2} = \sqrt{5},$$

$$\| \mathbf{v}_2 \| = \sqrt{\langle \mathbf{v}_2, \mathbf{v}_2 \rangle} = \sqrt{(-3)^2 + (-5)^2} = \sqrt{34}.$$

Observe that $\sqrt{13} \leqslant \sqrt{5} + \sqrt{34}$, and thus the triangle inequality is satisfied. Moreover, $\langle \mathbf{v}_1, \mathbf{v}_2 \rangle = (1)(-3) + (2)(-5) = -13$, and hence $|\langle \mathbf{v}_1, \mathbf{v}_2 \rangle| = 13$. Note that $13 \leqslant \sqrt{5} \cdot \sqrt{34}$ (verify this), and thus the Cauchy–Schwarz inequality is satisfied also.

By making use of the Cauchy–Schwarz inequality it is possible also to introduce the concept of *angle* into an inner-product space V. Let V be an arbitrary real inner-product space and let $\mathbf{u}$ and $\mathbf{v}$ be nonzero vectors in V. We define the **angle** θ **between $\mathbf{u}$ and $\mathbf{v}$** to be the angle θ such that

$$\cos \theta = \frac{\langle \mathbf{u}, \mathbf{v} \rangle}{\| \mathbf{u} \| \, \| \mathbf{v} \|}, \qquad 0 \leqslant \theta \leqslant \pi. \qquad \text{(4.36)}$$

This definition clearly reduces to the usual one in Euclidean 2-space and Euclidean 3-space (see (4.24)). That our definition is reasonable in V follows from the fact that for nonzero vectors $\mathbf{u}$ and $\mathbf{v}$ we can write the form (4.27) of the Cauchy–Schwarz inequality as (verify this)

$$-1 \leqslant \frac{\langle \mathbf{u}, \mathbf{v} \rangle}{\| \mathbf{u} \| \, \| \mathbf{v} \|} \leqslant 1.$$

Example 5 Find the cosine of the angle between the vectors $\mathbf{u} = (1, 0, 1, 1)$ and $\mathbf{v} = (2, 1, -1, 3)$ in Euclidean 4-space $\mathbb{R}^4$.

From (4.36) we have

$$\cos \theta = \frac{4}{\sqrt{3}\sqrt{15}} = \frac{4}{3\sqrt{5}} = \frac{4\sqrt{5}}{15} = 0.6 \quad \text{(approximately)}.$$

Example 6   Find the cosine of the angle between the two vectors $\mathbf{u} = (2, -1, 3, -2, 0)$ and $\mathbf{v} = (1, 3, 1, 1, 5)$.

From (4.36) we get

$$\cos \theta = \frac{\langle \mathbf{u}, \mathbf{v}\rangle}{\|\mathbf{u}\|\,\|\mathbf{v}\|} = \frac{0}{\|\mathbf{u}\|\,\|\mathbf{v}\|} = 0.$$

On the basis of this example and the situation in the usual two-dimensional and three-dimensional Euclidean space, we shall call two vectors $\mathbf{u}$ and $\mathbf{v}$ in an arbitrary inner-product space **orthogonal** (or *perpendicular*) if $\langle \mathbf{u}, \mathbf{v}\rangle = 0$. The next two examples illustrate why the term *orthogonal* is preferred over the term *perpendicular*.

Example 7   (for students who have studied calculus). Show that the polynomials $p(x) = x - 1$ and $q(x) = 3x - 1$ are orthogonal in the inner-product space P_1 of polynomials under the integral inner product.

We recall that

$$\langle p, q\rangle = \int_0^1 (t-1)(3t-1)dt = \int_0^1 (3t^2 - 4t + 1)dt$$

$$= t^3 - 2t^2 + t \Big|_0^1 = 0.$$

Example 8   Show that the matrices

$$A = \begin{bmatrix} 1 & 3 \\ -1 & 4 \end{bmatrix} \quad \text{and} \quad B = \begin{bmatrix} -5 & 2 \\ 5 & 1 \end{bmatrix}$$

are orthogonal under the trace inner product $\langle A, B\rangle = \operatorname{tr}(A^t B)$.

Observe that

$$A^t B = \begin{bmatrix} 1 & -1 \\ 3 & 4 \end{bmatrix} \begin{bmatrix} -5 & 2 \\ 5 & 1 \end{bmatrix} = \begin{bmatrix} -10 & 1 \\ 5 & 10 \end{bmatrix}$$

and $\operatorname{tr}(A^t B) = -10 + 10 = 0$. Hence $\langle A, B\rangle = 0$, and thus A and B are orthogonal under the given inner product.

A vector $\mathbf{v}$ in an inner-product space V is called a **unit vector** if $\|\mathbf{v}\| = 1$.

For example, the vectors $(1, 0, 0)$, $(0, 1, 0)$, $(0, 0, 1)$ are all unit vectors in $\mathbb{R}^3$ with the standard inner product (verify this). Also the vector $(1/\sqrt{5}, 2/\sqrt{5}, 0, 0)$ is a unit vector in Euclidean 4-space.

Example 9   (for students who have studied calculus). Find the value of a, so that the polynomial $p(x) = ax - 1$ is a unit vector in P_1 with the integral inner product.

Recall that

$$\|p\| = (\langle p, p \rangle)^{1/2} = \left(\int_0^1 p^2(t)\,dt \right)^{1/2}$$

$$= \left[\int_0^1 (a^2 t^2 - 2at + 1)\,dt \right]^{1/2}$$

$$= \left\{ \frac{a^2 t^3}{3} - at^2 + t \bigg|_0^1 \right\}^{1/2} = \left(\frac{a^2}{3} - a + 1 \right)^{1/2}.$$

Hence $\|p\| = 1$ implies that

$$\frac{a^2}{3} - a + 1 = 1 \qquad \text{or} \qquad \frac{a^2}{3} - a = 0,$$

whence $a = 0$ or $a = 3$. Thus, -1 and $3x - 1$ are each unit vectors in P_1.

Not only are the vectors $(1, 0, 0)$, $(0, 1, 0)$, and $(0, 0, 1)$ unit vectors in $\mathbb{R}^3$, but they form a basis for $\mathbb{R}^3$ and are mutually orthogonal. Such a basis for a vector space is called an orthonormal basis. That is:

A basis $S = \{\mathbf{v}_1, \mathbf{v}_2, \ldots\}$ for a real inner-product space V is an **orthonormal basis** if both of the following conditions are satisfied:

i) every $\mathbf{v}_i$ in S is a unit vector,

ii) the members of S are pairwise orthogonal, that is, $\langle \mathbf{v}_i, \mathbf{v}_j \rangle = 0$ for $i \neq j$.

In the next section we shall develop a method for converting a given basis into an orthonormal basis.

EXERCISES (4.3)

Find the length of each of the following vectors in a Euclidean n-space $\mathbb{R}^n$ under the standard inner products.

1. $(1, 3)$ **2.** $(0, -1)$ **3.** $(1, -1, 1)$ **4.** $(0, 0, 0)$

5. $(1/\sqrt{3}, 1/\sqrt{3}, 1/\sqrt{3})$ **6.** $(-1/\sqrt{2}, 1/\sqrt{2}, 0)$ **7.** $(1, 1, 1, 1)$

8. $(1, 2, 3, 4, 5)$ **9.** $(0, 2, -2, 0, 1, -1)$ **10.** $(1, -1, 0, -1, 1, 3)$

11–20. Convert each of the vectors **v** in Exercises 1–10 to unit vectors $\mathbf{v}/\|\mathbf{v}\|$, if possible.

In Exercises 21–25, which of the following pairs of vectors are orthogonal with respect to the standard (Euclidean) inner product in $\mathbf{R}^m$?

21. $\mathbf{u} = (1, 3)$, $\mathbf{v} = (3, -1)$ **22.** $\mathbf{u} = (0, -1)$, $\mathbf{v} = (14, 0)$

23. $\mathbf{u} = (1, 0, -1)$, $\mathbf{v} = (2, 19, 2)$ **24.** $\mathbf{u} = (1, 0, -1, 0)$, $\mathbf{v} = (0, 5, 0, -2)$

25. $\mathbf{u} = (1, 1, 1, 1)$, $\mathbf{v} = (-1, 1, -1, 1)$

26. The vectors $(1, 0, x)$ and $(x, 1, 1-x)$ are orthogonal in $\mathbf{R}^3$ under the standard inner product. Find x.

27. Under the Euclidean inner product, find an orthonormal basis for $\mathbf{R}^4$.

28. Find all vectors orthogonal to $(1, 0, 1)$ in Euclidean 3-space $\mathbf{R}^3$.

29. Verify that the triangle inequality is satisfied by the vectors $(1, 1, 0)$ and $(0, 1, 1)$ in $\mathbf{R}^3$.

30. Verify that the Cauchy–Schwarz inequality is satisfied by the vectors $(1, 2, -1)$ and $(3, 5, -4)$ in $\mathbf{R}^3$.

31. Let $\mathbf{u} = (2, 1, -4)$ and $\mathbf{v} = (10, 5, -20)$. Verify that the Cauchy–Schwarz inequality holds for these vectors in $\mathbf{R}^3$. Does equality hold? Are **u** and **v** linearly dependent?

32. Suppose that a vector **v** in an arbitrary real inner-product space V has the property that $\langle \mathbf{v}, \mathbf{w} \rangle = 0$ for *all* vectors **w** in V. Prove that $\mathbf{v} = \mathbf{0}$.

33. Let V be an inner-product space and let **v** be a fixed vector in V. Let S be the set of all vectors **s** in V such that $\langle \mathbf{s}, \mathbf{v} \rangle = 0$. Prove that S is a subspace of V. Interpret the result geometrically for Euclidean 2-space $\mathbf{R}^2$ and for Euclidean 3-space $\mathbf{R}^3$.

34. When does the equality hold in the triangle inequality? Give reasons. Interpret the results geometrically for a Euclidean 2-space $\mathbf{R}^2$.

For students who have studied calculus: Consider the space P_3 of polynomials of degree 3 or less, with the integral inner product.

35. Which of the basis vectors $1, x, x^2, x^3$ is a unit vector?

36. Are x^2 and x^3 orthogonal vectors in this space?

37. Is the standard basis $S = \{1, x, x^2, x^3\}$ an orthonormal basis for P_3?

38. Find a vector $q(x)$ in P_3 that is orthogonal to x and has unit length.

Let V be a vector space over the field of complex numbers. We define a *complex inner product* as a unique complex number $\langle \mathbf{v}, \mathbf{u} \rangle$ assigned to each ordered pair of vectors **u** and **v** from V, such that

i) $\langle \mathbf{v}, \mathbf{u} \rangle$ is a complex number $\alpha + i\beta = \xi$,

ii) $\langle \mathbf{u}, \mathbf{v} \rangle = \langle \overline{\mathbf{v}, \mathbf{u}} \rangle$, where the bar denotes the complex conjugate $\alpha - i\beta = \overline{\xi}$.

iii) $\langle \mu\mathbf{u} + \nu\mathbf{v}, \mathbf{w} \rangle = \mu\langle \mathbf{u}, \mathbf{w} \rangle + \nu\langle \mathbf{v}, \mathbf{w} \rangle$ for all (complex) scalars μ and ν and vectors **u**, **v**, and **w**.

iv) $\langle \mathbf{u}, \mathbf{u} \rangle \geqslant 0$. *Note.* Property (ii) implies that $\langle \mathbf{u}, \mathbf{u} \rangle$ is real (see Exercise 39 below.)

v) $\langle \mathbf{u}, \mathbf{u} \rangle = 0$ if and only if $\mathbf{u} = \mathbf{0}$.

39. Verify that $\langle \mathbf{u}, \mathbf{u} \rangle$ is always real.

40. Verify that $\langle \mathbf{u}, \gamma \mathbf{v} \rangle = \bar{\gamma} \langle \mathbf{u}, \mathbf{v} \rangle$.

41. Verify the Cauchy–Schwarz inequality: $\langle \mathbf{u}, \mathbf{v} \rangle \overline{\langle \mathbf{u}, \mathbf{v} \rangle} \leqslant \langle \mathbf{u}, \mathbf{u} \rangle \langle \mathbf{v}, \mathbf{v} \rangle$.

4.4 GRAM–SCHMIDT PROCESS

In this section we describe a method known as the Gram–Schmidt process, by means of which we can convert a given basis for an inner-product space into an *orthonormal* basis.

We recall that an *orthonormal basis* for an inner-product space V is a basis $\mathbf{v}_1, \mathbf{v}_2, \ldots, \mathbf{v}_n$ that has the following two properties:

1. Every one of the vectors $\mathbf{v}_1, \mathbf{v}_2, \ldots, \mathbf{v}_n$ is a unit vector, that is, $\|\mathbf{v}_i\| = 1$ for each $i = 1, \ldots, n$.

2. Any two *distinct* vectors $\mathbf{v}_i$ are orthogonal, that is, $\langle \mathbf{v}_i, \mathbf{v}_j \rangle = 0$ whenever $i \neq j$.

The usefulness of an orthonormal basis for a vector space becomes apparent from the following calculations. Let V be any real inner-product space and let $S = \{\mathbf{v}_1, \mathbf{v}_2, \ldots, \mathbf{v}_n\}$ be *any* arbitrary basis for **V**. Let **u** and **w** be any two vectors in V. Then

$$\mathbf{u} = a_1 \mathbf{v}_1 + a_2 \mathbf{v}_2 + \ldots + a_n \mathbf{v}_n,$$
$$\mathbf{w} = b_1 \mathbf{v}_1 + b_2 \mathbf{v}_2 + \ldots + b_n \mathbf{v}_n,$$

because S is a basis. Therefore, using the properties of the inner product, we have

$$\begin{aligned}
\langle \mathbf{u}, \mathbf{w} \rangle &= \langle a_1 \mathbf{v}_1 + a_2 \mathbf{v}_2 + \ldots + a_n \mathbf{v}_n, b_1 \mathbf{v}_1 + b_2 \mathbf{v}_2 + \ldots + b_n \mathbf{v}_n \rangle \\
&= a_1 b_1 \langle \mathbf{v}_1, \mathbf{v}_1 \rangle + a_1 b_2 \langle \mathbf{v}_1, \mathbf{v}_2 \rangle + \ldots + a_1 b_n \langle \mathbf{v}_1, \mathbf{v}_n \rangle \\
&\quad + a_2 b_1 \langle \mathbf{v}_2, \mathbf{v}_1 \rangle + a_2 b_2 \langle \mathbf{v}_2, \mathbf{v}_2 \rangle + \ldots + a_2 b_n \langle \mathbf{v}_2, \mathbf{v}_n \rangle \\
&\quad + \ldots + a_n b_1 \langle \mathbf{v}_n, \mathbf{v}_1 \rangle + \ldots + a_n b_n \langle \mathbf{v}_n, \mathbf{v}_n \rangle.
\end{aligned} \tag{4.37}$$

Thus, the value of $\langle \mathbf{u}, \mathbf{w} \rangle$ for any two vectors in V is completely determined by the values of the inner products of the basis vectors, that is, by $\langle \mathbf{v}_i, \mathbf{v}_j \rangle$ for each $i = 1, 2, \ldots, n, j = 1, 2, \ldots, n$.

Example 1 The vectors $\mathbf{v}_1 = (1, 1)$ and $\mathbf{v}_2 = (1, -2)$ form a basis for a Euclidean 2-space $\mathbb{R}^2$. Suppose $\mathbf{u} = (2, 3)$ and $\mathbf{w} = (-1, 4)$. We have (verify this)

$$\mathbf{u} = \tfrac{7}{3}\mathbf{v}_1 - \tfrac{1}{3}\mathbf{v}_2 \quad \text{and} \quad \mathbf{w} = \tfrac{2}{3}\mathbf{v}_1 - \tfrac{5}{3}\mathbf{v}_2.$$

Now $\langle \mathbf{v}_1, \mathbf{v}_1 \rangle = 2$, $\langle \mathbf{v}_1, \mathbf{v}_2 \rangle = -1 = \langle \mathbf{v}_2, \mathbf{v}_1 \rangle$, and $\langle \mathbf{v}_2, \mathbf{v}_2 \rangle = 5$. Therefore,

$$
\begin{aligned}
\langle \mathbf{u}, \mathbf{w} \rangle &= (\tfrac{7}{3})(\tfrac{2}{3}) \langle \mathbf{v}_1, \mathbf{v}_1 \rangle + \tfrac{7}{3}(-\tfrac{5}{3}) \langle \mathbf{v}_1, \mathbf{v}_2 \rangle \\
&\quad + (\tfrac{2}{3})(-\tfrac{1}{3}) \langle \mathbf{v}_2, \mathbf{v}_1 \rangle + (-\tfrac{1}{3})(-\tfrac{5}{3}) \langle \mathbf{v}_2, \mathbf{v}_2 \rangle \\
&= \tfrac{14}{9} \cdot 2 - \tfrac{35}{9}(-1) - \tfrac{2}{9}(-1) + \tfrac{5}{9}(5) \\
&= \frac{28 + 35 + 2 + 25}{9} = \frac{90}{9} = 10.
\end{aligned}
$$

This very messy calculation (minimally messy because of dimension 2) is in marked contrast to the easy computation $\langle \mathbf{u}, \mathbf{w} \rangle = 2(-1) + 3(4) = 10$. This latter computation is, however, based on the same principle as the former, except that here

$$\mathbf{u} = 2(1, 0) + 3(0, 1), \qquad \mathbf{w} = -1(1, 0) + 4(0, 1),$$

and $\{(1, 0), (0, 1)\}$ is an *orthonormal* basis for $\mathbb{R}^2$. In fact, if $S = \{\mathbf{v}_1, \mathbf{v}_2, \ldots, \mathbf{v}_n\}$ is an orthonormal basis for the inner-product space V, then

$$\langle \mathbf{v}_i, \mathbf{v}_j \rangle = \begin{cases} 0 & \text{if } i \neq j, \\ 1 & \text{if } i = j, \end{cases} \tag{4.38}$$

so that Eq. (4.37) is reduced to

$$\langle \mathbf{u}, \mathbf{w} \rangle = a_1 b_1 + a_2 b_2 + \ldots + a_n b_n, \tag{4.39}$$

which closely resembles the *standard inner product* in $\mathbb{R}^n$. But remember that V is an *arbitrary* real inner-product space and $\langle \ \rangle$ is an *arbitrary* real inner product.

Let us summarize this as a theorem.

Theorem 4.6

Let V be any real inner-product space and let $S = \{\mathbf{v}_1, \mathbf{v}_2, \ldots, \mathbf{v}_n\}$ be an orthonormal basis for V. If

$$\mathbf{u} = a_1 \mathbf{v}_1 + a_2 \mathbf{v}_2 + \ldots + a_n \mathbf{v}_n \qquad \text{and} \qquad \mathbf{w} = b_1 \mathbf{v}_1 + b_2 \mathbf{v}_2 + \ldots + b_n \mathbf{v}_n$$

are any vectors in V, then

$$\langle \mathbf{u}, \mathbf{w} \rangle = a_1 b_1 + a_2 b_2 + \ldots + a_n b_n.$$

As a second and similar result, we state the following theorem whose proof is along the same lines. We leave the proof to you as Exercise 21.

Theorem 4.7

Let $S = \{\mathbf{v}_1, \mathbf{v}_2, \ldots, \mathbf{v}_n\}$ be an orthonormal basis for the real inner-product space V. Then for any $\mathbf{u}$ in V, we have

$$\mathbf{u} = \sum_{i=1}^{n} \langle \mathbf{u}, \mathbf{v}_i \rangle \mathbf{v}_i. \tag{4.40}$$

This theorem states that the coefficients, by means of which $\mathbf{u}$ is written as a linear combination of the basis vectors from an orthonormal basis for V, are precisely the values of the inner products, namely $\langle \mathbf{u}, \mathbf{v}_i \rangle$, $i = 1, \ldots, n$.

Example 2 Note that

$$\mathbf{v}_1 = \left(\frac{1}{\sqrt{2}}, 0, \frac{1}{\sqrt{2}} \right), \qquad \mathbf{v}_2 = \left(\frac{1}{\sqrt{3}}, \frac{1}{\sqrt{3}}, -\frac{1}{\sqrt{3}} \right), \qquad \mathbf{v}_3 = \left(-\frac{1}{\sqrt{6}}, \frac{2}{\sqrt{6}}, \frac{1}{\sqrt{6}} \right)$$

form an orthonormal basis for $\mathbb{R}^3$ (verify this). Then $\mathbf{u} = (2, -1, 5)$ can be written as $\mathbf{u} = c_1 \mathbf{v}_1 + c_2 \mathbf{v}_2 + c_3 \mathbf{v}_3$, and from (4.40) we get

$$c_1 = \langle \mathbf{u}, \mathbf{v}_1 \rangle = \frac{7}{\sqrt{2}}, \qquad c_2 = \langle \mathbf{u}, \mathbf{v}_2 \rangle = \frac{-4}{\sqrt{3}}, \qquad c_3 = \langle \mathbf{u}, \mathbf{v}_3 \rangle = \frac{1}{\sqrt{6}}.$$

Thus,

$$\mathbf{u} = \frac{7}{\sqrt{2}} \mathbf{v}_1 - \frac{4}{\sqrt{3}} \mathbf{v}_2 + \frac{1}{\sqrt{6}} \mathbf{v}_3.$$

Verify this by direct calculation.

If we have an inner-product space V and an *arbitrary* basis S, we can use the vectors in S to arrive at a new basis T for V, which is an orthonormal basis. This process is named for the Danish actuary Jörgen Pederson Gram (1850–1916) and the German mathematician Erhardt Schmidt (1876–1959). The **Gram-Schmidt process** generalizes the idea of projecting a given vector along another vector and also of projecting it orthogonal to the given vector. Let us first describe the two-dimensional case.

Consider two vectors $\mathbf{u}$ and $\mathbf{v}$, as depicted in Fig. 4.10. By dropping a perpendicular from the terminal point A of $\mathbf{u}$ to the line along $\mathbf{v}$, we determine the point B. The vector $\mathbf{w}_1 = \overrightarrow{OB}$ is called the **projection of u along v**. The vector $\mathbf{w}_2 = \overrightarrow{BA}$ is perpendicular to $\mathbf{w}_1$ and is called the **projection of u orthogonal to v**. Note that

$$\mathbf{w}_2 = \mathbf{u} - \mathbf{w}_1 \tag{4.41}$$

so $\mathbf{u} = \mathbf{w}_1 + \mathbf{w}_2$ is the sum of its projections *along* and *orthogonal* to $\mathbf{v}$.

Let us find algebraic descriptions for these projections. First of all, it is evident that $\mathbf{w}_1$ is a scalar multiple of $\mathbf{v}$. Thus, $\mathbf{w}_1 = a\mathbf{v}$ and $\mathbf{u} = a\mathbf{v} + \mathbf{w}_2$. Now consider

$$\langle \mathbf{u}, \mathbf{v} \rangle = \langle a\mathbf{v} + \mathbf{w}_2, \mathbf{v} \rangle = a \langle \mathbf{v}, \mathbf{v} \rangle + \langle \mathbf{w}_2, \mathbf{v} \rangle.$$

But $\mathbf{w}_2$ is orthogonal to $\mathbf{v}$, so $\langle \mathbf{w}_2, \mathbf{v} \rangle = 0$. Therefore, $\langle \mathbf{u}, \mathbf{v} \rangle = a \langle \mathbf{v}, \mathbf{v} \rangle$ and $a = \langle \mathbf{u}, \mathbf{v} \rangle / \langle \mathbf{v}, \mathbf{v} \rangle$. Hence,

$$\mathbf{w}_1 = \frac{\langle \mathbf{u}, \mathbf{v} \rangle}{\langle \mathbf{v}, \mathbf{v} \rangle} \mathbf{v}, \quad (\mathbf{v} \neq \mathbf{0}). \tag{4.42}$$

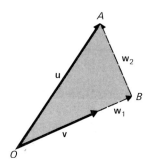

Figure 4.10

Substituting this in (4.41), we get that the projection of **u** orthogonal to **v** is

$$\mathbf{w}_2 = \mathbf{u} - \frac{\langle \mathbf{u}, \mathbf{v} \rangle}{\langle \mathbf{v}, \mathbf{v} \rangle} \mathbf{v}. \tag{4.43}$$

That $\mathbf{w}_2$ is indeed orthogonal to **v** is readily verified by calculating $\langle \mathbf{w}_2, \mathbf{v} \rangle$.

Example 3   Let $\mathbf{u} = (1, 3, -2)$ and $\mathbf{v} = (1, 0, 1)$. Find the projections of **u** along and orthogonal to **v**.

From (4.42), the projection of **u** *along* **v** is the vector

$$\mathbf{w}_1 = -\tfrac{1}{2}\mathbf{v} = (-\tfrac{1}{2}, 0, -\tfrac{1}{2}),$$

whereas the projection of **u** orthogonal to **v** is the vector

$$\mathbf{w}_2 = (1, 3, -2) - (-\tfrac{1}{2}, 0, -\tfrac{1}{2}) = (\tfrac{3}{2}, 3, -\tfrac{3}{2}).$$

Note now that if in (4.42) and (4.43) the vector **v** has unit length, that is, $\langle \mathbf{v}, \mathbf{v} \rangle = 1$, then (4.43) becomes

$$\mathbf{w}_2 = \mathbf{u} - \langle \mathbf{u}, \mathbf{v} \rangle \mathbf{v}. \tag{4.44}$$

Let us generalize this result to *n*-dimensions. The case of $n = 3$ is illustrated in Fig. 4.11.

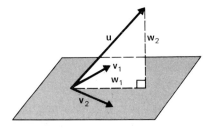

Figure 4.11

We have the following theorem, which is a fairly straightforward application of the discussion above. We omit the proof of the theorem.

Theorem 4.8

Let V be a real inner-product space and let $S = \{v_1, v_2, \ldots, v_k\}$ be a set of mutually orthogonal unit vectors from V. Let W be the subspace spanned by the set S, that is $W = L(S)$. Then any vector u in V can be written in the form $u = w_1 + w_2$, where w_1 is in W and w_2 is orthogonal to W (i.e., to every vector in W). This is accomplished by setting

$$w_1 = \langle u, v_1 \rangle v_1 + \langle u, v_2 \rangle v_2 + \ldots + \langle u, v_k \rangle v_k$$

and

$$w_2 = u - w_1.$$

Just as in the two- and three-dimensional cases, we call w_1 and w_2 the *components* of u in W and *orthogonal to* W, respectively. Note that the vector u is itself in the subspace W if and only if its component orthogonal to W is zero.

This theorem outlines the basic procedure used in the Gram–Schmidt process. In actually describing this process let us first focus our attention on the two-dimensional case once more. Then we will look at the three-dimensional case. The process continues to higher dimensions by the direct use of Theorem 4.8, as will be apparent.

Suppose that $\{v_1, v_2\}$ is a basis of an inner-product space V. Then $v_1 \neq 0$ (why?) and hence $\|v_1\| \neq 0$ (why?). Let

$$w_1 = \frac{v_1}{\|v_1\|}. \tag{4.45}$$

Then w_1 is the unit-vector basis for the one-dimensional subspace W. To see this, note that

$$\|w_1\| = \left\|\frac{v_1}{\|v_1\|}\right\| = \frac{1}{\|v_1\|} \cdot \|v_1\| = 1. \tag{4.46}$$

Now let w_2' be the component of the second-basis vector v_2 which is orthogonal to the subspace W spanned by w_1:

$$w_2' = v_2 - \langle w_1, v_2 \rangle w_1. \tag{4.47}$$

Can $w_2' = 0$? The answer is *no*. To prove it, suppose that $w_2' = 0$. Then by (4.47) and (4.45) we get

$$v_2 = \langle w_1, v_2 \rangle w_1 = \frac{\langle w_1, v_2 \rangle}{\|v_1\|} v_1. \tag{4.48}$$

In other words, if we assume that $w_2' = 0$, then, by (4.48), v_2 is a scalar multiple of v_1, which is impossible since $\mathbf{v}_1$, $\mathbf{v}_2$ are linearly independent (being a basis of V). Hence we conclude that $\mathbf{w}'_2 \neq \mathbf{0}$, and thus $||\mathbf{w}'_2|| \neq 0$ (why?).

Now, let $\mathbf{w}_2 = \mathbf{w}'_2/||\mathbf{w}'_2||$; hence $||\mathbf{w}_2|| = 1$ (why?).

The two unit vectors $\mathbf{w}_1$ and $\mathbf{w}_2$ form a linearly independent set of vectors in our two-dimensional vector space V. The set is, therefore, an orthonormal basis for V. We know this from Theorem 3.7; nevertheless, let us verify it by direct computation.

Note first that $\langle \mathbf{w}_1, \mathbf{w}_2 \rangle = 0$, and $||\mathbf{w}_1|| = 1$, $||\mathbf{w}_2|| = 1$. Moreover, if $\mathbf{x}$ is *any* vector in V, then

$$
\begin{aligned}
\mathbf{x} &= k_1 \mathbf{v}_1 + k_2 \mathbf{v}_2 \\
&= \{k_1 ||\mathbf{v}_1||\} \mathbf{w}_1 + k_2 \{\mathbf{w}'_2 + \langle \mathbf{w}_1, \mathbf{v}_2 \rangle \mathbf{w}_1\} \\
&= \{k_1 ||\mathbf{v}_1||\} \mathbf{w}_1 + k_2 \{||\mathbf{w}'_2|| \mathbf{w}_2 + \langle \mathbf{w}_1, \mathbf{v}_2 \rangle \mathbf{w}_1\};
\end{aligned}
$$

thus x is a linear combination of $\mathbf{w}_1$ and $\mathbf{w}_2$. We have shown that $\{\mathbf{w}_1, \mathbf{w}_2\}$ spans V; hence, it is an orthonormal basis of V.

Example 4 Let $\mathbf{v}_1 = (2, 3)$, $\mathbf{v}_2 = (-1, 4)$. Then,

$$
\mathbf{w}_1 = \frac{\mathbf{v}_1}{||\mathbf{v}_1||} = \frac{(2, 3)}{\sqrt{2^2 + 3^2}} = \frac{1}{\sqrt{13}} (2, 3).
$$

Note that

$$
\langle \mathbf{w}_1, \mathbf{v}_2 \rangle = \frac{1}{\sqrt{13}} \{(2)(-1) + (3)(4)\} = \frac{10}{\sqrt{13}}.
$$

Hence,

$$
\begin{aligned}
\mathbf{w}'_2 &= \mathbf{v}_2 - \langle \mathbf{w}_1, \mathbf{v}_2 \rangle \mathbf{w}_1 = (-1, 4) - \frac{10}{\sqrt{13}} \left(\frac{1}{\sqrt{13}} (2, 3) \right) \\
&= \left(-\frac{33}{13}, \frac{22}{13} \right).
\end{aligned}
$$

Therefore,

$$
\begin{aligned}
\mathbf{w}_2 &= \frac{\mathbf{w}'_2}{||\mathbf{w}'_2||} = \frac{1}{\sqrt{(-33/13)^2 + (22/13)^2}} \left(-\frac{33}{13}, \frac{22}{13} \right) \\
&= \frac{1}{\sqrt{1573}} (-33, 22).
\end{aligned}
$$

Thus

$$
\left\{ \frac{1}{\sqrt{13}} (2, 3), \frac{1}{\sqrt{1573}} (-33, 22) \right\}
$$

is an *orthonormal basis* of V.

This method can be extended step-by-step to the cases in which $n = 3, 4, 5$, etc., where n denotes the dimension of the inner-product space V. To illustrate, we construct an orthonormal basis for the case $n = 3$ and then indicate how Theorem 4.8 allows us to proceed step-by-step to $n = 4, 5$, etc.

Let $\{v_1, v_2, v_3\}$ be a given basis of V. Our construction involves essentially the following two steps:

Step 1. First, construct the orthonormal vectors w_1, w_2 exactly as we did when $n = 2$. Once this is done, define w_3' as the component of the vector v_3 orthogonal to the subspace W of V spanned by w_1 and w_2. Thus (see Theorem 4.8).

$$w_3' = v_3 - \langle w_1, v_3 \rangle w_1 - \langle w_2, v_3 \rangle w_2. \tag{4.49}$$

Step 2. We can argue as we did in the case of $n = 2$ and conclude that $w_3' \neq 0$. Thus $\| w_3' \| \neq 0$. Now define

$$w_3 = \frac{w_3'}{\| w_3' \|}. \tag{4.50}$$

Note that the formulas (4.49) and (4.50) tell us *how to extend the previously obtained orthonormal vectors w_1, w_2 into an orthonormal basis $\{w_1, w_2, w_3\}$ of V, when $n = 3$.*

Example 5 Let $v_1 = (1, -1, 0)$, $v_2 = (-1, 0, 1)$, and $v_3 = (0, 1, 1)$. Convert the basis $\{v_1, v_2, v_3\}$ of Euclidean 3-space V into an orthonormal basis.

Solution. It can be verified that $\{v_1, v_2, v_3\}$ is indeed a basis of V (check this). Now,

$$\|v_1\| = \sqrt{1^2 + (-1)^2 + 0^2} = \sqrt{2}.$$

Hence, by (4.45),

$$w_1 = \frac{v_1}{\|v_1\|} = \frac{1}{\sqrt{2}}(1, -1, 0),$$

that is,

$$w_1 = \frac{1}{\sqrt{2}}(1, -1, 0).$$

Also,

$$\langle w_1, v_2 \rangle = \frac{1}{\sqrt{2}}\{(1)(-1) + (-1)(0) + (0)(1)\} = -\frac{1}{\sqrt{2}};$$

hence,

$$w_2' = v_2 - \langle w_1, v_2 \rangle w_1 = (-1, 0, 1) + \frac{1}{\sqrt{2}}\left(\frac{1}{\sqrt{2}}(1, -1, 0)\right)$$

$$= (-\tfrac{1}{2}, -\tfrac{1}{2}, 1).$$

Thus,

$$\|\mathbf{w}_2'\| = \sqrt{(-\tfrac{1}{2})^2 + (-\tfrac{1}{2})^2 + 1^2} = \sqrt{\tfrac{3}{2}},$$

so

$$\mathbf{w}_2 = \frac{\mathbf{w}_2'}{\|\mathbf{w}_2'\|} = \sqrt{\tfrac{2}{3}}(-\tfrac{1}{2}, -\tfrac{1}{2}, 1).$$

Finally, to determine $\mathbf{w}_3$, we first find $\mathbf{w}_3'$. To this end, note that (verify this)

$$\langle \mathbf{w}_1, \mathbf{v}_3 \rangle = -\frac{1}{\sqrt{2}}; \qquad \langle \mathbf{w}_2, \mathbf{v}_3 \rangle = \sqrt{\frac{2}{3}} \cdot \frac{1}{2} = \frac{1}{\sqrt{6}},$$

and hence we see that

$$\mathbf{w}_3' = \mathbf{v}_3 - \langle \mathbf{w}_1, \mathbf{v}_3 \rangle \mathbf{w}_1 - \langle \mathbf{w}_2, \mathbf{v}_3 \rangle \mathbf{w}_2$$

$$= (0, 1, 1) + \frac{1}{2}(1, -1, 0) - \frac{1}{\sqrt{6}} \sqrt{\frac{2}{3}}\left(-\frac{1}{2}, -\frac{1}{2}, 1\right)$$

$$= \left(\frac{2}{3}, \frac{2}{3}, \frac{2}{3}\right).$$

Since

$$\|\mathbf{w}_3'\| = \sqrt{\left(\frac{2}{3}\right)^2 + \left(\frac{2}{3}\right)^2 + \left(\frac{2}{3}\right)^2} = \frac{2}{\sqrt{3}},$$

the vector $\mathbf{w}_3$ is

$$\mathbf{w}_3 = \frac{\sqrt{3}}{2}\left(\frac{2}{3}, \frac{2}{3}, \frac{2}{3}\right) = \left(\frac{1}{\sqrt{3}}, \frac{1}{\sqrt{3}}, \frac{1}{\sqrt{3}}\right).$$

The vectors $\mathbf{w}_1, \mathbf{w}_2, \mathbf{w}_3$ form an orthonormal basis for V.

The general case. Let $\{\mathbf{v}_1, \mathbf{v}_2, \mathbf{v}_3, \ldots, \mathbf{v}_n\}$ be a given basis of V and suppose that we have already constructed, step-by-step, *orthonormal vectors* $\mathbf{w}_1, \mathbf{w}_2, \mathbf{w}_3, \ldots, \mathbf{w}_{n-1}$ having the same linear span as $\{\mathbf{v}_1, \mathbf{v}_2, \ldots, \mathbf{v}_{n-1}\}$. Call this subspace W. To construct $\mathbf{w}_n$, define first $\mathbf{w}_n'$ as the component of $\mathbf{v}_n$ orthogonal to W as indicated in Theorem 4.8:

$$\mathbf{w}_n' = \mathbf{v}_n - \langle \mathbf{w}_1, \mathbf{v}_n \rangle \mathbf{w}_1 - \langle \mathbf{w}_2, \mathbf{v}_n \rangle \mathbf{w}_2 - \langle \mathbf{w}_3, \mathbf{v}_n \rangle \mathbf{w}_3 - \ldots - \langle \mathbf{w}_{n-1}, \mathbf{v}_n \rangle \mathbf{w}_{n-1}.$$
$$(4.51)$$

Next, from the fact that $\{\mathbf{w}_1, \ldots, \mathbf{w}_{n-1}\}$ and $\{\mathbf{v}_1, \ldots, \mathbf{v}_{n-1}\}$ have the same linear span W, it follows that $\mathbf{w}_n' \neq \mathbf{0}$ and hence $\|\mathbf{w}_n'\| \neq 0$.

Now define $\mathbf{w}_n$ as $\mathbf{w}_n = \mathbf{w}_n'/\|\mathbf{w}_n'\|$. Then $\{\mathbf{w}_1, \mathbf{w}_2, \ldots, \mathbf{w}_n\}$ is an orthonormal basis for V. (Why?)

EXERCISES (4.4)————————————————————————

In Exercises 1–8, convert the given basis for $\mathbb{R}^n$ into an orthonormal basis with respect to the Euclidean (standard) inner product in $\mathbb{R}^n$.

1. $\mathbf{v}_1 = (1, 1),\quad \mathbf{v}_2 = (2, 3)$ 2. $\mathbf{v}_1 = (0, -4),\quad \mathbf{v}_2 = (3, 0)$

3. $\mathbf{v}_1 = (-1, 4),\quad \mathbf{v}_2 = (0, 5)$ 4. $\mathbf{v}_1 = (1, -2),\quad \mathbf{v}_2 = (1, 2)$

5. $\mathbf{v}_1 = (1, 0, 1),\quad \mathbf{v}_2 = (0, 1, 1),\quad \mathbf{v}_3 = (1, 1, 0)$

6. $\mathbf{v}_1 = (0, 1, 1),\quad \mathbf{v}_2 = (0, 0, -1),\quad \mathbf{v}_3 = (-1, -1, -1)$

7. $\mathbf{v}_1 = (1, 1, 0, 0),\quad \mathbf{v}_2 = (0, -1, 0, 0),\quad \mathbf{v}_3 = (1, 0, 0, 1),\quad \mathbf{v}_4 = (0, 0, 1, 1)$

8. $\mathbf{v}_1 = (1, 0, 1, 0),\quad \mathbf{v}_2 = (0, 1, 0,1),\quad \mathbf{v}_3 = (1, 0, -1, 0),\quad \mathbf{v}_4 = (1, -1, -1, 1)$

9. Let $V = \mathbb{R}^3$ (cartesian 3-space) under the inner product

$$\langle (a_1, a_2, a_3), (b_1, b_2, b_3) \rangle = a_1 b_1 + 2a_2 b_2 + \tfrac{1}{2} a_3 b_3.$$

Convert the basis of Exercise 5 into an orthonormal basis with respect to this inner product.

10. Let V be the inner-product space of Exercise 9. Construct an orthonormal basis for V that includes the vector

$$\mathbf{v} = \left(\frac{1}{2}, \frac{\sqrt{6}}{4}, 0 \right).$$

11. Let $V = P_3$ be the space of polynomials with the inner product of Example 4 in Section 4.2. Is the standard basis $\{1, x, x^2, x^3\}$ orthonormal?

12. In the inner-product space of Exercise 11, find an orthonormal basis that includes the polynomial

$$p(x) = \frac{1 + x + x^2}{\sqrt{3}}.$$

13. In the inner-product space of Exercise 11, find an orthonormal basis that includes the appropriate scalar multiple of the polynomial $1 - x^2$.

14. Suppose that $\mathbf{v}_1, \mathbf{v}_2, \mathbf{v}_3$ are any *nonzero* vectors in an inner-product space V, and suppose $\langle \mathbf{v}_1, \mathbf{v}_2 \rangle = \langle \mathbf{v}_1, \mathbf{v}_3 \rangle = \langle \mathbf{v}_2, \mathbf{v}_3 \rangle = 0$. Prove that $\{\mathbf{v}_1, \mathbf{v}_2, \mathbf{v}_3\}$ is linearly independent.

15. Generalize Problem 14 to the case of n *nonzero* vectors $\mathbf{v}_1, \mathbf{v}_2, \ldots, \mathbf{v}_n$. Prove your assertions.

16. A set $S = \{\mathbf{v}_1, \mathbf{v}_2, \ldots, \mathbf{v}_n\}$ is called *orthonormal* if each vector $\mathbf{v}_i$ is of unit length and if $\langle \mathbf{v}_i, \mathbf{v}_j \rangle = 0$ for all *distinct* vectors $\mathbf{v}_i, \mathbf{v}_j$ in S. Prove that any orthonormal set is linearly independent. *Hint.* Assume $\alpha_1 \mathbf{v}_1 + \alpha_2 \mathbf{v}_2 + \ldots + \alpha_n \mathbf{v}_n = \mathbf{0}$. Consider

$$\langle \alpha_1 \mathbf{v}_1 + \alpha_2 \mathbf{v}_2 + \ldots + \alpha_n \mathbf{v}_n, \mathbf{v}_i \rangle \text{ for } i = 1, 2, \ldots, n.$$

Problems 17–20 are for students who have studied calculus. Consider the inner-product space P_n under the integral inner product.

17. Find a "standard" orthonormal basis for P_2.

18. Find an orthonormal basis for P_1 that includes a scalar multiple of the polynomial $p(x) = x + 2$.

19. Find an orthonormal basis for P_1 that includes a scalar multiple of the polynomial $q(x) = 3x + 2$.

20. Find an orthonormal basis for P_2 that includes a scalar multiple of the polynomial $h(x) = 2x + 1$.

21. Prove Theorem 4.7.

4.5 APPLICATION—LEAST SQUARES FIT

To construct a mathematical model describing the results of an experiment often involves "fitting" a curve to the given data. Suppose, for example, that in an experiment in mechanics we displace a spring by attaching various weights to it and then measure the amount of displacement (Fig. 4.12). Suppose the results are as indicated in the following table. Let us plot this data in Fig. 4.13.

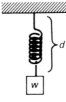

Figure 4.12

Weight w, lbs	Displacement d, in.
2	4.18
3	6.31
4	8.26
5	11.10
10	20.82

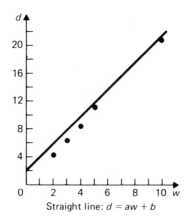

Straight line: $d = aw + b$

Figure 4.13

As we have indicated, the points in the table appear to almost lie along the straight line sketched in the figure. That they do not is attributable to one or both of the following factors: experimental errors in measurement or the spring displacement is not linear.

Let us suppose that, for various reasons, we disregard the second factor. The data "appear" to be nearly linear. Then our job is to determine the line that in some sense fits the data best.

Other data plots might best be approximated by other types of curves; we have indicated three different possibilities in Fig. 4.14. In each case the idea would be to choose the curve (by finding the coefficients) that fits the obtained data best. Let us first concentrate on fitting a straight line.

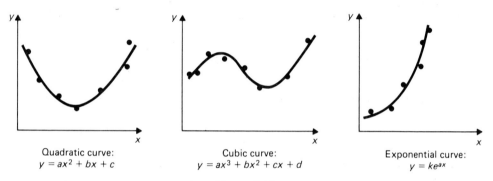

Quadratic curve:
$y = ax^2 + bx + c$

Cubic curve:
$y = ax^3 + bx^2 + cx + d$

Exponential curve:
$y = ke^{ax}$

Figure 4.14

Let us assume that n data points are experimentally determined:

$$(x_1, y_1), (x_2, y_2), \ldots, (x_n, y_n). \tag{4.52}$$

Through these points, we wish to find a straight line $y = ax + b$. If these points do indeed lie on the line, we have the following equations in the two unknown coefficients a and b:

$$
\begin{aligned}
y_1 &= ax_1 + b, \\
y_2 &= ax_2 + b, \\
&\ \ \vdots \\
y_n &= ax_n + b,
\end{aligned}
$$

or in matrix notation,

$$
\begin{bmatrix} y_1 \\ y_2 \\ \vdots \\ y_n \end{bmatrix} = \begin{bmatrix} x_1 & 1 \\ x_2 & 1 \\ \vdots & \vdots \\ x_n & 1 \end{bmatrix} \begin{bmatrix} a \\ b \end{bmatrix}. \tag{4.53}
$$

We abbreviate this by $Y = MS$, with S and Y the appropriate column vectors:

$$S = \begin{bmatrix} a \\ b \end{bmatrix}, \quad Y = [y_1, y_2, \ldots, y_n]^t.$$

If the given n data points (4.52) are collinear, then the system (4.53) has a unique solution $S = \begin{bmatrix} a \\ b \end{bmatrix}$. But if the points are not collinear, this system is inconsistent. Because the data points are experimentally obtained, this will be the usual case. We wish to find S, then, so that the difference between Y and MS is small. That is, we wish the Euclidean distance

$$\| Y - MS \| \tag{4.54}$$

to be small. Here we consider $\overline{\mathbb{R}}^n$, the space of n-dimensional column vectors, to be an inner-product space under the standard (Euclidean) inner product (see Example 6 of Section 4.2).

If $S' = \begin{bmatrix} a' \\ b' \end{bmatrix}$ is a vector such that (4.54) is a minimum, then the straight line

$$y = a'x + b'$$

is called the *least-squares fit* to the data. To justify this name, we note that minimizing $\| Y - MS' \|$ is the same as minimizing its square

$$\| Y - MS' \|^2 = (y_1 - a'x_1 - b')^2 + (y_2 - a'x_2 - b')^2 + \ldots + (y_n - a'x_n - b')^2.$$

From Fig. 4.15 we see that $d_i = | y_i - a'x_i - b' |$ is the vertical distance from the data point (x_i, y_i) and the point (x_i, y_i') on the line $y = a'x + b'$.

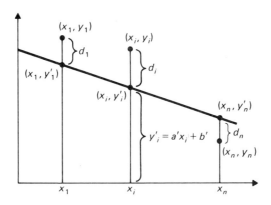

Figure 4.15

Thus the least-squares fit will minimize the sum of the squares of the vertical errors

$$d_1^2 + d_2^2 + \ldots + d_n^2.$$

To calculate the vector S' that does this, we note that Y is a fixed vector in $\overline{\mathbb{R}}^n$, and as S varies over all possible values, the vectors MS form a subspace of $\overline{\mathbb{R}}^n$, the column space W of the matrix M. That is,

$$MS = a \begin{bmatrix} x_1 \\ x_2 \\ \vdots \\ x_n \end{bmatrix} + b \begin{bmatrix} 1 \\ 1 \\ \vdots \\ 1 \end{bmatrix}.$$

It can be shown that if $Y - MS'$ is to have a minimum length, it must be orthogonal to this subspace W of $\overline{\mathbb{R}}^n$, that is the inner product

$$\langle MS, \ Y - MS' \rangle = (MS)^t (Y - MS')$$

must be zero for all S. Since $(MS)^t = (S)^t M^t$, we have

$$0 = (S)^t M^t (Y - MS') = (S)^t (M^t Y - M^t MS'). \tag{4.55}$$

Equation (4.55) states that the inner product $\langle S, M^t Y - M^t MS' \rangle = 0$ for *every* *vector* S. But then the fixed vector $M^t Y - M^t MS'$ must be the zero vector (why?). Hence,

$$M^t Y = M^t MS'. \tag{4.56}$$

Since M^t is a $2 \times n$ matrix, $M^t M$ is 2×2 (see Eq. (4.53)). Thus, if $M^t M$ is invertible, Eq. (4.56) has the solution

$$S' = (M^t M)^{-1} M^t Y. \tag{4.57}$$

Except for when the n data points given in (4.52) lie in a vertical line ($x_i = x_j$; $i, j = 1, 2, \ldots, n$) $M^t M$ is invertible (verify this as Exercise 12). Thus, (4.57) yields the vector $S' = \begin{bmatrix} a' \\ b' \end{bmatrix}$ that gives the coefficients of the line: $y = a'x + b'$. This is the least-squares fit to the data points of (4.52).

Example 1 Find the straight line that is the least-squares fit to the four points $(0, 2)$, $(1, 3)$, $(2, 5)$, $(3, 7)$.

To do this, we note that (4.53) becomes

$$\begin{bmatrix} 2 \\ 3 \\ 5 \\ 7 \end{bmatrix} = \begin{bmatrix} 0 & 1 \\ 1 & 1 \\ 2 & 1 \\ 3 & 1 \end{bmatrix} \begin{bmatrix} a \\ b \end{bmatrix},$$

$$Y = MS.$$

Hence

$$M^t M = \begin{bmatrix} 14 & 6 \\ 6 & 4 \end{bmatrix}, \qquad (M^t M)^{-1} = \begin{bmatrix} 0.2 & -0.3 \\ -0.3 & 0.7 \end{bmatrix}.$$

Therefore, from (4.57) we have

$$S' = (M^t M)^{-1} M^t Y$$

$$= \begin{bmatrix} 0.2 & -0.3 \\ -0.3 & 0.7 \end{bmatrix} \begin{bmatrix} 0 & 1 & 2 & 3 \\ 1 & 1 & 1 & 1 \end{bmatrix} \begin{bmatrix} 2 \\ 3 \\ 5 \\ 7 \end{bmatrix}$$

$$= \begin{bmatrix} 0.2 & -0.3 \\ -0.3 & 0.7 \end{bmatrix} \begin{bmatrix} 34 \\ 17 \end{bmatrix} = \begin{bmatrix} 1.7 \\ 1.7 \end{bmatrix},$$

so the desired line is $y = 1.7x + 1.7$.

Example 2 Find the line that is the least-squares fit to the data points of Fig. 4.12. From the table we obtain:

$$\begin{bmatrix} 4.18 \\ 6.31 \\ 8.26 \\ 11.10 \\ 20.82 \end{bmatrix} = \begin{bmatrix} 2 & 1 \\ 3 & 1 \\ 4 & 1 \\ 5 & 1 \\ 10 & 1 \end{bmatrix} \begin{bmatrix} a \\ b \end{bmatrix},$$

$$Y = MS,$$

so that

$$M^t M = \begin{bmatrix} 154 & 24 \\ 24 & 5 \end{bmatrix}, \qquad (M^t M)^{-1} = \frac{1}{194} \begin{bmatrix} 5 & -24 \\ -24 & 154 \end{bmatrix},$$

$$M^t Y = \begin{bmatrix} 324.03 \\ 50.67 \end{bmatrix}.$$

Thus,

$$S' = (M^t M)^{-1} M^t Y = \frac{1}{194} \begin{bmatrix} 404.07 \\ 26.46 \end{bmatrix} = \begin{bmatrix} 2.08 \\ 0.14 \end{bmatrix}.$$

The least-squares fit is, therefore, $d = 2.08w + 0.14$. Thus, according to Hooke's law, the spring constant is 2.08 lbs/in.

The method just used to find the straight line that is the least-squares fit to a set of data points can be generalized readily to apply to any function of the form

$$y = a_1 x_1 + a_2 x_2 + \ldots + a_n x_n. \tag{4.58}$$

Substituting the m data points $(x_{1i}, x_{2i}, \ldots, x_{ni}, y_i)$ into (4.58) yields a system of equations that can be written as follows:

$$
\begin{bmatrix} y_1 \\ y_2 \\ \vdots \\ y_m \end{bmatrix} = \begin{bmatrix} x_{11} & x_{21} & \cdots & x_{n1} \\ x_{12} & x_{22} & \cdots & x_{n2} \\ \vdots & \vdots & \vdots & \vdots \\ x_{1m} & x_{2m} & \cdots & x_{nm} \end{bmatrix} \begin{bmatrix} a_1 \\ a_2 \\ \vdots \\ a_n \end{bmatrix}.
$$
(4.59)

or

$$ Y = MS. $$

By the same argument, the minimizing vector S' is given by

$$ S' = (M^t M)^{-1} M^t Y. $$

In particular, if (4.58) is a polynomial of degree n:

$$ y = a_n x^n + a_{n-1} x^{n-1} + \ldots + a_1 x + a_0 $$

and the data points are (x_i, y_i), $i = 1, 2, \ldots, m$, we would have

$$
M = \begin{bmatrix} x_1^n & x_1^{n-1} & \cdots, & x_1 & 1 \\ x_2^n & x_2^{n-1} & \cdots, & x_2 & 1 \\ \vdots & \vdots & \vdots & & \vdots \\ x_m^n & x_m^{n-1} & \cdots, & x_m & 1 \end{bmatrix} \quad \text{with} \quad S = \begin{bmatrix} a_n \\ a_{n-1} \\ \vdots \\ a_1 \\ a_0 \end{bmatrix}.
$$
(4.60)

Example 3   Find the quadratic polynomial $y = ax^2 + bx + c$ that is the least-squares fit to the data points $(-2, 3), (-1, 1), (0, 2), (1, 3), (2, 5)$. Substituting these data points, we obtain

$$
\begin{bmatrix} 3 \\ 1 \\ 2 \\ 3 \\ 5 \end{bmatrix} = \begin{bmatrix} 4 & -2 & 1 \\ 1 & -1 & 1 \\ 0 & 0 & 1 \\ 1 & 1 & 1 \\ 4 & 2 & 1 \end{bmatrix} \begin{bmatrix} a \\ b \\ c \end{bmatrix},
$$

$$ Y = MS. $$

Thus,

$$
M^t M = \begin{bmatrix} 34 & 0 & 10 \\ 0 & 10 & 0 \\ 10 & 0 & 5 \end{bmatrix} \quad \text{and} \quad (M^t M)^{-1} = \begin{bmatrix} \frac{1}{14} & 0 & -\frac{1}{7} \\ 0 & \frac{1}{10} & 0 \\ -\frac{1}{7} & 0 & \frac{17}{35} \end{bmatrix},
$$

whence

$$
S' = \begin{bmatrix} a' \\ b' \\ c' \end{bmatrix} = \begin{bmatrix} \frac{1}{14} & 0 & -\frac{1}{7} \\ 0 & \frac{1}{10} & 0 \\ -\frac{1}{7} & 0 & \frac{17}{35} \end{bmatrix} \begin{bmatrix} 4 & 1 & 0 & 1 & 4 \\ -2 & -1 & 0 & 1 & 2 \\ 1 & 1 & 1 & 1 & 1 \end{bmatrix} \begin{bmatrix} 3 \\ 1 \\ 2 \\ 3 \\ 5 \end{bmatrix}
$$

$$
= \begin{bmatrix} \frac{1}{14} & 0 & -\frac{1}{7} \\ 0 & \frac{1}{10} & 0 \\ -\frac{1}{7} & 0 & \frac{17}{35} \end{bmatrix} \begin{bmatrix} 36 \\ 6 \\ 14 \end{bmatrix}
$$

$$
= \begin{bmatrix} \frac{4}{7} \\ \frac{3}{5} \\ \frac{58}{35} \end{bmatrix}
$$

Therefore the quadratic polynomial that gives the least-squares fit to these data points is

$$
y = \tfrac{4}{7}x^2 + \tfrac{3}{5}x + \tfrac{58}{35} = \tfrac{1}{35}[20x^2 + 21x + 58].
$$

Example 4 It has been observed that in an egg-production program the number y of eggs laid per day seems to be related to the amounts of two feed constants x_1 and x_2 by a linear equation of the form

$$
y = c_1 x_1 + c_2 x_2,
$$

where c_1 and c_2 are constants. To determine the relationship, a research program is undertaken in which the amounts x_1 and x_2 are varied. The results are as given in the following table:

x_1	x_2	y
1	0	4
0	1	5
1	1	6
2	1	5
1	2	4

Find the best approximation to the constants using the least-squares fit.

By substituting the given data points we obtain the matrix equation

$$\begin{bmatrix} 4 \\ 5 \\ 6 \\ 5 \\ 4 \end{bmatrix} = \begin{bmatrix} 1 & 0 \\ 0 & 1 \\ 1 & 1 \\ 2 & 1 \\ 1 & 2 \end{bmatrix} \begin{bmatrix} c_1 \\ c_2 \end{bmatrix},$$

$$Y = MS.$$

Therefore,

$$M^t M = \begin{bmatrix} 7 & 5 \\ 5 & 7 \end{bmatrix} \quad \text{and} \quad (M^t M)^{-1} = \begin{bmatrix} \frac{7}{24} & -\frac{5}{24} \\ -\frac{5}{24} & \frac{7}{24} \end{bmatrix}.$$

So

$$S' = \begin{bmatrix} c_1' \\ c_2' \end{bmatrix} = \begin{bmatrix} \frac{7}{24} & -\frac{5}{24} \\ -\frac{5}{24} & \frac{7}{24} \end{bmatrix} \begin{bmatrix} 1 & 0 & 1 & 2 & 1 \\ 0 & 1 & 1 & 1 & 2 \end{bmatrix} \begin{bmatrix} 4 \\ 5 \\ 6 \\ 5 \\ 4 \end{bmatrix} = \begin{bmatrix} 2 \\ 2 \end{bmatrix}.$$

Therefore $y = 2x_1 + 2x_2$ is the best least-squares-fit.

EXERCISES (4.5)

Find the straight line that is the least-squares fit to the following sets of data points:

1. $(1, 1)$, $(2, 2)$, $(3, 4)$ **2.** $(0, 3)$, $(1, 5)$, $(2, 9)$

3. $(0, 1.1)$, $(1, 2.4)$, $(2, 3.7)$ **4.** $(0, -1.6)$, $(1, -0.8)$, $(2, 3.5)$, $(3, 4.2)$

Find the quadratic $y = ax^2 + bx + c$ that is the least-squares fit to the following sets of data points:

5. $(-2, 1)$, $(-1, 3)$, $(0, 5)$, $(1, 4)$ **6.** $(-2, -1)$, $(-1, 2)$, $(0, 4)$, $(1, 1)$, $(2, -3)$.

7. $(0, -1.6)$, $(1, 0.8)$, $(2, 3.5)$, $(3, 4.2)$, $(4, 0.3)$

8. Find the cubic polynomial $y = ax^3 + bx^2 + cx + d$ that is the least-squares fit to the data points: $(-2, -8)$, $(-1, -1)$, $(0, 3)$, $(1, 1)$, $(2, -1)$, $(3, 0)$.

9. If $x_1, x_2, \ldots, x_m$ are linearly independent vectors in the real inner-product space V, then the $m \times m$ matrix $M = (k_{ij})$, where $k_{ij} = \langle x_i, x_j \rangle$, is called the *Gram matrix* associated with the x_i. Let v_j denote the jth column vector of M, that is,

$$v_j = [k_{1j}, k_{2j}, \ldots, k_{mj}]^t.$$

Suppose that $c_1 \mathbf{v}_1 + c_2 \mathbf{v}_2 + \ldots + c_m \mathbf{v}_m = \mathbf{0}$. Show that

$$0 = \sum_{j=1}^{m} c_j \langle \mathbf{x}_i, \mathbf{x}_j \rangle, \qquad i = 1, 2, \ldots, m.$$

10. With the concepts and notation of Exercise 9, let

$$\mathbf{u} = c_1 \mathbf{x}_1 + c_2 \mathbf{x}_2 + \ldots + c_m \mathbf{x}_m.$$

Show that $\langle \mathbf{x}_i, \mathbf{u} \rangle = 0$ for $i = 1, 2, \ldots, m$. Explain why $\mathbf{u} = \mathbf{0}$ and therefore the column vectors of M are linearly independent.

11. Show that if M is any $n \times n$ matrix with linearly independent column vectors, then $M^t M$ is an $n \times n$ nonsingular matrix.

12. Show that the matrix M in (4.53) has linearly independent columns if and only if at least two of the numbers $x_1, x_2, \ldots, x_n$ are distinct. Conclude from this that $M^t M$ is nonsingular if and only if the data points (4.52) do not lie in a vertical line in the xy-plane.

13. The owner of a business finds that his sales for the first five months of the year are 3.8, 4.2, 4.9, 5.3, 5.1 (in thousands of dollars). Plot these data points. Do they seem to lie on the graph of a. parabola?

14. Use the data in Exercise 13 to determine a quadratic $y = ax^2 + bx + c$ that is the least-squares fit.

5 LINEAR TRANSFORMATIONS

In this chapter we study linear transformations from a vector space U to a vector space V and their properties. In particular we discuss the kernel and range of a linear transformation, the matrix representation of a linear transformation, and orthogonal linear transformations.

5.1 DEFINITION AND EXAMPLES

You will recall from your previous mathematics courses that the concept of function is of primary importance. After spending the preceding two chapters discussing the internal structure of vector spaces, we turn now to functions dealing with transformations from one vector space to another. Remember that any function is made up of three things: two sets, the *domain* and *codomain*, and a *rule of correspondence* (Fig. 5.1). Thus:

If U is a set and V is a set, then a **function** f from U into V is a rule that associates with each member u of U a unique member $f(u)$ of V.

The set of all elements of the form $f(u)$ is called the **range** of f. Observe that the range of a function f is always contained in the codomain of f.

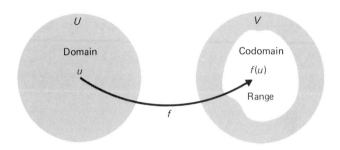

Figure 5.1

When the range of f is *exactly equal* to the codomain of f we say that the function f is **onto**. In other words, a function f from U to V is **onto** if every element v in V is of the form $v = f(u)$ for a suitably chosen element u in U.

Another useful concept is that of a one-to-one function.

A function f from U to V is *one-to-one* if distinct elements x, y in U have distinct function values $f(x), f(y)$ in V. Another way of saying this is the following: f is **one-to-one** if $f(x) = f(y)$ always implies that $x = y$ (where x, y are in U).

In calculus you dealt largely with a one-dimensional situation in which $U = V = R$ (the set of real numbers). We need now to lift our thoughts out of the one-dimensional world and consider multidimensional functions. The words **transformation** and **mapping** are used as synonyms for *function* when working with a multidimensional domain.

Example 1 Let U and V both be the Euclidean plane and let T be the transformation (function) that sends each point P: (a, b) of the plane to the point $T(P)$: $(2a, 2b)$. Thus, we stretch everything in U by a factor of 2 (see Fig. 5.2 for a diagram of this transformation). Note that the square region $ABCD$ in U is transformed into the square region $T(A)T(B)T(C)T(D)$ by T. In vector notation, if we consider $U = V = \mathbb{R}^2$ to be Euclidean 2-space, we have $T(\mathbf{u}) = 2\mathbf{u}$ for each vector $\mathbf{u}$ in U.

Example 2 Let U be 3-space and let V be the xy-plane. Consider T to be the transformation that projects every point in U into the xy-plane. We have indicated this projection T in Fig. 5.3.

Note that $T(a, b, c) = (a, b)$ for each vector $\mathbf{u} = (a, b, c)$ in $\mathbb{R}^3$. Thus each vector $\mathbf{u}$ in $\mathbb{R}^3$ is essentially projected orthogonally onto $\mathbb{R}^2$ considered as a subspace of $\mathbb{R}^3$ (see Section 4.4). Hence,

$$T(\mathbf{u}) = \langle \mathbf{u}, \mathbf{e}_1 \rangle \mathbf{e}_1 + \langle \mathbf{u}, \mathbf{e}_2 \rangle \mathbf{e}_2,$$

where $\mathbf{e}_1$ and $\mathbf{e}_2$ are the standard basis vectors for $\mathbb{R}^2$ in $\mathbb{R}^3$.

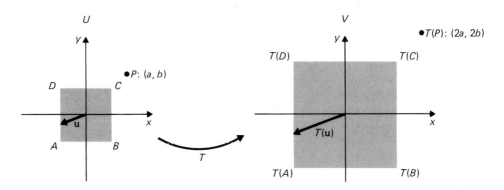

Figure 5.2

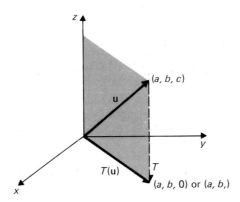

Figure 5.3

The transformations of Examples 1 and 2 have special properties distinguishing them from other transformations between vector spaces. We note that in both examples it is true that

$$T(\mathbf{u} + \mathbf{v}) = T(\mathbf{u}) + T(\mathbf{v}), \quad \text{and} \quad T(a\mathbf{u}) = aT(\mathbf{u}) \tag{5.1}$$

for *all* vectors $\mathbf{u}$ and $\mathbf{v}$ in U and *all* scalars a. You can quickly verify this for Example 1 (see also Example 3). In the case of the transformation in Example 2, let

$$\mathbf{u} = (u_1, u_2, u_3) \quad \text{and} \quad \mathbf{v} = (v_1, v_2, v_3).$$

Then $\mathbf{u} + \mathbf{v} = (u_1 + v_1, u_2 + v_2, u_3 + v_3)$; therefore,

$$T(\mathbf{u}) = (u_1, u_2), \quad T(\mathbf{v}) = (v_1, v_2), \quad \text{and} \quad T(\mathbf{u} + \mathbf{v}) = (u_1 + v_1, u_2 + v_2),$$

so $T(\mathbf{u} + \mathbf{v}) = T(\mathbf{u}) + T(\mathbf{v})$. Also note that $a\mathbf{u} = (au_1, au_2, au_3)$, so

$$T(a\mathbf{u}) = (au_1, au_2) = a(u_1, u_2) = aT(\mathbf{u}).$$

Not all transformations possess properties (5.1). For example, suppose we translate each point (a, b) in the Euclidean plane to the point $(a + 1, b + 1)$ (see Fig. 5.4).

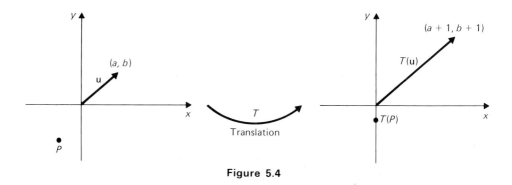

Figure 5.4

Note that, if $\mathbf{u} = (u_1, u_2)$ and $\mathbf{v} = (v_1, v_2)$, then

$$T(\mathbf{u}) = (u_1 + 1, u_2 + 1) \qquad \text{and} \qquad T(\mathbf{v}) = (v_1 + 1, v_2 + 1).$$

Therefore, $T(\mathbf{u} + \mathbf{v}) = (u_1 + v_1 + 1, u_2 + v_2 + 1)$. This is *not* the same as

$$T(\mathbf{u}) + T(\mathbf{v}) = (u_1 + 1, u_2 + 1) + (v_1 + 1, v_2 + 1)$$
$$= (u_1 + v_1 + 2, u_2 + v_2 + 2).$$

Transformations between vector spaces U and V that do satisfy *both* properties of (5.1) are called *linear transformations*. The transformation of Fig. 5.4 is *not linear*, because it fails to satisfy the first of these (actually it fails to satisfy the second property also). Formally we have the following *definition*:

Let U and V be any two (real) vector spaces. A **function** $T: U \to V$ from U into V is called a **linear transformation** if and only if for all vectors $\mathbf{u}$ and $\mathbf{v}$ in U and scalars (real numbers) a we have:

$$T(\mathbf{u} + \mathbf{v}) = T(\mathbf{u}) + T(\mathbf{v}),$$
$$T(a\mathbf{u}) = aT(\mathbf{u}). \tag{5.2}$$

We shall devote the rest of this section to examples of linear transformations. Note that the first property states that we obtain the same result if we add two vectors in U and then transform the resultant to a vector of V as if we had transformed the two vectors separately and then added their two images as vectors in V. What is the interpretation of the second property?

Example 3 Let $U = V = \mathbb{R}^2$ be Euclidean 2-space (i.e., a plane); and consider the transformation for $\mathbf{u} = (u_1, u_2)$ (see Fig. 5.5):

$$T(\mathbf{u}) = T(u_1, u_2) = (2u_1, -u_2).$$

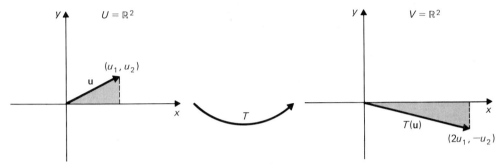

Figure 5.5

Observe that, if $\mathbf{u} = (u_1, u_2)$ and $\mathbf{v} = (v_1, v_2)$ are any two vectors in U, then

$$T(\mathbf{u}) = (2u_1, -u_2) \quad \text{and} \quad T(\mathbf{v}) = (2v_1, -v_2),$$

so that

$$\begin{aligned} T(\mathbf{u} + \mathbf{v}) &= T(u_1 + v_1, u_2 + v_2) = (2(u_1 + v_1), -(u_2 + v_2)) \\ &= (2u_1 + 2v_1, -u_2 - v_2) = (2u_1, -u_2) + (2v_1, -v_2) \\ &= T(\mathbf{u}) + T(\mathbf{v}). \end{aligned}$$

Also for any scalar (real number) a we get

$$\begin{aligned} T(a\mathbf{u}) &= T(au_1, au_2) = (2au_1, -au_2) \\ &= a(2u_1, -u_2) = aT(\mathbf{u}). \end{aligned}$$

Since this transformation T satisfies both properties listed in the definition, it is a *linear transformation* from $\mathbb{R}^2$ to $\mathbb{R}^2$.

Remark. In the above example we denoted $T((u_1, u_2))$ by $T(u_1, u_2)$ to simplify the notation. Generally speaking, we shall continue to use this simplification in the notation.

It is not difficult to show that the definition of linear transformation given above is equivalent to the following *alternative form* (see Exercise 14).

Theorem 5.1
A function $T: U \to V$ is a linear transformation if and only if T has the following

property: For all vectors **x**, **y** *in U and all scalars k, l,*

$$T(k\mathbf{x} + l\mathbf{y}) = kT(\mathbf{x}) + lT(\mathbf{y}). \tag{5.3}$$

This alternative form of the definition of a linear transformation is often convenient to use in verifying that a particular function T is indeed a linear transformation.

Example 4 Let $U = \mathbb{R}^2$ (a plane, as in Example 3) and $V = \mathbb{R}^3$ (3-space); define $T: U \to V$ by

$$T(x_1, x_2) = (x_1, -x_2, x_1 - x_2).$$

You should have no trouble verifying that, for all vectors $\mathbf{u} = (x_1, x_2), \mathbf{u}' = (x'_1, x'_2)$ in $\mathbb{R}^2$ and all scalars k, k',

$$\begin{aligned} T(k\mathbf{u} + k'\mathbf{u}') &= T(k(x_1, x_2) + k'(x'_1, x'_2)) \\ &= kT((x_1, x_2)) + k'T((x'_1, x'_2)) \\ &= kT(\mathbf{u}) + k'T(\mathbf{u}'). \end{aligned}$$

Hence, T is a linear transformation.

Example 5 The function $T: U \to U$ defined by $T(\mathbf{x}) = \mathbf{x}$ for all $\mathbf{x}$ in U is readily seen to be a linear transformation. It is called the *identity linear transformation* and is usually denoted by I.

Example 6 The function $T: U \to U$ defined by $T(\mathbf{x}) = \mathbf{0}$ for all $\mathbf{x}$ in U is again easily seen to be a linear transformation. This linear transformation "collapses" the vector space U into the zero vector and is called the *zero linear transformation*; it is denoted by 0.

Example 7 Let A be any $m \times n$ real matrix. We define a function $T: \overline{\mathbb{R}^n} \to \overline{\mathbb{R}^m}$ from the vector space of column n-tuples to the space of column m-tuples by

$$T(X) = AX.$$

This T is also a linear transformation, as you can verify by the properties of matrix multiplication. In particular, if

$$A = \begin{bmatrix} 1 & 2 & 0 & 3 \\ 0 & 1 & 8 & 1 \\ -1 & 0 & 5 & 0 \end{bmatrix} \quad \text{and} \quad X = \begin{bmatrix} x_1 \\ x_2 \\ x_3 \\ x_4 \end{bmatrix},$$

we have

$$T(X) = AX = \begin{bmatrix} 1 & 2 & 0 & 3 \\ 0 & 1 & 8 & 1 \\ -1 & 0 & 5 & 0 \end{bmatrix} \begin{bmatrix} x_1 \\ x_2 \\ x_3 \\ x_4 \end{bmatrix} = \begin{bmatrix} x_1 + 2x_2 + 3x_4 \\ x_2 + 8x_3 + x_4 \\ -x_1 + 5x_3 \end{bmatrix}.$$

Thus, for example,

$$T\left(\begin{bmatrix} 1 \\ 0 \\ -1 \\ 2 \end{bmatrix}\right) = \begin{bmatrix} 7 \\ -6 \\ -6 \end{bmatrix}.$$

We shall call the linear transformation in this example *multiplication by A.* Linear transformations of this kind are called **matrix transformations**.

Example 8   As a special case of Example 7, let θ be a fixed angle and let $T_\theta: \mathbb{R}^2 \to \mathbb{R}^2$ be multiplication by the matrix

$$A = \begin{bmatrix} \cos\theta & -\sin\theta \\ \sin\theta & \cos\theta \end{bmatrix}.$$

If X is the vector

$$X = \begin{bmatrix} x \\ y \end{bmatrix},$$

then

$$T_\theta(X) = AX = \begin{bmatrix} \cos\theta & -\sin\theta \\ \sin\theta & \cos\theta \end{bmatrix} \begin{bmatrix} x \\ y \end{bmatrix} = \begin{bmatrix} x\cos\theta - y\sin\theta \\ x\sin\theta + y\cos\theta \end{bmatrix}.$$

Geometrically, if $\mathbb{R}^2$ is identified with the plane, then $T_\theta(X)$ is the vector that results from rotating through the angle θ (see Fig. 5.6).

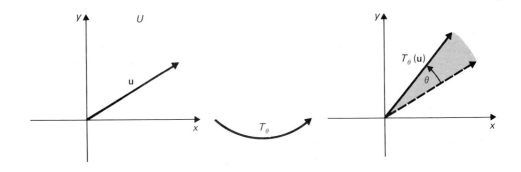

Figure 5.6

You can verify that this is indeed a rotation of $\mathbb{R}^2$ through the angle θ. (see Exercise 24.)

Example 9   Consider the function $T: \mathbb{R}^3 \rightarrow P_2$ from Euclidean 3-space to the vector space of polynomials of degree two or less given by $T(a, b, c) = ax^2 + bx + c$. It is easily verified that this is also a linear transformation.

Example 10   Show that the transformation $T: \mathbb{R}^3 \rightarrow \mathbb{R}^3$ given by $T(x, y, z) = (x, 1, 1)$ is *not linear*.

   Although T is surely a transformation (function) from $\mathbb{R}^3$ to $\mathbb{R}^3$ (because the description clearly assigns a unique vector $T(\mathbf{u})$ to each vector $\mathbf{u}$), it fails to be linear. To see this for $\mathbf{u} = (x, y, z)$ and k any real number, note that

$$T(k\mathbf{u}) = T(kx, ky, kz) = (kx, 1, 1) \neq k(x, 1, 1) \quad \text{when} \quad k \neq 1.$$

Example 11   (For students who have studied calculus) The properties of the derivative of a function show that the transformation D from the vector space of differentiable functions to the space of all functions given by

$$D(f) = \frac{df}{dx} = f'$$

is a linear transformation (see Exercise 25). Under this transformation, $D(x^2) = 2x$, $D(\sin x) = \cos x$, etc. Moreover, it is also true that the transformation L from the space of integrable functions to the space of real numbers given by

$$L(f) = \int_0^1 f(x)dx$$

is a linear transformation (see Exercise 29).

EXERCISES (5.1)

In Exercises 1–9, find which of the given functions $T: U \rightarrow V$ (where $U = V = \mathbb{R}^2$) are linear transformations; here $\mathbf{u} = (x_1, x_2)$ represents an arbitrary vector in $\mathbb{R}^2$.

1. $T(x_1, x_2) = (-x_1, x_2)$ **2.** $T(x_1, x_2) = (x_1 + 1, x_2)$

3. $T(x_1, x_2) = (x_1, x_2 - 2)$ **4.** $T(x_1, x_2) = (x_1, x_1)$

5. $T(x_1, x_2) = (2x_1, -3x_2)$ **6.** $T(x_1, x_2) = (x_1 + 2x_2, -x_1 + 3x_2)$

7. $T(x_1, x_2) = (2x_1 - 5x_2, 0)$

8. $T(x_1, x_2) = (x_1 + 5x_2, x_2)$; this linear transformation is called a *shear*.

9. $T(x_1, x_2) = (5x_1, x_2)$; this linear transformation is called a *dilation*.

10. Show that the function T in Example 1 is a linear transformation.

11. Show that the function T in Example 4 is a linear transformation.

12. Show that the function T in Example 5 is a linear transformation.

13. Show that the function T in Example 6 is a linear transformation.

14. Prove that the definition of a linear transformation given by Theorem 5.1 is equivalent to the definition originally given. *Hint.* In proving that the second definition implies the first definition, note that $T(x + y) = T(1 \cdot x + 1 \cdot y)$, etc.

15. Let $T: \mathbb{R}^2 \to \mathbb{R}^2$ be defined by $T(x_1, x_2) = (0, x_2)$. Show that T is a linear transformation.

16. Consider the transformation $T: \mathbb{R}^n \to \mathbb{R}^m$ of Example 7.
    a) Verify that if A is any fixed $m \times n$ matrix, then $T(X) = AX$ is linear.
    b) Use the matrix A given in Example 7 to compute $T(X)$ for both

$$X = \begin{bmatrix} 1 \\ 1 \\ 0 \\ 1 \end{bmatrix} \quad \text{and} \quad X = \begin{bmatrix} 1 \\ 2 \\ 3 \\ 5 \end{bmatrix}.$$

17. Let A be a fixed $n \times n$ matrix. Verify that, if X is any $n \times n$ matrix, then the function $T_A(X) = AX - XA$ is a linear transformation on the vector space M_n of $n \times n$ matrices.

18. Let $S = \{\mathbf{u}_1, \mathbf{u}_2, \ldots, \mathbf{u}_n\}$ be a basis for the vector space U and let $T: U \to V$ be a linear transformation. Show that if $V = U$ and $T(\mathbf{u}_i) = \mathbf{u}_i$ for each $i = 1, 2, \ldots, n$, then T is the identity transformation on U.

19. If $T: U \to V$ and $S = \{\mathbf{u}_1, \mathbf{u}_2, \ldots, \mathbf{u}_n\}$ are as in Exercise 18, show that for each $\mathbf{u}$ in U, $T(\mathbf{u})$ is a linear combination of the vectors $T(\mathbf{u}_i)$, $i = 1, 2, \ldots, n$, in V.

20. In the notation of Exercises 18 and 19, does the set $T(S) = \{T(\mathbf{u}_1), \ldots, T(\mathbf{u}_n)\}$ necessarily span V? Give reasons.

21. Let U, V, S, T, and $T(S)$ be as in Exercises 18–20. Prove that the set $T(S)$ spans a subspace W of V.

22. Is the set $T(S)$ in Exercise 21 necessarily a basis for W? Why?

23. Verify that matrix transformations (as in Example 7) are indeed linear transformations from $\mathbb{R}^n$ to $\mathbb{R}^m$.

24. Verify that the transformation of Example 8 is a rotation of the plane through the angle θ. *Hint.* Consider the angle ϕ between the vector $\mathbf{v}$ and the positive x-axis and denote $\|\mathbf{v}\|$ by r. Show that, if $\mathbf{v} = (x, y)$, then $x = r \cos \phi$ and $y = r \sin \phi$. Consider $T(\mathbf{v})$.

Exercises 25–30 are for students who have studied calculus.

25. Prove that the differential operator $D(f) = f'$ is a linear transformation from the vector space K of all functions f with continuous first derivatives on the closed interval $[a, b]$ into the space C of all functions continuous on $[a, b]$.

26. Let D^2 and D^3 denote the second and the third derivatives, respectively, and let f be a vector from the vector space M of all functions with continuous first, second, and third derivatives.
    Show that the transformation $T: M \to C$ given by $T(f) = D^3 - 2D^2 + D$ is linear.

27. Compute $T(x^3 - 3x + 1)$ for the transformation T of Exercise 26.

28. Let D^k denote the kth derivative. Show that the operator

$$P = D^n + a_{n-1} D^{n-1} + \ldots + a_1 D$$

is linear for real numbers a_i, $i = 1, 2, \ldots, n - 1$.

29. Show that the integral operator L of Example 11 is a linear transformation.

30. Compute $L(x^3 - 3x + 1)$.

5.2 KERNEL AND RANGE OF A LINEAR TRANSFORMATION

In this section we single out two subspaces, known as the *kernel* and *range* of a linear transformation, and briefly discuss their properties. We begin by showing that a linear transformation always takes zero to zero in the following sense:

Theorem 5.2
If $T: U \to V$ is a linear transformation of a vector space U into vector space V, then $T(0) = 0$.

To prove this theorem note that since $0 + 0 = 0$, therefore

$$T(0 + 0) = T(0). \tag{5.4}$$

But, by the definition of a linear transformation,

$$T(0 + 0) = T(0) + T(0). \tag{5.5}$$

Combining (5.4) and (5.5), we get $T(0) + T(0) = T(0)$, and hence $T(0) = 0$ (why?).

Theorem 5.2 shows us that a linear transformation $T: U \to V$ always takes the zero vector of U to the zero vector of V. It may well happen that $T(x) = 0$ even when $x \neq 0$ (see Example 6 of Section 5.1 for the extreme case where every x goes to 0). What can we say about those vectors x in U that satisfy the equation $T(x) = 0$? It turns out that these vectors x form a *subspace* of U. Before proving this, however, we first introduce some terminology to describe these vectors.

Let $T: U \to V$ be a linear transformation of a vector space U into a vector space V. The set of all vectors x in U such that $T(x) = 0$ is called the **kernel** of T. It is also called the **null space** of T by many authors. Consider the following example.

Example 1 Let $U = V = \mathbb{R}^2$ be Euclidean 2-space (i.e., the plane) and let $T: U \to V$ be defined by

$$T(x_1, x_2) = (x_1, 0). \tag{5.6}$$

We leave it to you to verify that this T, known as a *projection*, is a linear transformation. What is the kernel of this projection? The answer is (verify this):

Kernel of T = Set of all vectors $(0, x_2)$, where x_2 is real.

In other words, the kernel of the linear transformation "*projection on the subspace spanned by* $\{x_1\}$" is the set of all points on the x_2-axis.

Note that this kernel is indeed a subspace of V. This is not a coincidence, as the following theorem asserts:

Theorem 5.3
The kernel K of a linear transformation $T: U \to V$ is always a subspace of U.

To prove this theorem, we recall that, by Theorem 3.3, it suffices to prove that (i) the kernel K is not empty, (ii) it is closed with respect to vector addition, and (iii) it is closed with respect to scalar multiplication. To prove this, first note that, by Theorem 5.2, $T(\mathbf{0}) = \mathbf{0}$ and hence $\mathbf{0}$ is in the kernel K of T; thus K is not empty. Next, suppose that $\mathbf{x}$ and $\mathbf{y}$ are both in K. Then, by definition of kernel,

$$T(\mathbf{x}) = \mathbf{0} \quad \text{and} \quad T(\mathbf{y}) = \mathbf{0}. \tag{5.7}$$

Using (5.7) and the fact that T is a linear transformation, we get

$$T(\mathbf{x} + \mathbf{y}) = T(\mathbf{x}) + T(\mathbf{y}) = \mathbf{0} + \mathbf{0} = \mathbf{0}.$$

We have thus shown that $T(\mathbf{x} + \mathbf{y}) = \mathbf{0}$ and hence $\mathbf{x} + \mathbf{y}$ is in the kernel K. Now suppose k is a scalar and the vector $\mathbf{x}$ is in the kernel K of T. Then $T(\mathbf{x}) = \mathbf{0}$ and hence (give reasons)

$$T(k\mathbf{x}) = kT(\mathbf{x}) = k \cdot \mathbf{0} = \mathbf{0};$$

that is $T(k\mathbf{x}) = \mathbf{0}$. Thus $k\mathbf{x}$ is in the kernel K. Therefore, the kernel K is a subspace of U. This proves the theorem.

Example 2   Let $T: \mathbb{R}^3 \to \mathbb{R}^2$ be the transformation $T(x, y, z) = (x - y, x - z)$. If $\mathbf{u} = (x, y, z)$ belongs to the kernel of T, then $T(\mathbf{u}) = \mathbf{0}$. That is, $(x - y, x - z) = (0, 0)$. Therefore, $x - y = 0$, $x - z = 0$. Hence $x = y = z$, so that each vector in the kernel of T is a scalar multiple of the vector $\mathbf{v} = (1, 1, 1)$. This vector forms a basis for the kernel K of the transformation T. Therefore K is a one-dimensional subspace of $\mathbb{R}^3$.

The kernel of a transformation is a subspace of the *domain* U of the transformation. Let us now focus our attention on the *codomain* V of the transformation $T: U \to V$.

Example 3   Let $T: \mathbb{R}^3 \to \mathbb{R}^4$ be the transformation $T(x, y, z) = (x + y, 0, x + z, 0)$. Describe those vectors in $\mathbb{R}^4$ that are images of vectors in $\mathbb{R}^3$ under this transformation T.

From the definition of T we can see immediately that those vectors in $\mathbb{R}^4$ that have nonzero second or fourth components, such as $(1, -1, 1, 1)$, cannot be images $T(\mathbf{u})$ of any vector $\mathbf{u}$ in $\mathbb{R}^3$ under the transformation T. Just which vectors $(a, 0, b, 0)$ are these images?

We seek numbers a and b such that $a = x + y$ and $b = x + z$. For every two

For every two
real numbers a and b, the vector

$$(a, 0, b, 0) = a(1, 0, 0, 0) + b(0, 0, 1, 0) \tag{5.8}$$

is $T(\mathbf{u})$, where $\mathbf{u} = (b - 1, a - b + 1, 1)$ is a vector in $\mathbb{R}^3$. In fact, for each real number t, if $\mathbf{u}_t = (b - t, a - b + t, t)$, then $T(\mathbf{u}_t) = (a, 0, b, 0)$. At any rate, those vectors in $\mathbb{R}^4$ that are images under T of vectors in $\mathbb{R}^3$ have the form (5.8). Therefore, they form a two-dimensional subspace of $\mathbb{R}^4$, namely the linear span of the two vectors $(1, 0, 0, 0)$ and $(0, 0, 1, 0)$. Let us give a name to this collection of images.

Let $T: U \rightarrow V$ be a linear transformation of a vector space U into a vector space V. The set of all vectors $T(\mathbf{x})$ in V (where $\mathbf{x}$ is in U) is called the **range** (or **image**) of T.

In other words, the range of T is the set of all vectors in V of the form $T(\mathbf{x})$, where $\mathbf{x}$ is in U.

The *kernel* of T is a subspace of the *domain* U. The *range* of T is a subspace of the *codomain* V. You should have no trouble proving this last fact as Theorem 5.4. The diagram in Fig. 5.7 summarizes this.

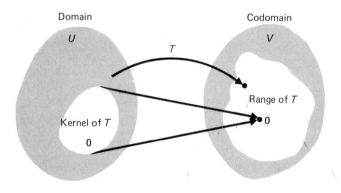

Figure 5.7

Theorem 5.4

The range of a linear transformation $T: U \rightarrow V$ is a subspace of V.

The following example illustrates the range.

Example 4 Consider again the projection linear transformation $T: U \rightarrow V$ in Example 1. In view of (5.6), we see that the range of T is the set of all vectors $(x_1, 0)$, where x_1 is real. Thus the range of T is precisely the set of all points on the x_1-axis. Note that this is a *subspace* of $\mathbb{R}^2$.

Example 5   Find the range of the transformation T of Example 2.

Here we have $T: \mathbb{R}^3 \to \mathbb{R}^2$ with (a, b) in $\mathbb{R}^2$ being the image $T(\mathbf{u})$ of a vector $\mathbf{u} = (x, y, z)$ in $\mathbb{R}^3$ when $a = x - y$ and $b = x - z$.

But this system of equations has augmented matrix

$$\begin{bmatrix} 1 & -1 & 0 & a \\ 1 & 0 & -1 & b \end{bmatrix},$$

which is equivalent to

$$\begin{bmatrix} 1 & 0 & -1 & b \\ 0 & 1 & -1 & b-a \end{bmatrix}.$$

Therefore, every (a, b) in $\mathbb{R}^2$ is the image $T(\mathbf{u})$ of a vector

$$\mathbf{u} = (b + t, \, b - a + t, \, t)$$

in $\mathbb{R}^3$ for all t. Thus all of $\mathbb{R}^2$ is the range of T.

In Example 3 we found the range of the given transformation. Its kernel is all vectors in $\mathbb{R}^3$ of the form $(x, -x, -x)$, as you can readily verify. These vectors are spanned by the vector $(1, -1, -1)$. So the kernel of the transformation in Example 3 has dimension one.

It is instructive to take a closer look at the results of these examples. We summarize them in the following table:

Examples	Linear transformation	Kernel	Range
1 and 4	$T(x_1, x_2) = (x_1, 0)$	$x_2(0, 1)$	$x_1(1, 0)$
2 and 5	$T(x, y, z) = (x - y, x - z)$	$x(1, 1, 1)$	$a(1, 0) + b(0, 1)$
3	$T(x, y, z) = (x + y, 0, x + z, 0)$	$x(1, -1, -1)$	$a(1, 0, 0, 0) + b(0, 0, 1, 0)$

Note that in each case the dimension of the kernel plus the dimension of the range is equal to the dimension of the domain of T. This, it turns out, is always the case for a linear transformation. We have the following theorem whose proof we append at the end of this section.

Theorem 5.5

Let $T: U \to V$ be a linear transformation. Then,

Dimension of kernel of T + Dimension of range of T

$$= \textit{Dimension of domain } U \textit{ of } T.$$

As a further illustration of Theorem 5.5, consider the following example.

Example 6   Let $T: \mathbb{R}^4 \to \mathbb{R}^3$ be given by

$$T(x_1, x_2, x_3, x_4) = (0, x_1 - x_2, x_3 - x_4).$$

Then $T(x_1, x_2, x_3, x_4) = \mathbf{0}$ if and only if $x_1 - x_2 = 0$ and $x_3 - x_4 = 0$, that is, if $x_1 = x_2$ and $x_3 = x_4$. Thus vectors $\mathbf{u} = (a, a, b, b)$ form the kernel of T. These are spanned by $(1, 1, 0, 0)$ and $(0, 0, 1, 1)$, so the dimension of the kernel of T is 2. Those vectors $\mathbf{v}$ in $\mathbb{R}^3$ that are images $T(\mathbf{x})$ of vectors $\mathbf{x}$ in $\mathbb{R}^4$ must have zero first component. However, given any vector of the form $(0, s, t)$ in $\mathbb{R}^3$, you can verify that it is the image of at least the vector $(s, 0, t, 0)$ in $\mathbb{R}^4$. Hence it lies in the range of T, thus the dimension of the range of T is 2. Therefore, as indicated in Theorem 5.5,

Dimension of kernel of $T +$ Dimension of range of T

$$= \text{Dimension of } \mathbb{R}^4.$$

Example 7   Let $T_A: \mathbb{R}^n \to \mathbb{R}^m$ be multiplication by the $m \times n$ matrix A, where $A = (a_{ij})$, $i = 1, 2, \ldots, m$; $j = 1, 2, \ldots, n$. The kernel of T_A consists of all those column vectors

$$X = \begin{bmatrix} x_1 \\ x_2 \\ \vdots \\ x_n \end{bmatrix},$$

that are solutions to the equation $AX = 0$, that is, to the homogeneous system of equations

$$a_{11}x_1 + a_{12}x_2 + \ldots + a_{1n}x_n = 0,$$
$$a_{21}x_1 + a_{22}x_2 + \ldots + a_{2n}x_n = 0,$$
$$\vdots \qquad\qquad\qquad \vdots$$
$$a_{m1}x_1 + a_{m2}x_2 + \ldots + a_{mn}x_n = 0.$$

This is the *solution space* of this system.

The range of T_A consists of all column vectors

$$B = \begin{bmatrix} b_1 \\ b_2 \\ \vdots \\ b_m \end{bmatrix}$$

such that $AX = B$, that is, such that the system $AX = B$ is consistent. Hence, it is composed of those vectors B that lie in the *column space* of A.

We noted earlier that the kernel of a linear transformation T is often called the *null space* of T. The dimension of the kernel (or null space) of T is called the **nullity** of T. Also, the dimension of the range subspace of T is called the **rank** of T.

Accordingly, we may restate Theorem 5.5 in the following short form:

$$\text{Nullity of } T + \text{Rank of } T = \text{Dimension of domain of } T.$$

This fact is also known as *Sylvester's law of nullity*.

Suppose now that U has the set of vectors $S = \{\mathbf{u}_1, \mathbf{u}_2, \ldots, \mathbf{u}_n\}$ as a basis. If $\mathbf{u}$ is any vector in U, then $\mathbf{u}$ can be written as a linear combination of the basis vectors:

$$\mathbf{u} = a_1 \mathbf{u}_1 + a_2 \mathbf{u}_2 + \ldots + a_n \mathbf{u}_n. \tag{5.9}$$

If $T: U \rightarrow V$ is a linear transformation, then

$$\begin{aligned} T(\mathbf{u}) &= T(a_1 \mathbf{u}_1 + a_2 \mathbf{u}_2 + \ldots + a_n \mathbf{u}_n) \\ &= a_1 T(\mathbf{u}_1) + a_2 T(\mathbf{u}_2) + \ldots + a_n T(\mathbf{u}_n). \end{aligned} \tag{5.10}$$

Therefore, *the action of T on U is determined completely by its action on a basis of U. The vectors $T(\mathbf{u}_1)$, $T(\mathbf{u}_2)$, $\ldots$, $T(\mathbf{u}_n)$ span the range of T in V.* They may not be a basis, however, since we are not certain that they are linearly independent. The set

$$\begin{aligned} T(1, 0, 0, 0) &= (0, 1, 0), \\ T(0, 1, 0, 0) &= (0, -1, 0), \\ T(0, 0, 1, 0) &= (0, 0, 1), \\ T(0, 0, 0, 1) &= (0, 0, -1) \end{aligned}$$

of images of the standard basis for $\mathbb{R}^4$ under the transformation T of Example 6 is a spanning set for the range of T but is not a basis. To find a basis for the range of T we need, in this case, merely write the vectors $T(\mathbf{u}_i)$ as the rows of a matrix and row-reduce it as we did in Chapter 3. Therefore,

$$\begin{bmatrix} 0 & 1 & 0 \\ 0 & -1 & 0 \\ 0 & 0 & 1 \\ 0 & 0 & -1 \end{bmatrix} \rightarrow \begin{bmatrix} 0 & 1 & 0 \\ 0 & 0 & 1 \\ 0 & 0 & 0 \\ 0 & 0 & 0 \end{bmatrix}$$

shows that the range of this T is spanned by the two vectors $(0, 1, 0)$ and $(0, 0, 1)$ and has dimension two, as we noted in Example 6.

Example 8   Let $T_A: \mathbb{R}^4 \rightarrow \mathbb{R}^3$ be multiplication by the matrix

$$A = \begin{bmatrix} 1 & 1 & -1 & 2 \\ 2 & 1 & 4 & 3 \\ 5 & 6 & 1 & 9 \end{bmatrix}$$

(see Example 7). Find a basis for the range of T_A and a basis for the kernel of T_A.

Let us see what T_A does to a basis for $\overline{\mathbb{R}}^4$. We have

$$T_A(e_1) = A \begin{bmatrix} 1 \\ 0 \\ 0 \\ 0 \end{bmatrix} = \begin{bmatrix} 1 \\ 2 \\ 5 \end{bmatrix}, \qquad T_A(e_2) = A \begin{bmatrix} 0 \\ 1 \\ 0 \\ 0 \end{bmatrix} = \begin{bmatrix} 1 \\ 1 \\ 6 \end{bmatrix},$$

$$T_A(e_3) = A \begin{bmatrix} 0 \\ 0 \\ 1 \\ 0 \end{bmatrix} = \begin{bmatrix} -1 \\ 4 \\ 1 \end{bmatrix}, \qquad T_A(e_4) = A \begin{bmatrix} 0 \\ 0 \\ 0 \\ 1 \end{bmatrix} = \begin{bmatrix} 2 \\ 3 \\ 9 \end{bmatrix}.$$

Note that these vectors are the columns of the matrix A. In the next section we shall show that this always happens.

To find a basis for the range, we write the matrix $M = A^t$ and row-reduce it to the matrix N:

$$M = \begin{bmatrix} 1 & 2 & 5 \\ 1 & 1 & 6 \\ -1 & 4 & 1 \\ 2 & 3 & 9 \end{bmatrix} \rightarrow N = \begin{bmatrix} 1 & 0 & 0 \\ 0 & 1 & 0 \\ 0 & 0 & 1 \\ 0 & 0 & 0 \end{bmatrix}.$$

Thus, the range of T_A has dimension three, and is spanned by the three standard basis vectors for $\overline{\mathbb{R}}^3$. To find a basis for the kernel of T_A we seek vectors X in $\overline{\mathbb{R}}^4$ such that $AX = 0$. The augmented matrix for this system is $[A:0]$. Since row-reduction of this matrix will not affect the last column of zeros, we need only row-reduce A. This A is row-equivalent to

$$C = \begin{bmatrix} 1 & 0 & 0 & \frac{11}{6} \\ 0 & 1 & 0 & 0 \\ 0 & 0 & 1 & -\frac{1}{6} \end{bmatrix}.$$

Therefore,

$$\text{if} \quad \begin{cases} x_1 = -\frac{11}{6}x_4, \\ x_2 = 0, \\ x_3 = \frac{1}{6}x_4, \end{cases} \quad \text{then} \quad x = \begin{bmatrix} x_1 \\ x_2 \\ x_3 \\ x_4 \end{bmatrix}$$

is in the kernel of T_A. So the column vector

$$\begin{bmatrix} -11 \\ 0 \\ 1 \\ 6 \end{bmatrix}$$

spans the kernel of T_A. Note that dimension of kernel of T_A is 1, dimension of range of T_A is 3, and dimension of $\mathbb{R}^4$ is 4, concurring with Theorem 5.5.

Optional Proof of Theorem 5.5. First, consider the case with kernel $T = \{\mathbf{0}\}$. Suppose that $\{\mathbf{u}_1, \mathbf{u}_2, \ldots, \mathbf{u}_n\}$ is a basis of U (the domain of the linear transformation T). The discussion preceding Example 8 shows that $\{T(\mathbf{u}_1), T(\mathbf{u}_2), \ldots, T(\mathbf{u}_n)\}$ is a basis of range T since kernel $T = \{\mathbf{0}\}$. In this case we have that the dimension of kernel T is 0 and the dimension of range T is n; thus,

Dimension of kernel T + Dimension of range T = Dimension of U.

Now let us assume that kernel $T \neq \{\mathbf{0}\}$. Then the dimension of kernel T must be at least 1 (why?). Let the dimension of U be n, and let the dimension of kernel T be r, where $1 \leqslant r \leqslant n$.

If $r = n$, then the kernel of T is *all* of U (why?) and hence $T(\mathbf{u}) = \mathbf{0}$ for *all* vectors $\mathbf{u}$ in U. This implies that the range of T is just the zero vector and thus *range* $T = \{\mathbf{0}\}$. Hence, the dimension of range T is 0 and thus

the dimension of kernel T is n,
the dimension of range T is 0,
the dimension of U is n.

Theorem 5.5 is thus verified in this case also.

The only case left, then, is that in which $1 \leqslant r < n$, where r is the dimension of kernel T.

Let $S' = \{\mathbf{u}_1, \mathbf{u}_2, \ldots, \mathbf{u}_r\}$ be a basis for the kernel of T. By Theorem 3.9 we can extend S' to a basis S for U by adding some $n - r$ vectors $\mathbf{u}_{r+1}, \mathbf{u}_{r+2}, \ldots, \mathbf{u}_n$. We shall show that the set of $n - r$ vectors $H = \{T(\mathbf{u}_{r+1}), T(\mathbf{u}_{r+2}), \ldots, T(\mathbf{u}_n)\}$ is a basis for the range of T. First, to show that they span *range* T, let $T(\mathbf{v})$ be any vector in the range of T. Since $\mathbf{v}$ is in U, it is a linear combination of the basis vectors $\mathbf{u}_1, \mathbf{u}_2, \ldots,$ $\mathbf{u}_n$, say,

$$\mathbf{v} = k_1 \mathbf{u}_1 + k_2 \mathbf{u}_2 + \ldots + k_n \mathbf{u}_n,$$

so

$$T(\mathbf{v}) = k_1 T(\mathbf{u}_1) + k_2 T(\mathbf{u}_2) + \ldots + k_r T(\mathbf{u}_r) + k_{r+1} T(\mathbf{u}_{r+1}) + \ldots + k_n T(\mathbf{u}_n)$$
$$= \mathbf{0} + k_{r+1} T(\mathbf{u}_{r+1}) + \ldots + k_n T(\mathbf{u}_n)$$

because $\mathbf{u}_1, \ldots, \mathbf{u}_r$ lie in the kernel of T. Thus, H spans the range of T. Moreover, the set H is linearly independent for if

$$\mathbf{0} = b_{r+1} T(\mathbf{u}_{r+1}) + b_{r+2} T(\mathbf{u}_{r+2}) + \ldots + b_n T(\mathbf{u}_n),$$

then

$$\mathbf{0} = T(b_{r+1} \mathbf{u}_{r+1} + b_{r+2} \mathbf{u}_{r+2} + \ldots + b_n \mathbf{u}_n).$$

So the vector $\mathbf{w} = b_{r+1}\mathbf{u}_{r+1} + b_{r+2}\mathbf{u}_{r+2} + \ldots + b_n\mathbf{u}_n$ is in the kernel of T. Since S' is a basis for the kernel, $\mathbf{w}$ is also a linear combination of the vectors $\mathbf{u}_1, \mathbf{u}_2, \ldots, \mathbf{u}_r$, say,

$$\mathbf{w} = b_1\mathbf{u}_1 + b_2\mathbf{u}_2 + \ldots + b_r\mathbf{u}_r,$$

hence,

$$b_1\mathbf{u}_1 + b_2\mathbf{u}_2 + \ldots + b_r\mathbf{u}_r = b_{r+1}\mathbf{u}_{r+1} + \ldots + b_n\mathbf{u}_n.$$

Therefore,

$$-b_1\mathbf{u}_1 - b_2\mathbf{u}_2 - \ldots - b_r\mathbf{u}_r + b_{r+1}\mathbf{u}_{r+1} + \ldots + b_n\mathbf{u}_n = \mathbf{0}$$

and all the b_i are zero because S is a basis for U. Therefore H is linearly independent. Since H is a basis for the range of T, the dimension of range T is $n-r$. Thus,

$$\text{Dimension of kernel } T + \text{Dimension of range } T = n.$$

This completes the proof.

EXERCISES (5.2) ─────────────────────────────────────

Suppose that $T_A : \mathbb{R}^2 \to \mathbb{R}^2$ is multiplication by the matrix $\begin{bmatrix} 2 & -1 \\ -6 & 3 \end{bmatrix}$.

1. Show that $\begin{bmatrix} 4 \\ 8 \end{bmatrix}$ is in ker T_A.   2. Show that $\begin{bmatrix} 1 \\ -3 \end{bmatrix}$ is in range T_A.

3. Is $\begin{bmatrix} 1 \\ 5 \end{bmatrix}$ in the range of T_A? Explain.   4. Find $T_A\begin{bmatrix} x \\ y \end{bmatrix}$.

5. Find a basis for the kernel of T_A.   6. Find a basis for the range of T_A.

7. Find the kernel and range of the linear transformation in Example 1 of Section 5.1. Confirm Theorem 5.5 for this example.

8. Find the kernel and range of the linear transformation in Example 2 of Section 5.1. Confirm Theorem 5.5 for this example.

9. Find the kernel and range of the linear transformation in Example 6 of Section 5.1. Confirm Theorem 5.5 in this case.

10. Let T be the linear transformation in Exercise 8 of Exercises 5.1. Find the kernel and range of this linear transformation and confirm Theorem 5.5.

11. Find the kernel and range of the linear transformation in Example 7 of Section 5.1. Confirm Theorem 5.5.

12. Prove Theorem 5.4.

13. Let P_n be the vector space of polynomials of degree $\leqslant n$. Define the *differentiation operator* $D: P_n \to P_{n-1}$ by the following differentiation formula:

$$D(a_0 + a_1 x + a_2 x^2 + a_3 x^3 + \ldots + a_n x^n) = a_1 + 2a_2 x + 3a_3 x^2 + \ldots + na_n x^{n-1}.$$

Prove that D is a linear transformation. Find the kernel and range of the linear transformation D. Confirm Theorem 5.5.

14. Use Theorem 5.5 and the results of Example 7 to prove that, if A is an $m \times n$ matrix, then the dimension of the solution space of A is $n - \text{rank}\ (A)$.

15. Suppose that $T: U \to V$ is a linear transformation and suppose that $\{\mathbf{u}_1, \mathbf{u}_2, \ldots, \mathbf{u}_n\}$ is a basis for U. Prove that $\{T(\mathbf{u}_1), T(\mathbf{u}_2), \ldots, T(\mathbf{u}_n)\}$ is a basis for the range of T if and only if the kernel of T is $\{\mathbf{0}\}$.

5.3 MATRIX REPRESENTATION OF A LINEAR TRANSFORMATION

In this section we shall show that every linear transformation from a finite-dimensional vector space U into a finite-dimensional vector space V can be regarded as a matrix transformation T_A of the type considered in the examples of Sections 5.1 and 5.2.

In particular we show that a given linear transformation $T: U \to V$ from a vector space U of dimension n to a vector space V of dimension m can be thought of as a matrix transformation $T_A: \mathbb{R}^n \to \mathbb{R}^m$ from the space of $n \times 1$ matrices to the space of $m \times 1$ matrices given by

$$T_A X = AX. \tag{5.11}$$

First of all, let us show that every vector $\mathbf{u}$ in a finite-dimensional vector space can be represented by a column vector ($n \times 1$ matrix).

Let $S = \{\mathbf{u}_1, \mathbf{u}_2, \ldots, \mathbf{u}_n\}$ be a basis for the n-dimensional vector space U. In Exercise 13 you are asked to show that there exist *unique* scalars $a_1, a_2, \ldots, a_n$ such that

$$\mathbf{u} = a_1 \mathbf{u}_1 + a_2 \mathbf{u}_2 + \ldots + a_n \mathbf{u}_n.$$

Then we represent the vector $\mathbf{u}$ by the column vector ($n \times 1$ matrix) consisting of these unique scalars called the **coordinates of u with respect to the basis** S. Denote this by writing

$$[\mathbf{u}]_S = \begin{bmatrix} a_1 \\ a_2 \\ \vdots \\ a_n \end{bmatrix}. \tag{5.12}$$

We call the representation (5.12) of $[\mathbf{u}]_S$ the **coordinatization of u with respect to** S or, more simply, the **S-coordinatization of u**.

Example 1   Let $V = \mathbb{R}^2$ be a Euclidean 2-space and let $S = E = \{(1, 0), (0, 1)\}$ be the standard basis. Then the E-coordinatization of the vector $\mathbf{u} = (3, -1)$ is

$$[\mathbf{u}]_E = \begin{bmatrix} 3 \\ -1 \end{bmatrix}$$

because, of course, $\mathbf{u} = 3(1, 0) - 1(0, 1)$. More generally, the E-coordinatization of the vector $\mathbf{x} = (x_1, x_2)$ of $\mathbb{R}^2$ is

$$[\mathbf{x}]_E = \begin{bmatrix} x_1 \\ x_2 \end{bmatrix}.$$

Example 2 Let $V = P_2$ be the space of polynomials of degree two or less. Let $S = E = \{1, x, x^2\}$ be the standard basis. Then if $p(x) = ax^2 + bx + c$ is a polynomial in P_2, we have

$$[p(x)]_E = \begin{bmatrix} c \\ b \\ a \end{bmatrix}.$$

In particular,

$$[1 - x^2]_E = \begin{bmatrix} 1 \\ 0 \\ -1 \end{bmatrix}.$$

Example 3 Let $V = \mathbb{R}^3$ and let

$$S = \{\mathbf{v}_1 = (1, 1, 1), \quad \mathbf{v}_2 = (0, 1, 1), \quad \mathbf{v}_3 = (0, 0, 1)\}$$

be a basis (verify that it is). Then if $\mathbf{v} = (2, -3, 4)$, we find that

$$\mathbf{v} = 2\mathbf{v}_1 + (-5)\mathbf{v}_2 + 7\mathbf{v}_3$$

by solving for the coefficients in the linear combination

$$(2, -3, 4) = c_1(1, 1, 1) + c_2(0, 1, 1) + c_3(0, 0, 1)$$

(check this). Therefore,

$$[\mathbf{v}]_S = \begin{bmatrix} 2 \\ -5 \\ 7 \end{bmatrix}.$$

Theorem 5.6

The correspondence $\phi_S: U \to \mathbb{R}^n$ between the n-dimensional vector space U with basis S and the vector space $\mathbb{R}^n$ of $n \times 1$ column vectors (matrices) given by $\phi_S(\mathbf{v}) = [\mathbf{v}]_S$; that is, the S-coordinatization of $\mathbf{v}$, has the following properties:

i) *ϕ_S is one-to-one and onto $\mathbb{R}^n$ (see Section 5.1 for definition of these concepts),*

ii) *$\phi_S(\mathbf{u} + \mathbf{v}) = \phi_S(\mathbf{u}) + \phi_S(\mathbf{v})$ for all $\mathbf{u}, \mathbf{v}$ in U,*

iii) $\phi_S(k\mathbf{v}) = k\phi_S(\mathbf{v})$ *for all scalars k and all* **v** *in U,*
iv) $\phi_S(\mathbf{0}) = \mathbf{0}$,
 v) $\phi_S(-\mathbf{v}) = -\phi_S(\mathbf{v})$,
vi) *kernel* $\phi_S = \mathbf{0}$,
vii) *range* $\phi_S = \overline{\mathbb{R}^n}$.

Proof. We shall leave most of the details as exercises. Parts (ii) and (iii) say essentially that ϕ_S is a linear transformation and part (i) is equivalent to parts (vi) and (vii) together. We shall prove part (ii). Let $S = \{\mathbf{v}_1, \mathbf{v}_2, \ldots, \mathbf{v}_n\}$ be a basis for U. Then, for any **u**, **v** in U, there exist unique scalars α_i and β_i, where $i = 1, 2, \ldots, n$, such that

$$\mathbf{u} = \alpha_1\mathbf{v}_1 + \alpha_2\mathbf{v}_2 + \ldots + \alpha_n\mathbf{v}_n,$$
$$\mathbf{v} = \beta_1\mathbf{v}_1 + \beta_2\mathbf{v}_2 + \ldots + \beta_n\mathbf{v}_n.$$

Therefore (verify this)

$$\mathbf{u} + \mathbf{v} = (\alpha_1 + \beta_1)\mathbf{v}_1 + (\alpha_2 + \beta_2)\mathbf{v}_2 + \ldots + (\alpha_n + \beta_n)\mathbf{v}_n,$$

so that the S-coordinatizations for the vectors **u**, **v**, and $\mathbf{u} + \mathbf{v}$ are

$$[\mathbf{u}]_S = \begin{bmatrix} \alpha_1 \\ \alpha_2 \\ \vdots \\ \alpha_n \end{bmatrix}, \quad [\mathbf{v}]_S = \begin{bmatrix} \beta_1 \\ \beta_2 \\ \vdots \\ \beta_n \end{bmatrix}, \quad [\mathbf{u} + \mathbf{v}]_S = \begin{bmatrix} \alpha_1 + \beta_1 \\ \alpha_2 + \beta_2 \\ \vdots \\ \alpha_n + \beta_n \end{bmatrix}.$$

The properties of matrix addition then allow us to conclude that

$$\phi_S(\mathbf{u} + \mathbf{v}) = [\mathbf{u} + \mathbf{v}]_S = [\mathbf{u}]_S + [\mathbf{v}]_S = \phi_S(\mathbf{u}) + \phi_S(\mathbf{v}),$$

as desired. Part (iii) is proved similarly.

Let U now be an n-dimensional vector space with basis $N = \{\mathbf{u}_1, \mathbf{u}_2, \ldots, \mathbf{u}_n\}$ and let V be an m-dimensional vector space with basis $S = \{\mathbf{v}_1, \mathbf{v}_2, \ldots, \mathbf{v}_m\}$. Let $T: U \to V$ be a linear transformation. Let **u** be in U. Then **u** can be expressed uniquely in the form

$$\mathbf{u} = \alpha_1\mathbf{u}_1 + \alpha_2\mathbf{u}_2 + \ldots + \alpha_n\mathbf{u}_n. \tag{5.13}$$

Also since T is a linear transformation,

$$T(\mathbf{u}) = \alpha_1 T(\mathbf{u}_1) + \alpha_2 T(\mathbf{u}_2) + \ldots + \alpha_n T(\mathbf{u}_n). \tag{5.14}$$

Each of the vectors $T(\mathbf{u}_i)$, $i = 1, 2, \ldots, n$ is a vector in the codomain V of the transformation T. Since S is a basis for V, each of these vectors is expressible uniquely as a linear combination of the vectors $\mathbf{v}_1, \mathbf{v}_2, \ldots, \mathbf{v}_m$ in S. Therefore, we have

$$T(\mathbf{u}_i) = \sum_{j=1}^{m} a_{ji}\mathbf{v}_j$$

or, in expanded form,

$$T(\mathbf{u}_1) = a_{11}\mathbf{v}_1 + a_{21}\mathbf{v}_2 + \ldots + a_{m1}\mathbf{v}_m$$
$$T(\mathbf{u}_2) = a_{12}\mathbf{v}_1 + a_{22}\mathbf{v}_2 + \ldots + a_{m2}\mathbf{v}_m$$
$$\vdots \qquad \vdots \tag{5.15}$$
$$T(\mathbf{u}_n) = a_{1n}\mathbf{v}_1 + a_{2n}\mathbf{v}_2 + \ldots + a_{mn}\mathbf{v}_m$$

Now we form the matrix A whose ith column vector is the S-coordinatization of the vector $T(\mathbf{u}_i)$. This matrix is

$$A = \begin{bmatrix} a_{11} & a_{12} & \cdots & a_{1n} \\ a_{21} & a_{22} & \cdots & a_{2n} \\ \vdots & \vdots & \vdots & \vdots \\ a_{m1} & a_{m2} & \cdots & a_{mn} \end{bmatrix}. \tag{5.16}$$

$$[T(\mathbf{u}_1)]_S \quad [T(\mathbf{u}_2)]_S \qquad [T(\mathbf{u}_n)]_S$$

We define the **matrix representation** of the transformation $T: U \to V$ *with respect to the bases N and S*, respectively, to be the matrix A of (5.16) and write this in symbols

$$A = [T]_S^N.$$

We now proceed to show that, if $\mathbf{u}$ is in U, then $T(\mathbf{u})$ can be computed as a matrix transformation as follows:

$$[T(\mathbf{u})]_S = [T]_S^N [\mathbf{u}]_N. \tag{5.17}$$

That is, the S-coordinatization of the vector $T(\mathbf{u})$ is obtained by matrix multiplication: *Multiply the N-coordinatization of the vector $\mathbf{u}$ in U by the matrix representation of the transformation $T: U \to V$ with respect to N and S (from N to S)*, as indicated in (5.17). To see this, let $\mathbf{u}$ be in U. Then, using (5.13) we obtain

$$[\mathbf{u}]_N = \begin{bmatrix} \alpha_1 \\ \alpha_2 \\ \vdots \\ \alpha_n \end{bmatrix}$$

From (5.14)–(5.15) it can be verified that (check this)

$$[T(\mathbf{u})]_S = \begin{bmatrix} \beta_1' \\ \beta_2' \\ \vdots \\ \beta_m' \end{bmatrix},$$

where

$$\beta'_1 = a_{11}\alpha_1 + a_{12}\alpha_2 + \ldots + a_{1n}\alpha_n,$$
$$\beta'_2 = a_{21}\alpha_1 + a_{22}\alpha_2 + \ldots + a_{2n}\alpha_n,$$

$$\qquad \qquad \qquad \qquad \qquad \qquad \qquad \qquad \qquad \text{(5.18)}$$

$$\beta'_m = a_{m1}\alpha_1 + a_{m2}\alpha_2 + \ldots + a_{mn}\alpha_n.$$

Or, using (5.16), we get

$$[T(\mathbf{u})]_S = A[\mathbf{u}]_N.$$

Example 4 Let $U = V = \mathbb{R}^2$ be a Euclidean 2-space. Find the matrix representation of the linear transformation of Example 1 of Section 5.1 relative to the standard basis $E = \{\mathbf{e}_1 = (1, 0), \mathbf{e}_2 = (0, 1)\}$ of $\mathbb{R}^2$ and illustrate (5.17) for this T.

Recall that this transformation was given by $T(x_1, x_2) = (2x_1, 2x_2)$. To compute the matrix A we find $T(\mathbf{e}_1)$ and $T(\mathbf{e}_2)$ and then write these as column vectors (with respect to E). Clearly,

$$T(\mathbf{e}_1) = T(1, 0) = (2, 0) \qquad \text{and} \qquad T(\mathbf{e}_2) = T(0, 1) = (0, 2),$$

so

$$A = [T]_E^E = \begin{bmatrix} 2 & 0 \\ 0 & 2 \end{bmatrix}.$$

When the bases S and N are the same, we usually write only the subscript, so $A = [T]_E$. To illustrate (5.17) write the arbitrary vector $\mathbf{x} = (x_1, x_2)$ as

$$[x]_E = \begin{bmatrix} x_1 \\ x_2 \end{bmatrix}.$$

Then note that

$$[T(\mathbf{x})]_E = \begin{bmatrix} 2x_1 \\ 2x_2 \end{bmatrix} = \begin{bmatrix} 2 & 0 \\ 0 & 2 \end{bmatrix} \begin{bmatrix} x_1 \\ x_2 \end{bmatrix} = [T]_E^E[\mathbf{x}]_E.$$

Example 5 Find the matrix representation of the linear transformation in Example 4 of Section 5.1 with respect to the standard bases for $\mathbb{R}^2$ and $\mathbb{R}^3$. Illustrate (5.17) for this T.

Recall that this transformation was given by

$$T(x_1, x_2) = (x_1, -x_2, x_1 - x_2). \qquad \qquad \text{(5.19)}$$

We again compute $T(\mathbf{e}_1)$ and $T(\mathbf{e}_2)$, then coordinatize these with respect to the basis E for $\mathbb{R}^3$ and use them as the column vectors of the matrix. Thus

$$T(\mathbf{e}_1) = T(1, 0) = (1, 0, 1),$$
$$T(\mathbf{e}_2) = T(0, 1) = (0, -1, -1),$$

so

$$A = [T]_E = \begin{bmatrix} 1 & 0 \\ 0 & -1 \\ 1 & -1 \end{bmatrix}.$$

To illustrate (5.17), we note that if $\mathbf{x} = (x_1, x_2)$, then

$$[\mathbf{x}]_E = \begin{bmatrix} x_1 \\ x_2 \end{bmatrix},$$

so

$$[T]_E[\mathbf{x}]_E = \begin{bmatrix} 1 & 0 \\ 0 & -1 \\ 1 & -1 \end{bmatrix} \begin{bmatrix} x_1 \\ x_2 \end{bmatrix} = \begin{bmatrix} x_1 \\ -x_2 \\ x_1 - x_2 \end{bmatrix} = [T(\mathbf{x})]_E.$$

We shall henceforth call the matrix representation of a transformation T with respect to a standard basis (as in Examples 4 and 5) the **standard matrix representation**.

EXERCISES (5.3)

In Exercises 1–6, find the standard matrix representations $[T]_E$ of the given linear transformations.

1. The linear transformation in Example 2 of Section 5.1.
2. The linear transformation in Example 3 of Section 5.1.
3. The linear transformation in Exercise 8 of Exercises 5.1.
4. The linear transformation in Exercise 9 of Exercises 5.1.
5. The linear transformation in Example 6 of Section 5.2.
6. The linear transformation in Problem 13 of Exercises 5.2 with $n = 3$.
7. Let $T: U \rightarrow U$ be the identity linear transformation given in Example 5 of Section 5.1, where U is a Euclidean 3-space. Find the standard matrix representation of T.
8. Let $T: U \rightarrow U$ be the zero linear transformation $[T(\mathbf{x}) = \mathbf{0}$ for all $\mathbf{x}$ in $U]$, where U is Euclidean 2-space. Find the standard matrix representation of T.
9. Let $T: P_1 \rightarrow P_2$ be given by $T(p(x)) = xp(x)$. Find the matrix representation $[T]_H^G$ of this transformation with respect to the bases

$$G = \{u_1 = 1, u_2 = x\}, \quad H = \{v_1 = 1, v_2 = x, v_3 = x^2\}.$$

   Then use this matrix to compute $[T(p(x))]$ for $p(x) = 4x + 1$.
10. Let $T: P_1 \rightarrow P_2$ be the same as given in Exercise 9.
   a) Show that $u_1 = 1 + x$ and $u_2 = 1 - x$ form a basis K for P_1.
   b) Show that $v_1 = 1 + x$, $v_2 = 1 - x^2$, $v_3 = 1 - x$ form a basis M for P_2.

c) Find the matrix $[T]_M^K$.
d) Use the results of part (c) to compute $[T(p)]_M$ for $p(x) = 4x + 1$ and compare with Exercise 9.

11. Show the validity of the following method for verifying that a set $S = \{v_1, v_2, \ldots, v_n\}$ of vectors from an n-dimensional vector space V is a basis of V.

Step 1. Coordinatize each v_i with respect to the standard basis E of v, that is, find $[v_i]_E$.

Step 2. Form the matrix A whose columns are the column vectors $[v_i]_E$.

Step 3. Find the rank of A by row reduction or by column operations (row-reduce A'). Then if n is the rank of A then S is a basis.

12. Let V be the ordinary xy-plane. Consider the transformation

$$T(x, y) = (x \cos\theta + y \sin\theta, \ -x \sin\theta + y \cos\theta).$$

a) Show that T is a linear transformation.
b) Show that T is a rotation of the axes through an angle. What is this angle?
c) Find the standard matrix representation $A = [T]_E^E$.
d) Show that $\det A = 1$.

13. Prove that if **u** is a vector in U and $\{u_1, u_2, \ldots, u_n\}$ is a basis of U, then **u** can be expressed *uniquely* as $u = a_1 u_1 + a_2 u_2 + \ldots + a_n u_n$ for some scalars $a_1, a_2, \ldots, a_n$.

5.4 THE ALGEBRA OF LINEAR TRANSFORMATIONS

In this section we shall consider operations involving linear transformations together with some of the laws governing these operations. Specifically, we shall define the sum, scalar product, and product of transformations. It can then be seen that the algebra of linear transformations behaves just the same as the algebra of matrices. This last fact, of course, is to be expected since we demonstrated in the previous section that each linear transformation on a finite-dimensional vector space can be thought of as a matrix multiplication.

Since, after all, linear transformations are functions, it is not surprising to learn that we can give meaning to their sum and scalar product.

Let $T_1: U \to V$ and $T_2: U \to V$ be linear transformations from the vector space U into the vector space V, then the **sum** $T_1 + T_2$ is the function $T_1 + T_2: U \to V$ defined by

$$(T_1 + T_2)(u) = T_1(u) + T_2(u) \quad \text{for all } u \text{ in } U. \tag{5.20}$$

If k is any real number, then the **scalar product** kT_1 is the function $kT_1: U \to V$ defined by

$$(kT_1)(u) = k(T_1(u)) \quad \text{for all } u \text{ in } U. \tag{5.21}$$

Example 1   Let $U = V = \mathbb{R}^2$ and let T_1 and T_2 be defined by

$$T_1(x_1, x_2) = (x_2, x_1) \quad \text{and} \quad T_2(x_1, x_2) = (2x_1, 2x_2).$$

Then $T_1 + T_2$ is the transformation given by

$$(T_1 + T_2)(x_1, x_2) = T_1(x_1, x_2) + T_2(x_1, x_2) = (x_2, x_1) + (2x_1, 2x_2)$$
$$= (x_2 + 2x_1, x_1 + 2x_2),$$

while for the real number π the transformation πT_1 is given by

$$(\pi T_1)(x_1, x_2) = \pi T_1(x_1, x_2) = \pi(x_2, x_1) = (\pi x_2, \pi x_1).$$

By checking the properties listed in Section 5.1, you can verify that the sum of two linear transformations and the product of a scalar and a linear transformation are also linear transformations (see Exercises 23, 24).

Since linear transformations are functions, we expect that function composition might also result in a linear transformation. Hence there is another operation on linear transformations, generally called **multiplication**, defined as follows: Suppose that

$$T_1: U \to V \quad \text{and} \quad T_2: V \to W \tag{5.22}$$

are linear transformations. The *product*.

$$T_2 T_1: U \to W \tag{5.23}$$

is defined by the formula

$$(T_2 T_1)(\mathbf{u}) = T_2(T_1(\mathbf{u})), \quad \text{for all } \mathbf{u} \text{ in } U. \tag{5.24}$$

It is extremely important to emphasize here that *order is very essential* in (5.24). Indeed, we *cannot* be certain that the product $T_1 T_2$ (in the opposite order) even makes sense.

The product $T_2 T_1$ is also frequently called the *composition* of T_2 and T_1 and is sometimes denoted by $T_2 \circ T_1$. You can verify that the product $T_2 T_1$ is also a linear transformation (see Exercise 25).

Example 2   Let T_1 and T_2 be the linear transformations from $\mathbb{R}^2$ to $\mathbb{R}^2$ given in Example 1. In this case, both $T_1 T_2$ and $T_2 T_1$ are defined. Indeed, we have the highly unusual case where $T_1 T_2 = T_2 T_1$:

$$T_1 T_2(x_1, x_2) = T_1(2x_1, 2x_2) = (2x_2, 2x_1),$$
$$T_2 T_1(x_1, x_2) = T_2(x_2, x_1) = (2x_2, 2x_1).$$

But consider the following example.

Example 3   Let $U = V = \mathbb{R}^2$. The linear transformations T_1 and T_2 are given by

$$T_1(x_1, x_2) = (x_1 + 2x_2, -x_2) \quad \text{and} \quad T_2(x_1, x_2) = (-x_1, 4x_1 + x_2).$$

Then (verify this)

$$T_1 T_2(x_1, x_2) = T_1(-x_1, 4x_1 + x_2) = (7x_1 + 2x_2, -4x_1 - x_2),$$

while

$$T_2 T_1(x_1, x_2) = T_2(x_1 + 2x_2, -x_2) = (-x_1 - 2x_2, 4x_1 + 7x_2).$$

So here $T_1 T_2 \neq T_2 T_1$, even though both products are defined.

This example shows that for linear transformations, as well as for matrices, the commutative law for multiplication does *not* hold. In fact, it turns out that *linear transformations obey the same laws of algebra as do matrices.* Indeed, the usual commutative law for addition, the associative laws for addition and multiplication, and the two distributive laws are all true for linear transformations (see Theorems 1.3 and 1.5). pp 34, 42

Continuing the comparison with matrices, we note that some linear transformations also have inverses in the following sense.

A linear transformation $T: U \to V$ is **invertible** if we can find a transformation $S: V \to U$ (going in the opposite direction) that brings us back, in the sense that

$$ST(\mathbf{u}) = \mathbf{u} \text{ for } all \text{ } \mathbf{u} \text{ in } U, \tag{5.25}$$

$$TS(\mathbf{v}) = \mathbf{v} \text{ for } all \text{ } \mathbf{v} \text{ in } V, \tag{5.26}$$

as illustrated in Fig. 5.8. In this case, we say that T has an **inverse** S (and vice versa).

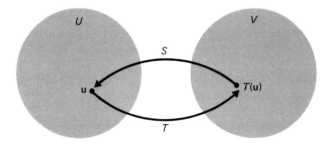

Figure 5.8

To simplify matters, we will confine our discussion to the case when the domain and codomain of the linear transformation T are the *same* vector space U, that is, $T: U \to U$. In this case we say that T is a *linear transformation on the vector space U.*

Not all such linear transformations have inverses, however. For example, if $T: \mathbb{R}^2 \to \mathbb{R}^2$ is defined by

$$T(x_1, x_2) = (x_1, 0), \tag{5.27}$$

then no S that satisfies properties (5.25) and (5.26) can possibly exist. To prove this, suppose that such an S were to exist. Observe that by (5.27) we have

$$T(0, 1) = (0, 0) \quad \text{and} \quad T(0, 0) = (0, 0),$$

and hence $T(0, 1) = T(0, 0)$. Now, applying S to both sides of this equation we would get

$$ST(0, 1) = ST(0, 0)$$

or

$$(0, 1) = (0, 0) \quad \text{(by (5.25))},$$

which is a contradiction. This shows that no S satisfying (5.25) and (5.26) exists, that is, T has *no* inverse.

When T *does* have an inverse S such that $ST = TS = I$, then this inverse is unique, as can be proved (see Exercise 29). We shall then denote S by T^{-1}. Thus, if $T: U \to U$ has an inverse transformation $T^{-1}: U \to U$, then $TT^{-1} = T^{-1}T = I$, where I is the identity linear transformation on U.

When does T^{-1} exist? Clearly, T^{-1} cannot exist if there are two distinct vectors **u** and **v** in U such that $T(\mathbf{u}) = T(\mathbf{v})$. As before if T^{-1} were to exist and $T(\mathbf{u}) = T(\mathbf{v})$, then

$$\mathbf{u} = T^{-1}T(\mathbf{u}) = T^{-1}T(\mathbf{v}) = \mathbf{v}.$$

Therefore, T^{-1} cannot exist if $T(\mathbf{u}) = \mathbf{0}$ for any *nonzero* vector **u**. The following theorem gives the complete answer. We leave the proof as an exercise for you.

Theorem 5.7
Let $T: U \to U$ be a linear transformation and let $G = \{\mathbf{u}_1, \mathbf{u}_2, \ldots, \mathbf{u}_n\}$ be a basis of U. Then $T^{-1}: U \to U$ exists if and only if <u>any</u> (and hence all) of the following equivalent conditions hold:

   i) *kernel of $T = \{\mathbf{0}\}$,*
   ii) *range of $T = U$,*
   iii) *$\{T(\mathbf{u}_1), T(\mathbf{u}_2), \ldots, T(\mathbf{u}_n)\}$ is a basis of U.*

As in the case of matrices, whenever T_1 and T_2 are both invertible linear transformations of U onto U, then $T_1 T_2$ is also invertible and in fact

$$(T_1 T_2)^{-1} = T_2^{-1} T_1^{-1}.$$

In other words, *the inverse of the product is equal to the product of the inverses in the reverse order.*

Moreover, $(T_1^{-1})^{-1} = T_1$, that is, *the inverse of the inverse of T_1 is T_1 itself.*

Example 4   Let $U = P_2$ be the space of polynomials of degree 2 or less. Let $T: P_2 \to P_2$

be the following linear transformation (verify that it is indeed a linear transformation):

$$T(ax^2 + bx + c) = (a - b)x^2 + (a + c)x + (a + b).$$

Then the transformation T^{-1} is given by

$$T^{-1}(ax^2 + bx + c) = \tfrac{1}{2}(a + c)x^2 + \tfrac{1}{2}(c - a)x + \tfrac{1}{2}(2b - a - c), \qquad \textbf{(5.28)}$$

as can be verified by calculating

$$
\begin{aligned}
TT^{-1}(ax^2 + bx + c) &= T(\tfrac{1}{2}(a + c)x^2 + \tfrac{1}{2}(c - a)x + \tfrac{1}{2}(2b - a - c)) \\
&= [\tfrac{1}{2}(a + c) - \tfrac{1}{2}(c - a)]x^2 \\
&\quad + [\tfrac{1}{2}(a + c) + \tfrac{1}{2}(2b - a - c)]x \\
&\quad + [\tfrac{1}{2}(a + c) + \tfrac{1}{2}(c - a)] \\
&= ax^2 + bx + c
\end{aligned}
$$

Perhaps the easiest way to find T^{-1}, (in general) is to represent T by a matrix. This is the substance of the following theorem stated without proof.

Theorem 5.8

The linear transformation $T: U \rightarrow U$ is invertible if and only if any matrix representation A of T is nonsingular. Moreover, A^{-1} represents T^{-1}.

Example 5   Let $T: \mathbb{R}^2 \rightarrow \mathbb{R}^2$ be the linear transformation that maps each vector in the plane to its symmetric image about the x-axis (see Fig. 5.9).

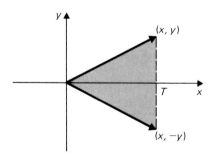

Figure 5.9

To find the standard matrix representation of T we note that $T(1, 0) = (1, 0)$, while $T(0, 1) = (0, -1)$. Hence T is represented by the matrix

$$A = \begin{bmatrix} 1 & 0 \\ 0 & -1 \end{bmatrix}.$$

It is easy to verify that A^{-1} exists and equals the matrix A itself; therefore, $T^{-1} = T$.

As a less trivial illustration of Theorem 5.8, note that, with respect to the standard basis $E = \{x^2, x, 1\}$ for P_2, the transformation of Example 4 can be represented by the matrix (verify this)

$$A = \begin{bmatrix} 1 & -1 & 0 \\ 1 & 0 & 1 \\ 1 & 1 & 0 \end{bmatrix}.$$

Then, using the matrix-inversion algorithm, we find that

$$A^{-1} = \begin{bmatrix} \frac{1}{2} & 0 & \frac{1}{2} \\ -\frac{1}{2} & 0 & \frac{1}{2} \\ -\frac{1}{2} & 1 & -\frac{1}{2} \end{bmatrix}.$$

Hence (verify this also), T^{-1} is obtained from A^{-1}. Thus

$$\left[T^{-1}(ax^2 + bx + c) \right]_E = A^{-1} \begin{bmatrix} a \\ b \\ c \end{bmatrix} = \begin{bmatrix} \frac{1}{2}(a+c) \\ \frac{1}{2}(c-a) \\ -\frac{1}{2}a + b - \frac{1}{2}c \end{bmatrix}.$$

Compare with (5.28).

EXERCISES (5.4)——————————————————————————————————

In Exercises 1–8 let T_1 and T_2 be the linear transformations of Examples 1 and 2.

1. Compute $\frac{1}{2}T_1 T_2 - 2T_2 T_1$.
2. Find the standard matrix representation for T_1.
3. Find the standard matrix representation for T_2.
4. Find the standard matrix representation for $T_1 + T_2$.
5. Find the standard matrix representation for $T_1 T_2$.
6. Find the standard matrix representation $[T_1^{-1}]$ for T_1^{-1}.
7. Find the standard matrix representation $[T_2^{-1}]$ for T_2^{-1}.
8. Show that the standard matrix representation for $(T_1 T_2)^{-1}$ is $[T_2^{-1}][T_1^{-1}]$.

9–16. Repeat Exercises 1–8 for the transformations T_1 and T_2 on $\mathbb{R}^3$ given by

$$T_1(x, y, z) = (x - y, z - x, z - y) \quad \text{and} \quad T_2(x, y, z) = (z, y, z).$$

17. Let $T: \mathbb{R}^3 \to \mathbb{R}^2$ be the transformation $T(x, y, z) = (x - y + z, -2x + z)$. Write the standard matrix representation for T.

18. Let $S: \mathbb{R}^2 \to \mathbb{R}^3$ be the transformation $S(x, y) = (x - y, 2x - 2y, 2x - y)$. Write the standard matrix representation for S.

19. With T and S an in Exercises 17 and 18, find TS and ST. Note that TS is the identity transformation on $\mathbb{R}^2$. *Hint.* Use the matrix representations.

20. Refer to Exercise 19. Find the kernel of the transformation ST and the range of ST. Explain why ST is not the identity transformation on $\mathbb{R}^3$.

21. Verify that the transformation T of Example 4 is linear.

22. Find the standard matrix representation for the transformation T of Example 4.

23. Show that the sum of two linear transformations defined in (5.20) is a linear transformation.

24. Show that the product of a scalar and a linear transformation defined in (5.21) is a linear transformation.

25. Show that the product of two linear transformations (if defined) is a linear transformation.

In Exercises 26–28, sketch a proof of Theorem 5.7.

26. Prove part (i).

27. Prove part (ii).

28. Prove part (iii).

29. Prove that if $T: U \to U$ is an invertible linear transformation, then its inverse T^{-1} is unique.

5.5 CHANGE OF BASIS AND SIMILARITY

In this section we compare the matrix representation of a linear transformation $T: U \to U$ relative to a *given* basis of U with the matrix representation of $T: U \to U$ relative to *another* basis of U. This leads us to the important concept of *similarity of matrices*. Let us begin with an example.

Example 1 Let $T: \mathbb{R}^3 \to \mathbb{R}^3$ be the linear transformation defined by

$$T(x, y, z) = (x + y, y + z, z + x)$$

(verify that T is indeed a linear transformation).

Then with respect to the standard basis for $\mathbb{R}^3$, namely,

$$E = \{e_1 = (1, 0, 0), \quad e_2 = (0, 1, 0), \quad e_3 = (0, 0, 1)\},$$

T is represented by the matrix

$$A = [T]_E = \begin{bmatrix} 1 & 1 & 0 \\ 0 & 1 & 1 \\ 1 & 0 & 1 \end{bmatrix}$$
$$\quad\quad T(e_1) \quad T(e_2) \quad T(e_3)$$

It is not difficult to see that the set

$$G = \{u_1 = (1, -1, 0), u_2 = (1, 0, -1), u_3 = (0, 1, 1)\}$$

is also a basis for $\mathbb{R}^3$. Relative to this basis, the matrix $[T]_G$ representing T is computed as follows (verify this):

$$T(u_1) = (0, -1, 1) = u_1 - u_2,$$
$$T(u_2) = (1, -1, 0) = u_1,$$
$$T(u_3) = (1, 2, 1) \quad = \quad u_2 + 2u_3.$$

Therefore, the matrix representation of T with respect to G is

$$B = [T]_G = \begin{bmatrix} 1 & 1 & 0 \\ -1 & 0 & 1 \\ 0 & 0 & 2 \end{bmatrix}.$$

$$T(u_1) \quad T(u_2) \quad T(u_3)$$

How are A and B related as matrices? The answer is provided by the following theorem whose proof we omit.

Theorem 5.9

Let $A = [T]_G$ be the matrix representation of a linear transformation $T: U \to U$ with respect to a basis G for U, and let $B = [T]_H$ be the matrix representation of the same transformation T with respect to a different basis H for U. If S is the transition matrix from the basis H to the basis G, then

$$A = SBS^{-1}. \tag{5.29}$$

The **transition matrix** S mentioned in this theorem is calculated as follows for our example. Consider the coordinatizations of the basis vectors u_1, u_2, and u_3 of G in the basis E. Form the matrix S whose columns are these coordinatizations. Thus,

$$S = \begin{bmatrix} 1 & 1 & 0 \\ -1 & 0 & 1 \\ 0 & -1 & 1 \end{bmatrix}.$$

This matrix is called the *transition matrix from the basis G to the basis E* or the *change of basis matrix from G to E*. It can be verified that S is nonsingular and that its inverse is the following matrix (check this):

$$S^{-1} = \begin{bmatrix} \frac{1}{2} & -\frac{1}{2} & \frac{1}{2} \\ \frac{1}{2} & \frac{1}{2} & -\frac{1}{2} \\ \frac{1}{2} & \frac{1}{2} & \frac{1}{2} \end{bmatrix}$$

You can also readily verify that the columns of S^{-1} are the coordinatizations of e_1, e_2, and e_3 with respect to the basis G. That is,

$$e_1 = \tfrac{1}{2}u_1 + \tfrac{1}{2}u_2 + \tfrac{1}{2}u_3,$$
$$e_2 = -\tfrac{1}{2}u_1 + \tfrac{1}{2}u_2 + \tfrac{1}{2}u_3,$$
$$e_3 = \tfrac{1}{2}u_1 - \tfrac{1}{2}u_2 + \tfrac{1}{2}u_3.$$

The relationship between the matrices A and B given in (5.29) is an interesting one, and is worth studying in its own right.

A given $n \times n$ matrix A is said to be **similar** to the $n \times n$ matrix B if there exists an invertible (nonsingular) $n \times n$ matrix S such that

$$A = SBS^{-1}. \tag{5.30}$$

Example 2   Let

$$A = \begin{bmatrix} 1 & 0 \\ 0 & -1 \end{bmatrix} \quad \text{and} \quad B = \begin{bmatrix} -1 & 0 \\ 0 & 1 \end{bmatrix}. \tag{5.31}$$

Is A similar to B?

In order for A to be similar to B, there must exist a 2×2 *nonsingular* matrix S such that (5.30) holds. Now, if we multiply (5.30) by S on the right, we get the equation

$$AS = SB. \tag{5.32}$$

So we are now looking for a 2×2 *nonsingular* matrix S for which (5.32) holds. Of course, we do *not* even know that such a matrix S exists. Nevertheless, we can try to solve (5.32) for the unknown matrix S and then test such an S (if it exists) to see whether it satisfies (5.30). Suppose, then, that

$$S = \begin{bmatrix} a & b \\ c & d \end{bmatrix}, \tag{5.33}$$

where a, b, c, d are unknown scalars. Substituting (5.31) and (5.33) into (5.32), we get

$$\begin{bmatrix} 1 & 0 \\ 0 & -1 \end{bmatrix} \begin{bmatrix} a & b \\ c & d \end{bmatrix} = \begin{bmatrix} a & b \\ c & d \end{bmatrix} \begin{bmatrix} -1 & 0 \\ 0 & 1 \end{bmatrix}. \tag{5.34}$$

Simplifying (5.34), we get

$$\begin{bmatrix} a & b \\ -c & -d \end{bmatrix} = \begin{bmatrix} -a & b \\ -c & d \end{bmatrix} \tag{5.35}$$

For (5.35) to hold, we must have $a = -a$ and $-d = d$, and hence $a = 0, d = 0$. Substituting these values in (5.33), we get

$$S = \begin{bmatrix} 0 & b \\ c & 0 \end{bmatrix}. \tag{5.36}$$

Because S must be *nonsingular*, we must have $b \neq 0$ and $c \neq 0$ (why?). Let us choose

$b = 1, c = 1$ for convenience in computing S_r^{-1} although any nonzero b and c would do. Then we have in our particular case

$$S = \begin{bmatrix} 0 & 1 \\ 1 & 0 \end{bmatrix}. \tag{5.37}$$

You should have no trouble verifying that S is nonsingular and that

$$S^{-1} = \begin{bmatrix} 0 & 1 \\ 1 & 0 \end{bmatrix}. \tag{5.38}$$

Now that we have a *candidate for a solution* to Eq. (5.30), we substitute to get

$$SBS^{-1} = \begin{bmatrix} 0 & 1 \\ 1 & 0 \end{bmatrix} \begin{bmatrix} -1 & 0 \\ 0 & 1 \end{bmatrix} \begin{bmatrix} 0 & 1 \\ 1 & 0 \end{bmatrix} = \begin{bmatrix} 1 & 0 \\ 0 & -1 \end{bmatrix} = A.$$

Hence, A is similar to B.

Example 3   Show that the only matrix similar to the identity matrix

$$I_2 = \begin{bmatrix} 1 & 0 \\ 0 & 1 \end{bmatrix}$$

is I_2 itself.

Suppose that A is *any* 2×2 matrix similar to I_2. Then (by definition) there exists a nonsingular 2×2 matrix S such that

$$A = SI_2 S^{-1}. \tag{5.39}$$

The right side of (5.39) can be simplified (give reasons) to

$$SI_2 S^{-1} = S(I_2 S^{-1}) = SS^{-1} = I_2. \tag{5.40}$$

Combining (5.39) and (5.40), we conclude that $A = I_2$ and the proof is complete.

The relation of similarity has the following attractive features:

1. Reflexivity
   A is similar to A for every $n \times n$ matrix A.

   Proof. $A = IAI^{-1}$, where I is the identity matrix.

2. Symmetry
   If A is similar to B, then B is similar to A.

   Proof. Suppose that $A = SBS^{-1}$ for some nonsingular matrix S. Then solving for B, we get $B = (S^{-1})A(S^{-1})^{-1}$. [Why?] Thus, $B = PAP^{-1}$, where $P = S^{-1}$ is also nonsingular. Hence, B is similar to A.

3. Transitivity

If A is similar to B and B is similar to C, then A is similar to C.

Proof. Suppose A is similar to B and B is similar to C. Then, for some *nonsingular* matrices P and Q, we have

$$A = PBP^{-1} \quad \text{and} \quad B = QCQ^{-1}.$$

Hence [give reasons]

$$A = P(QCQ^{-1})P^{-1} = (PQ)C(Q^{-1}P^{-1})$$
$$= (PQ)C(PQ)^{-1};$$

that is,

$$A = SCS^{-1}, \quad \text{with} \quad S = PQ.$$

Hence A is similar to C. This is an example of an important mathematical idea which we now define.

An **equivalence relation** is a relation that is reflexive, symmetric, and transitive.

We have just demonstrated that the relation of similarity of square matrices is an equivalence relation. You can also verify that another example of an equivalence relation on matrices is given by the concept of row-equivalence discussed in Chapter 1. One of the reasons why an equivalence relation on a set is of importance is that it divides, or "partitions", the objects in question into mutually disjoint subsets known as **equivalence classes**, such that every object belongs to *exactly one* equivalence class. This fact, when applied to the similarity equivalence relation, yields the following important theorem.

Theorem 5.10

All matrices similar to a given $n \times n$ matrix A belong to a class called a similarity class. Every $n \times n$ matrix belongs to exactly one similarity class, and no two distinct similarity classes have any elements (i.e., matrices) in common.

We discover that these similarity classes, when applied to the matrix representations of a given linear transformation, differ precisely as the linear transformations differ.

In Chapter 6 we shall discover a method for finding the "simplest" member of the similarity class containing some special matrices.

EXERCISES (5.5)————————————————————————————————

1. Show that the only 3×3 matrix that is similar to the identity 3×3 matrix I_3 is I_3 itself. Generalize this to $n \times n$ matrices.

2. Show that if A is similar to B, then det A = det B.

Hint. What can you say about the determinant of a product? Also, how does det S^{-1} compare with det S?

3. Is the converse of Exercise 2 true? If so, prove it. If not, give a counterexample.

4. Can a singular matrix be similar to a nonsingular matrix? Give reasons.

5. Prove or disprove: If A and B are similar matrices, then A and B are both singular together or both nonsingular together.

Determine whether the given matrices are similar or not.

6. $A = \begin{bmatrix} 0 & 1 \\ 0 & 0 \end{bmatrix}$, $B = \begin{bmatrix} 0 & 0 \\ 1 & 0 \end{bmatrix}$

7. $A = \begin{bmatrix} 1 & 1 \\ 0 & 1 \end{bmatrix}$, $B = \begin{bmatrix} 1 & 0 \\ 1 & 1 \end{bmatrix}$

8. $A = \begin{bmatrix} 1 & 0 \\ 0 & 0 \end{bmatrix}$, $B = \begin{bmatrix} 0 & 0 \\ 0 & 1 \end{bmatrix}$

9. $A = \begin{bmatrix} 1 & 0 & 0 \\ 0 & 1 & 0 \\ 0 & 0 & -1 \end{bmatrix}$, $B = \begin{bmatrix} -1 & 0 & 0 \\ 0 & 1 & 0 \\ 0 & 0 & 1 \end{bmatrix}$

10. $A = \begin{bmatrix} 1 & 0 & 0 \\ 0 & -1 & 0 \\ 0 & 0 & -1 \end{bmatrix}$, $B = \begin{bmatrix} -1 & 0 & 0 \\ 0 & -1 & 0 \\ 0 & 0 & 1 \end{bmatrix}$

In Exercises 11–20, let $T: \mathbb{R}^3 \to \mathbb{R}^3$ be the linear transformation

$$T(x, y, z) = (y - x, 0, z - x).$$

11. Write the standard matrix representation for T. $[T]_E$

12. Find the rank and the nullity of T.

13. Let $G = \{\mathbf{u}_1 = (1, 0, 1), \mathbf{u}_2 = (0, -1, -1), \mathbf{u}_3 = (1, 1, 0)\}$ be another basis for $\mathbb{R}^3$. Find the transition matrix S from the basis G to the standard basis E of $\mathbb{R}^3$.

14. Find the transition matrix from the standard basis E of $\mathbb{R}^3$ to the basis G of Exercise 13.

15. Find the matrix representation of T with respect to the basis G.

16. Show that the matrices of Exercises 11 and 15 are similar.

17. Let $H = \{\mathbf{v}_1 = (1, 1, -1), \mathbf{v}_2 = (-1, 1, -1), \mathbf{v}_3(0, 1, 1)\}$ be a basis for $\mathbb{R}^3$. Find the transition matrix from the standard basis E of $\mathbb{R}^3$ to the basis H.

18. Find the transition matrix from the basis G of Exercise 13 to the basis H of Exercise 17.

19. Find the matrix representation of T with respect to the basis H of Exercise 17.

20. Show that the matrices of Exercises 15 and 19 are similar.

21. Prove that similar matrices have the same rank.

22. Prove that if A and B are similar, then so are A^n and B^n for every positive integer n.

23. Give an example of two matrices A and B that are row-equivalent but are not similar. *Hint.* Consider Example 3.

5.6 ORTHOGONAL LINEAR TRANSFORMATIONS

In some applications we are interested only in those linear transformations that preserve the length of a vector and the angle between two vectors, when these are defined in the vector space. Remember that these ideas are meaningful in real inner-product spaces (you should review the definitions and concepts of Chapter 4). Let us look at a simple example in $\mathbb{R}^2$. We have already noted that Euclidean 2-space can be interpreted geometrically as the plane.

Suppose we rotate the plane through an angle of $30°$, as discussed in the following example.

Example 1   Let $T_{30°}: \mathbb{R}^2 \to \mathbb{R}^2$ be the rotation of the plane through $30°$. From Fig. 5.10 we see that the point $P: (a, b)$ is rotated by $T_{30°}$ to the point $Q: (a', b')$.

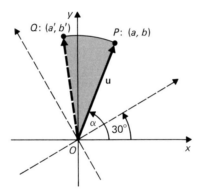

Figure 5.10

If $\overrightarrow{OP} = \mathbf{u}$ makes an angle α with the positive x-axis, then $\overrightarrow{OQ} = T_{30°}(\mathbf{u})$ makes an angle $\alpha + 30°$ with the same axis. Set $\|\mathbf{u}\| = |\overrightarrow{OP}| = |\overrightarrow{OQ}| = r$. Then $a = r \cos \alpha$ and $b = r \sin \alpha$, so that

$$a' = r \cos(\alpha + 30°) = r(\cos \alpha \cos 30° - \sin \alpha \sin 30°)$$
$$= r \cos \alpha \cos 30° - r \sin \alpha \sin 30° = \frac{\sqrt{3}}{2} a - \frac{1}{2} b.$$

Similarly,

$$b' = r \sin(\alpha + 30°) = r \sin \alpha \cos 30° + r \cos \alpha \sin 30°$$
$$= \frac{\sqrt{3}}{2} b + \frac{1}{2} a.$$

We rewrite these equations as

$$a' = \frac{\sqrt{3}}{2}a - \frac{1}{2}b \quad \text{and} \quad b' = \frac{1}{2}a + \frac{\sqrt{3}}{2}b.$$

Therefore,

$$T_{30^\circ}(a, b) = \left(\frac{\sqrt{3}}{2}a - \frac{1}{2}b, \frac{1}{2}a + \frac{\sqrt{3}}{2}b\right)$$

and its standard matrix representation is (verify this)

$$A = [T_{30^\circ}]_E = \begin{bmatrix} \frac{\sqrt{3}}{2} & -\frac{1}{2} \\ \frac{1}{2} & \frac{\sqrt{3}}{2} \end{bmatrix}.$$

This rotation does indeed preserve the length of a vector and the angle between two vectors in the plane. Let us verify that it *preserves inner products.* Let $\mathbf{u} = (u_1, u_2)$ and $\mathbf{v} = (v_1, v_2)$ be two vectors in $\mathbb{R}^2$. Then the standard inner product $\langle u, v \rangle$ gives $\langle u, v \rangle = u_1 v_1 + u_2 v_2$.

Let us denote T_{30° by T. Then

$$T(\mathbf{u}) = \left(\frac{\sqrt{3}}{2}u_1 - \frac{1}{2}u_2, \frac{1}{2}u_1 + \frac{\sqrt{3}}{2}u_2\right),$$

$$T(\mathbf{v}) = \left(\frac{\sqrt{3}}{2}v_1 - \frac{1}{2}v_2, \frac{1}{2}v_1 + \frac{\sqrt{3}}{2}v_2\right)$$

and

$$\langle T(\mathbf{u}), T(\mathbf{v}) \rangle = \left(\frac{\sqrt{3}}{2}u_1 - \frac{1}{2}u_2\right)\left(\frac{\sqrt{3}}{2}v_1 - \frac{1}{2}v_2\right) + \left(\frac{1}{2}u_1 + \frac{\sqrt{3}}{2}u_2\right)\left(\frac{1}{2}v_1 + \frac{\sqrt{3}}{2}v_2\right)$$

$$= \frac{3}{4}u_1 v_1 - \frac{\sqrt{3}}{4}u_1 v_2 - \frac{\sqrt{3}}{4}u_2 v_1 + \frac{1}{4}u_2 v_2$$

$$+ \frac{1}{4}u_1 v_1 + \frac{\sqrt{3}}{4}u_1 v_2 + \frac{\sqrt{3}}{4}u_2 v_1 + \frac{3}{4}u_2 v_2$$

$$= u_1 v_1 + u_2 v_2 = \langle \mathbf{u}, \mathbf{v} \rangle.$$

Thus $\langle T(\mathbf{u}), T(\mathbf{v}) \rangle = \langle \mathbf{u}, \mathbf{v} \rangle$.

For reasons that will become clearer as we proceed, we call T an *orthogonal linear transformation.* More generally:

If $T: U \to U$ is a linear transformation defined on the real inner-product space U, we say that T is an **orthogonal linear transformation** if, for each $\mathbf{u}, \mathbf{v}$ in U, we have $\langle T(\mathbf{u}), T(\mathbf{v}) \rangle = \langle \mathbf{u}, \mathbf{v} \rangle$; that is, T *preserves inner products.*

Example 2   Let $T: \mathbb{R}^2 \to \mathbb{R}^2$ be the following transformation studied in Section 5.1:

$$T(x_1, x_2) = (-x_2, x_1).$$

Now let $\mathbf{u} = (u_1, u_2)$ and $\mathbf{v} = (v_1, v_2)$ be arbitrary vectors in $\mathbb{R}^2$ (here $\mathbb{R}^2$ is Euclidean 2-space with the Euclidean inner product). Let us compute the inner product of $T(\mathbf{u})$ and $T(\mathbf{v})$. Since

$$T(\mathbf{u}) = (-u_2, u_1) \quad \text{and} \quad T(\mathbf{v}) = (-v_2, v_1),$$

therefore

$$\langle T(\mathbf{u}), T(\mathbf{v}) \rangle = (-u_2)(-v_2) + u_1 v_1$$
$$= u_2 v_2 + u_1 v_1 = u_1 v_1 + u_2 v_2 = \langle \mathbf{u}, \mathbf{v} \rangle.$$

So T is orthogonal.

Observe that T preserves lengths also. For, let $\mathbf{v} = (x_1, x_2)$, where x_1, x_2 are real. Then

$$\| \mathbf{v} \| = \sqrt{\langle \mathbf{v}, \mathbf{v} \rangle} = \sqrt{x_1^2 + x_2^2}.$$

On the other hand,

$$\| T(\mathbf{v}) \| = \sqrt{\langle T(\mathbf{v}), T(\mathbf{v}) \rangle} = \sqrt{(-x_2)^2 + x_1^2} = \sqrt{x_1^2 + x_2^2}.$$

Comparing, we see that $\| T(\mathbf{v}) \| = \| \mathbf{v} \|$ for all vectors v, and hence T preserves length.

We now state and partially prove another interesting characterization of an orthogonal linear transformation.

Theorem 5.11

Let U be an inner-product space, and let $T: U \to U$ be a linear transformation. Then T is orthogonal if and only if T preserves lengths in the sense that $\|T(\mathbf{u})\| = \|\mathbf{u}\|$ for all $\mathbf{u}$ in U.

To prove one part of this theorem, first observe that if T is orthogonal, then surely

$$\| \mathbf{u} \|^2 = \langle \mathbf{u}, \mathbf{u} \rangle = \langle T(\mathbf{u}), T(\mathbf{u}) \rangle = \| T(\mathbf{u}) \|^2$$

for all $\mathbf{u}$ in U. Therefore, $\| T(\mathbf{u}) \| = \| \mathbf{u} \|$.

Now suppose that T is an orthogonal linear transformation. Then by what we have just shown it preserves lengths. But if T preserves lengths, it also preserves inner products (see Exercise 32). Moreover, in Section 4.3 we noted that if θ is an angle between two nonzero vectors $\mathbf{v}_1$ and $\mathbf{v}_2$ in an inner-product space, then

$$\cos \theta = \frac{\langle \mathbf{v}_1, \mathbf{v}_2 \rangle}{\| \mathbf{v}_1 \| \, \| \mathbf{v}_2 \|}.$$

Since this expression involves inner products and lengths, we can conclude:

Corollary 1

An orthogonal linear transformation preserves angles too.

An orthogonal linear transformation is also called an **isometry**. The term isometry comes from the Greek language and means "of equal measure or dimensions." The measure intended in the present situation is the norm (or length), which, of course, is preserved under an orthogonal linear transformation.

It is useful to note that it is sufficient to verify that inner products are preserved only for all pairs of members of a basis for V to demonstrate that T is an orthogonal linear transformation. This is the content of the following corollary. The proof is left to you as an exercise.

Corollary 2

Let $S = \{v_1, v_2, \ldots, v_n\}$ be a basis for the real inner-product space V. Then the linear transformation $T: V \to V$ is orthogonal if and only if $\langle T(v_i), T(v_j) \rangle = \langle v_i, v_j \rangle$ for each pair of vectors v_i and v_j in S.

Let us return briefly to Example 2 and compute the matrix representation for T.

Example 3   Calculate the matrix representation of the linear transformation $T(x, y) = (-y, x)$ with respect to the standard (orthonormal) basis for $\mathbb{R}^2$.

It is clear that

$$B = [T]_E = \begin{bmatrix} 0 & -1 \\ 1 & 0 \end{bmatrix}.$$
$$\;\; T(e_1) \quad T(e_2)$$

Note that

$$B^{-1} = \begin{bmatrix} 0 & 1 \\ -1 & 0 \end{bmatrix} = B^t.$$

Also note that, for the matrix A of Example 1, we have

$$A^{-1} = \begin{bmatrix} \dfrac{\sqrt{3}}{2} & \dfrac{1}{2} \\ -\dfrac{1}{2} & \dfrac{\sqrt{3}}{2} \end{bmatrix} = A^t.$$

The properties of the matrices A and B are of interest to us.

An $n \times n$ real matrix P is called an **orthogonal matrix** if

$$P^t P = I_n = PP^t.$$

The matrices A and B are orthogonal.

Example 4 The following matrices are orthogonal:

$$I_n, \quad \begin{bmatrix} 0 & 1 \\ 1 & 0 \end{bmatrix}, \quad \begin{bmatrix} 0 & 0 & 1 \\ 0 & 1 & 0 \\ 1 & 0 & 0 \end{bmatrix}, \quad \begin{bmatrix} 1 & 0 & 0 & 0 \\ 0 & 0 & 1 & 0 \\ 0 & 1 & 0 & 0 \\ 0 & 0 & 0 & 1 \end{bmatrix},$$

$$\begin{bmatrix} \dfrac{1}{\sqrt{2}} & -\dfrac{1}{\sqrt{3}} & \dfrac{1}{\sqrt{6}} \\[2ex] 0 & \dfrac{1}{\sqrt{3}} & \dfrac{2}{\sqrt{6}} \\[2ex] \dfrac{1}{\sqrt{2}} & \dfrac{1}{\sqrt{3}} & -\dfrac{1}{\sqrt{6}} \end{bmatrix},$$

as can be easily verified by computing the product $P^t P$.

Orthogonal linear transformations and orthogonal matrices are related by the following theorem stated here without proof. You should verify this result for the special situations given in Examples 1, 2 and 3.

Theorem· 5.12
Let $T: V \to V$ be a linear transformation and let $S = \{v_1, v_2, \ldots, v_n\}$ be an orthonormal basis for the real inner-product space V. Then T is an orthogonal transformation if and only if $[T]_S$ is an orthogonal matrix.

We remarked earlier that the choice of the word *orthogonal* to describe a transformation that preserves inner products would become apparent. Look at the column vectors of the orthogonal matrices in Examples 3 and 4. As you can easily check, they are mutually orthonormal as vectors in $\mathbb{R}^n$. In fact we have the following:

Theorem 5.13
The column vectors of an orthogonal matrix P are mutually orthonormal.

The proofs of this theorem and its corollary below are left as exercises for you.

Corollary
The column vectors of an $n \times n$ real matrix A are mutually orthonormal if and only if the row vectors of A are mutually orthonormal.

Applications of the ideas developed in this chapter are the subject of the last two chapters of this book.

EXERCISES (5.6)

Which of the following matrices are orthogonal?

1. $\begin{bmatrix} \dfrac{1}{2} & \dfrac{1}{3} \\[2mm] -\dfrac{1}{2} & \dfrac{1}{3} \end{bmatrix}$
  2. $\begin{bmatrix} \dfrac{1}{\sqrt{2}} & -\dfrac{1}{\sqrt{2}} \\[2mm] \dfrac{1}{\sqrt{2}} & \dfrac{1}{\sqrt{2}} \end{bmatrix}$
  3. $\begin{bmatrix} \dfrac{3}{5} & \dfrac{4}{5} \\[2mm] \dfrac{4}{5} & -\dfrac{3}{5} \end{bmatrix}$

4. $\begin{bmatrix} \dfrac{12}{13} & -\dfrac{5}{13} \\[2mm] -\dfrac{5}{13} & -\dfrac{12}{13} \end{bmatrix}$
  5. $\begin{bmatrix} \dfrac{1}{\sqrt{2}} & -\dfrac{1}{\sqrt{2}} & 0 \\[2mm] 0 & \dfrac{1}{\sqrt{2}} & -\dfrac{1}{\sqrt{2}} \\[2mm] -\dfrac{1}{\sqrt{2}} & 0 & \dfrac{1}{\sqrt{2}} \end{bmatrix}$

6. $\begin{bmatrix} \cos\theta & \sin\theta & 0 \\ \sin\theta & -\cos\theta & 0 \\ 0 & 0 & 1 \end{bmatrix}$
  7. $\begin{bmatrix} \dfrac{1}{\sqrt{2}} & \dfrac{1}{\sqrt{2}} & 0 \\[2mm] \dfrac{1}{\sqrt{3}} & -\dfrac{1}{\sqrt{3}} & \dfrac{1}{\sqrt{3}} \\[2mm] -\dfrac{1}{\sqrt{6}} & \dfrac{1}{\sqrt{6}} & \dfrac{2}{\sqrt{6}} \end{bmatrix}$

Determine which of the following linear transformations on $\mathbb{R}^n$ with the standard inner product are orthogonal.

8. $T(\alpha_1, \alpha_2) = (\tfrac{3}{5}\alpha_1 + \tfrac{4}{5}\alpha_2, \tfrac{4}{5}\alpha_1 - \tfrac{3}{5}\alpha_2)$

9. $T(\alpha_1, \alpha_2, \alpha_3) = \left(\alpha_3, \dfrac{\alpha_1\sqrt{3}}{2} + \dfrac{\alpha_2}{2}, \dfrac{\alpha_1}{2} - \dfrac{\alpha_2\sqrt{3}}{2}\right)$

10. $T(\alpha_1, \alpha_2, \alpha_3) = (\tfrac{3}{5}\alpha_1 - \tfrac{4}{5}\alpha_2, \alpha_3, \tfrac{4}{5}\alpha_2 + \tfrac{3}{5}\alpha_3)$

11. $T(\alpha_1, \alpha_2, \alpha_3) = (\tfrac{5}{13}\alpha_1 + \tfrac{12}{13}\alpha_3, \tfrac{12}{13}\alpha_2 - \tfrac{5}{13}\alpha_3, \alpha_1)$

12–15. Write the matrix representation $P = [T]_E$, with respect to the standard basis, of each linear transformation in Exercises 8–11.

Exercises 16–19 are for students who have studied calculus. Let $T: P_1 \to P_1$ be the linear transformation on the vector space of real linear polynomials with the integral inner product $\langle p, q \rangle = \int_0^1 p(t)q(t)\,dt$ defined by

$$T(ax + b) = xb\sqrt{3} + \frac{a\sqrt{3}}{3}.$$

16. Is the standard basis $\{x, 1\}$ for P_1 orthonormal with respect to the integral inner product?

17. Is the basis $S = \{1, \sqrt{3}\,(2x - 1)\}$ for P_1 orthonormal with respect to the integral inner product?

18. Represent the transformation T by a matrix $P = [T]_S$ with respect to the basis S.

19. Determine whether or not T is an orthogonal transformation with respect to the integral inner product.

20. Show that every 2×2 orthogonal matrix P must have either form A or B, where

$$A = \begin{bmatrix} \cos\phi & -\sin\phi \\ \sin\phi & \cos\phi \end{bmatrix}, \quad B = \begin{bmatrix} \cos\phi & \sin\phi \\ \sin\phi & -\cos\phi \end{bmatrix}.$$

21. Show geometrically that the matrix A in Exercise 20 represents, with respect to the standard basis for the plane, a rotation about the origin through an angle ϕ.

22. Show that the matrix B in Exercise 20 represents, with respect to the standard basis for the plane, a reflection of the plane in the line through the origin whose angle of inclination is $\phi/2$.

23. Use the results of Exercises 20–22 to show that an orthogonal matrix P represents a rotation of the plane if and only if det $P = 1$.

In Exercises 24–26, let V be an inner-product space and let k be a fixed scalar such that $k > 1$. Let $T: V \to V$ be defined by $T(\mathbf{v}) = k\mathbf{v}$ for all $\mathbf{v}$ in V.

24. Show that T is a linear transformation.

25. Show that for all nonzero vectors $\mathbf{v}$, $\mathbf{w}$ we get

$$\frac{\langle T(\mathbf{v}), T(\mathbf{w}) \rangle}{\| T(\mathbf{v}) \| \, \| T(\mathbf{w}) \|} = \frac{\langle \mathbf{v}, \mathbf{w} \rangle}{\| \mathbf{v} \| \, \| \mathbf{w} \|}.$$

26. Conclude that T preserves angles but not lengths or inner products. *Remark.* Such a linear transformation is called a *magnification*.

27. Are the linear transformations T in Exercises 24–26 orthogonal? Give reasons.

In Exercises 28–30, suppose that V is a Euclidean 2-space, and suppose $T: V \to V$ is defined by $T(x_1, x_2) = (x_2, -x_1)$, where x_1, x_2 are real.

28. Is T a linear transformation?

29. Is T an orthogonal linear transformation? Why?

30. Does T preserve lengths? inner products? angles? Explain.

31. Let V be an inner product space and let $T: V \to V$ be a linear transformation. Suppose that T preserves orthogonality in the sense that whenever $\langle \mathbf{v}, \mathbf{v}' \rangle = 0$, then also $\langle T(\mathbf{v}), T(\mathbf{v}') \rangle = 0$. Does this force T to be an isometry? Give reasons.

32. Prove that if $T: V \to V$ is a linear transformation of an inner-product space V such that T preserves lengths, then T preserves inner products. *Hint.* Consider $\| T(u + v) \|^2$ and $\| u + v \|^2$.

6
EIGENVALUES, EIGENVECTORS, AND QUADRATIC FORMS

One often applies linear algebra to a situation where one knows a linear transformation T and is concerned with those vectors $\mathbf{x}$ and those scalars a for which the equation

$$T(\mathbf{x}) = a\mathbf{x}$$

is valid. We shall see an example of this in Chapter 7 when we find fixed-point vectors for Markov matrices. In that example we will require only that $a = 1$. The more general problem and some of its ramifications are the topic of this chapter.

6.1 EIGENVALUES AND EIGENVECTORS

Let us introduce this concept with an example from biology.

Example 1 Consider an ecosystem containing m species of life. Define the population vector $\mathbf{n}(t)$ of the ecosystem to be the column vector with m entries, whose ith entry $n_i(t)$ is the population of the ith species at time t. We assume that there is a matrix

$A(t)$, called the transition matrix of the ecosystem from time t to time $t + 1$, such that

$$\mathbf{n}(t + 1) = A(t)\mathbf{n}(t).$$

The entries in the matrix $A(t)$ are numbers that reflect the possibility that an individual member of the given species will survive to time $t + 1$ or affect the survival of other species, or that new individuals will come into existence during this interval.

In a stable ecosystem the value of $\mathbf{n}(t + 1)$ is proportional to that of $\mathbf{n}(t)$; that is, at time $t + 1$ the species in the system will still be in the same proportion as at time t. This gives rise to the problem: For what values of $\mathbf{n}(t)$ and proportionality constant λ does $A(t)\mathbf{n}(t) = \lambda\mathbf{n}(t)$?

The general form of this problem is interesting enough and is applied so often that we give the following definition:

Let A be an $n \times n$ matrix. A scalar λ is called an **eigenvalue** of the matrix A corresponding to the nonzero **eigenvector** $\mathbf{x}$ if

$$A\mathbf{x} = \lambda\mathbf{x}. \tag{6.1}$$

It is clear that the zero vector would satisfy Equation (6.1) for any scalar λ, so zero *is not allowed* to be an eigenvector.

Example 2   Given the matrix

$$A = \begin{bmatrix} 1 & 0 & 1 \\ 1 & 2 & 0 \\ 3 & 0 & 1 \end{bmatrix},$$

show that $\lambda = 2$ is an eigenvalue, and that a corresponding eigenvector is

$$\mathbf{x} = \begin{bmatrix} 0 \\ 1 \\ 0 \end{bmatrix}.$$

Direct computation shows that (6.1) is satisfied:

$$A\mathbf{x} = \begin{bmatrix} 1 & 0 & 1 \\ 1 & 2 & 0 \\ 3 & 0 & 1 \end{bmatrix} \cdot \begin{bmatrix} 0 \\ 1 \\ 0 \end{bmatrix} = \begin{bmatrix} 0 \\ 2 \\ 0 \end{bmatrix} = 2\mathbf{x}.$$

To find the eigenvalues and eigenvectors for a given matrix A we first note that we may write Equation (6.1) in matrix form as

$$\lambda I\mathbf{x} - A\mathbf{x} = \mathbf{0} \quad \text{or} \quad (\lambda I - A)\mathbf{x} = \mathbf{0}. \tag{6.2}$$

Equation (6.2) is the matrix equation for a system of homogeneous linear equations. It will have a nontrivial solution if and only if the determinant of the coefficient matrix $(\lambda I - A)$ is zero. We have the following theorem.

Theorem 6.1

The scalar λ is an eigenvalue for the $n \times n$ matrix A if and only if

$$\det(\lambda I - A) = 0. \qquad (6.3)$$

$$\det(T - \lambda I) = 0.$$

Equation (6.3) is called the **characteristic equation** of the matrix A and the eigenvalue λ is frequently called a *characteristic value* of A. Other names in use are *proper value* and *latent root*.

Example 3 Find all of the eigenvalues for the matrix

$$A = \begin{bmatrix} 1 & -2 \\ 0 & 3 \end{bmatrix}.$$

Note that

$$\lambda I - A = \begin{bmatrix} \lambda & 0 \\ 0 & \lambda \end{bmatrix} - \begin{bmatrix} 1 & -2 \\ 0 & 3 \end{bmatrix} = \begin{bmatrix} \lambda - 1 & 2 \\ 0 & \lambda - 3 \end{bmatrix}.$$

Therefore, the characteristic equation for A is

$$\det \begin{bmatrix} \lambda - 1 & 2 \\ 0 & \lambda - 3 \end{bmatrix} = (\lambda - 1)(\lambda - 3) = 0.$$

Hence A has eigenvalues 1 and 3. The corresponding eigenvectors $\mathbf{x}$ for A are found by substituting these values for λ separately into Equation (6.2) and solving the resulting systems of homogeneous equations. Thus, for $\lambda = 3$,

$$\begin{bmatrix} 3-1 & 2 \\ 0 & 3-3 \end{bmatrix} \begin{bmatrix} x_1 \\ x_2 \end{bmatrix} = \begin{bmatrix} 0 \\ 0 \end{bmatrix} \quad \text{or} \quad \begin{bmatrix} 2 & 2 \\ 0 & 0 \end{bmatrix} \begin{bmatrix} x_1 \\ x_2 \end{bmatrix} = \begin{bmatrix} 0 \\ 0 \end{bmatrix}.$$

All solutions to this system are seen to be proportional to the vector

$$\mathbf{x} = \begin{bmatrix} 1 \\ -1 \end{bmatrix}.$$

Thus, this vector $\mathbf{x}$ is an eigenvector for A corresponding to the eigenvalue 3; that is, $A\mathbf{x} = 3\mathbf{x}$. This is readily verified by the computation

$$\begin{bmatrix} 1 & -2 \\ 0 & 3 \end{bmatrix} \cdot \begin{bmatrix} 1 \\ -1 \end{bmatrix} = 3 \begin{bmatrix} 1 \\ -1 \end{bmatrix}.$$

A similar calculation with the eigenvalue 1 results in the homogeneous system

$$\begin{bmatrix} 0 & 2 \\ 0 & -2 \end{bmatrix} \cdot \begin{bmatrix} x_1 \\ x_2 \end{bmatrix} = \begin{bmatrix} 0 \\ 0 \end{bmatrix}.$$

All solutions to this system are proportional to the eigenvector

$$\mathbf{x} = \begin{bmatrix} 1 \\ 0 \end{bmatrix}.$$

If A is an $n \times n$ matrix and λ_0 is an eigenvalue for A, then the homogeneous system of linear equations $(\lambda_0 I - A)\mathbf{x} = \mathbf{0}$ has nontrivial solutions. The set of all solution vectors $\mathbf{x}$ form a vector space called the **eigenspace of A corresponding to** λ_0. Thus, the eigenvectors of A corresponding to the eigenvalue λ_0 together with the zero vector form the eigenspace of A corresponding to λ_0. In Examples 2 and 3 the eigenspaces were each one-dimensional. Consider, however, the following example.

Example 4   Find a basis for each eigenspace of the matrix

$$A = \begin{bmatrix} 2 & -1 & 0 \\ -1 & 2 & 0 \\ 0 & 0 & 3 \end{bmatrix}.$$

We find that the characteristic equation $\det(\lambda I - A) = 0$ for A is (verify this)

$$(\lambda - 3)^2 (\lambda - 1) = 0.$$

For $\lambda_0 = 3$, we solve

$$(3I - A)\mathbf{x} = \mathbf{0},$$

which is

$$\begin{bmatrix} 1 & 1 & 0 \\ 1 & 1 & 0 \\ 0 & 0 & 0 \end{bmatrix} \begin{bmatrix} x_1 \\ x_2 \\ x_3 \end{bmatrix} = \begin{bmatrix} 0 \\ 0 \\ 0 \end{bmatrix}.$$

Solving this system, we see that x_3 is arbitrary and $x_1 = -x_2$, so let $x_3 = s, x_2 = t$, and $x_1 = -t$. The existence of two independent parameters s and t indicates that the eigenspace of A corresponding to $\lambda = 3$ has dimension two. A basis for this space consists of the two linearly independent vectors

$$\mathbf{u} = \begin{bmatrix} -1 \\ 1 \\ 0 \end{bmatrix} \quad \text{and} \quad \mathbf{v} = \begin{bmatrix} 0 \\ 0 \\ 1 \end{bmatrix}.$$

These two vectors are easily obtained by setting $s = 0, t = 1$, and then $s = 1, t = 0$. They are obviously linearly independent. Furthermore, they span the eigenspace corresponding to 3. In verifying this, note that any eigenvector $\mathbf{x}$ corresponding to the eigenvalue 3 can be written as a linear combination of **u** and **v** as follows:

$$\mathbf{x} = \begin{bmatrix} -t \\ t \\ s \end{bmatrix} = t\mathbf{u} + s\mathbf{v}.$$

For the other eigenvalue $\lambda = 1$ we find that

$$(I - A)\mathbf{x} = \mathbf{0}.$$

has solutions (verify this)

$$\mathbf{x} = \begin{bmatrix} t \\ t \\ 0 \end{bmatrix} = t \begin{bmatrix} 1 \\ 1 \\ 0 \end{bmatrix}.$$

Therefore, the vector

$$\mathbf{w} = \begin{bmatrix} 1 \\ 1 \\ 0 \end{bmatrix}$$

is a basis for the eigenspace of A corresponding to the eigenvalue 1.

We have discussed eigenvalues and eigenvectors for $n \times n$ matrices. Suppose

$$T: V \to V$$

is a linear transformation of the vector space V into itself; then the *eigenvalues* and *eigenvectors* of T are defined similarly, that is, they are solutions to the equation

$$T(\mathbf{x}) = \lambda\mathbf{x}, \quad \mathbf{x} \neq \mathbf{0}.$$

It can be verified that the eigenvectors of T for a given eigenvalue λ_0, together with the zero vector, make up the kernel of the transformation $(\lambda_0 I - T)$, where I is the identity transformation given by $I(\mathbf{x}) = \mathbf{x}$. The kernel of the transformation $\lambda_0 I - T$ is called the *eigenspace* of T *corresponding to* λ_0.

Example 5   Let $V = \mathbb{R}^2$ and let **w** be a fixed vector in V. Let $T: V \to V$ be a projection onto **w**. We can find eigenvalues and eigenvectors for T geometrically, since we seek solutions to the equation $T(\mathbf{x}) = \lambda\mathbf{x}$. Every vector parallel to **w** is of the form $\mathbf{v} = a\mathbf{w}$, where a is a scalar. Since T projects onto **w**, in this case we would have

$$T(\mathbf{v}) = T(a\mathbf{w}) = aT(\mathbf{w}) = a\mathbf{w} = \mathbf{v}.$$

So $\mathbf{v} = a\mathbf{w}$ is an eigenvector corresponding to the eigenvalue $\lambda = 1$.

If a nonzero vector **v** is orthogonal to **w**, then $T(\mathbf{v}) = \mathbf{0} = 0 \cdot \mathbf{v}$, so **v** is an eigenvector corresponding to the eigenvalue $\lambda = 0$.

If **v** is any other vector in $\mathbb{R}^2$, neither parallel nor orthogonal to **w**, then $T(\mathbf{v})$ is not a scalar multiple of **v**, as you can see from Fig. 6.1. It is not parallel to **v** at all, so it cannot be a characteristic vector for T.

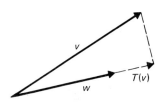

Figure 6.1

Therefore, the eigenvalues for a projection in $\mathbb{R}^2$ are $\lambda = 1$ and $\lambda = 0$, with eigenvectors respectively parallel or orthogonal to the vector onto which the projection goes.

In general, to compute the eigenvalues and corresponding eigenvectors of a linear transformation $T: V \to V$, one simply selects the matrix representation A of T with respect to *any* basis for V and then calculates the characteristic equation for A. The eigenvalues and corresponding eigenvectors for A will be those of T. The fact that these are independent of the choice of basis for V and hence of the choice of the matrix representation for T is the result of the work done in Chapter 5. Let us summarize this as the following theorem.

Theorem 6.2

Let $T: V \to V$ be a linear transformation on the finite-dimensional vector space V. If S and S' are bases for V, and if A and A' are the matrix representations of T relative to S and S', respectively, then the eigenvalues A and A' are equal. That is, similar matrices have the same eigenvalues.

Proof. Since A and A' are both matrix representations of T, they are similar matrices. Therefore, for some invertible matrix P, we have

$$A = P^{-1}A'P.$$

Hence,

$$\lambda I - A = \lambda I - P^{-1}A'P = \lambda P^{-1}IP - P^{-1}A'P = P^{-1}\lambda IP - P^{-1}A'P$$
$$= P^{-1}(\lambda I - A')P.$$

Because of this, the characteristic equations are

$$0 = \det(\lambda I - A) = \det(P^{-1}(\lambda I - A')P) = (\det P^{-1}) \cdot (\det(\lambda I - A'))(\det P)$$
$$= (\det P^{-1}) \cdot (\det P) \cdot (\det(\lambda I - A')) = \det(\lambda I - A').$$

Thus, A and A' have the same eigenvalues. Furthermore if x is an eigenvector of A corresponding to the value λ, then Px is an eigenvector of A' corresponding to λ.

Example 6　Let T be the transformation on the space P_2 of real polynomials of degree two or less defined by

$$T(c + bx + ax^2) = (5c - a) + 2bx + (2a - c)x^2.$$

Pick the standard basis $\{1, x, x^2\}$ for P_2. The matrix representation for T relative to this basis is (verify this)

$$A = \begin{bmatrix} 5 & 0 & -1 \\ 0 & 2 & 0 \\ -1 & 0 & 2 \end{bmatrix}.$$

The characteristic equation $\det(\lambda I - A) = 0$ for A, hence for T, is

$$(\lambda - 2)(\lambda^2 - 7\lambda + 9) = 0.$$

The roots of this equation, hence the eigenvalues of A, are

$$\lambda = 2, \quad \frac{7}{2} + \frac{\sqrt{13}}{2}, \quad \text{and} \quad \frac{7}{2} - \frac{\sqrt{13}}{2}.$$

Corresponding to each of these, we have the following eigenvectors (verify this):

For $\lambda_1 = 2$:
$$\begin{bmatrix} 0 \\ t \\ 0 \end{bmatrix} = tx \text{ (note that } T(tx) = 2tx).$$

For $\lambda_2 = \dfrac{7 + \sqrt{13}}{2}$:
$$\begin{bmatrix} \dfrac{-3 - \sqrt{13}}{2}t \\ 0 \\ t \end{bmatrix} = t\left(\frac{-3 - \sqrt{13}}{2} + 0x + x^2 \right).$$

For $\lambda_3 = \dfrac{7 - \sqrt{13}}{2}$:
$$\begin{bmatrix} \dfrac{-3 + \sqrt{13}}{2}t \\ 0 \\ t \end{bmatrix} = t\left(\frac{-3 + \sqrt{13}}{2} + 0x + x^2 \right).$$

　　In general, finding the eigenvalues of the transformation T or of an $n \times n$ matrix A is the same problem as finding the roots of a polynomial in λ. This is not always a simple task and the techniques can be quite involved. The fundamental ideas for solving polynomial equations developed in college algebra are needed. Often some (or all) of the roots of the characteristic equation for a given *real* matrix are not real numbers. However, we shall defer the discussion of complex eigenvalues to more advanced courses.

In Theorem 6.2 we proved that similar matrices have the same eigenvalues since they have the same characteristic equation. The converse is, however, false. The two matrices

$$\begin{bmatrix} 1 & 0 \\ 0 & 1 \end{bmatrix} \quad \text{and} \quad \begin{bmatrix} 1 & 1 \\ 0 & 1 \end{bmatrix}$$

have the same eigenvalues, yet they are not similar. (Why not?)

EXERCISES (6.1)

In Exercises 1–10, for each of the given matrices (a) write the characteristic equation, (b) find the eigenvalues of the matrix, and (c) find an eigenvector corresponding to each eigenvalue.

1. $\begin{bmatrix} 3 & 1 \\ 1 & 3 \end{bmatrix}$
2. $\begin{bmatrix} 0 & 2 \\ 8 & 0 \end{bmatrix}$
3. $\begin{bmatrix} 10 & -9 \\ 4 & -2 \end{bmatrix}$

4. $\begin{bmatrix} \frac{1}{2} & \frac{1}{2} \\ \frac{1}{2} & \frac{1}{2} \end{bmatrix}$
5. $\begin{bmatrix} 0.3 & 0.7 \\ 0.5 & 0.5 \end{bmatrix}$
6. $\begin{bmatrix} 0 & 0 \\ 0 & 0 \end{bmatrix}$

7. $\begin{bmatrix} 3 & -1 \\ 2 & 2 \end{bmatrix}$
8. $\begin{bmatrix} 1 & 2 & 0 \\ 0 & 2 & -1 \\ 0 & 0 & 3 \end{bmatrix}$

9. $\begin{bmatrix} 1 & -1 & 0 \\ 0 & 1 & -1 \\ 0 & 0 & 0 \end{bmatrix}$
10. $\begin{bmatrix} -15 & 16 & 32 \\ -4 & 5 & 8 \\ -4 & 4 & 9 \end{bmatrix}$

11. Find bases for the eigenspaces of the matrix in Exercise 5.

12. Find bases for the eigenspaces of the matrix in Exercise 10.

In Exercises 13–18, find the eigenvalues and eigenvectors of the given linear transformation T. Sketch figures.

13. T is a reflection in $\mathbb{R}^2$ through the line along the vector $\mathbf{w}$.

14. T is a projection in $\mathbb{R}^2$ orthogonal to a given vector $\mathbf{w}$.

15. T is a reflection in $\mathbb{R}^3$ through the line along a given vector $\mathbf{w}$.

16. T is a projection in $\mathbb{R}^3$ onto $\mathbf{w}$.

17. T is a projection in $\mathbb{R}^3$ orthogonal to $\mathbf{w}$.

18. T is a clockwise rotation in $\mathbb{R}^2$ of 90° followed by a reflection in the y-axis.

In Exercises 19–24, find the eigenspaces associated with each eigenvalue of the given matrix.

19. $\begin{bmatrix} 4 & 1 & 0 \\ 1 & 4 & 0 \\ 0 & 0 & 2 \end{bmatrix}$
20. $\begin{bmatrix} 5 & 0 & 1 \\ 1 & 1 & 0 \\ -7 & 1 & 0 \end{bmatrix}$
21. $\begin{bmatrix} -1 & 0 & 0 \\ 0 & 3 & 1 \\ 0 & 1 & 3 \end{bmatrix}$

22. $\begin{bmatrix} 0 & 0 & 2 & 0 \\ 1 & 0 & 1 & 0 \\ 0 & 1 & -2 & 0 \\ 0 & 0 & 0 & 1 \end{bmatrix}$ 23. $\begin{bmatrix} 1 & 2 & 1 \\ 0 & 2 & 1 \\ 0 & 0 & 3 \end{bmatrix}$ 24. $\begin{bmatrix} 10 & -9 & 0 & 0 \\ 4 & -2 & 0 & 0 \\ 0 & 0 & -2 & -5 \\ 0 & 0 & -1 & 2 \end{bmatrix}$

In Exercises 25–28 let T be the transformation in the space P_2 of quadratic polynomials given by

$$T(c + bx + ax^2) = (4c + a) + (b - 2c)x + (a - 2c)x^2.$$

25. Write the matrix representation A for T relative to the standard basis $\{1, x, x^2\}$.
26. Find the characteristic equation of A.
27. Find the eigenvalues of T.
28. Find bases for the corresponding eigenspaces of T.

In Exercises 29–32 let T be the transformation on the space M_2 of real 2×2 matrices given by

$$T\left(\begin{bmatrix} a & b \\ c & d \end{bmatrix}\right) = \begin{bmatrix} 10a - 9b & 4a - 2b \\ -2c - 7d & c + 2d \end{bmatrix}.$$

29. Find the (4×4) matrix representation A for T relative to the standard basis for M_2.
30. Find the characteristic equation for A.
31. Find the eigenvalues of T.
32. Find bases for the corresponding eigenspaces of T.
33. Show that $\lambda = 0$ is an eigenvalue for a matrix A if and only if A is not invertible.
34. Prove that the eigenvalues of an upper triangular matrix A are the diagonal entries a_{ii} of A.
35. Prove that the two matrices

$$A = \begin{bmatrix} 1 & 0 & 0 \\ 0 & -1 & 1 \\ 0 & 0 & -1 \end{bmatrix} \quad \text{and} \quad B = \begin{bmatrix} 1 & 0 & 0 \\ 0 & -1 & 0 \\ 0 & 0 & -1 \end{bmatrix}$$

are not similar even though they have the same eigenvalues.
Hint. Show that if $AP = PB$, then P is singular.

36. Show that the *real* matrix

$$A = \begin{bmatrix} -1 & 2 \\ -2 & 1 \end{bmatrix}$$

has no eigenvalues but that as a *complex* matrix it has complex eigenvalues and eigenvectors.

37. Find the eigenspaces of the rotation of the plane through $45°$ corresponding to each eigenvalue.
38. Show that if $A\mathbf{x} = \lambda\mathbf{x}$, then $A^2\mathbf{x} = \lambda^2\mathbf{x}$.

39. If the characteristic values of the matrix A are $\lambda = 1$ and $\lambda = -2$, what are the characteristic values of A^2?

40. Show that the characteristic equation for the 2×2 matrix $A = (a_{ij})$ is

$$\lambda^2 - (a_{11} + a_{22})\lambda + \det A = 0.$$

41. Show that the characteristic equation for the 3×3 matrix $A = (a_{ij})$ is

$$\lambda^3 - (a_{11} + a_{22} + a_{33})\lambda^2$$

$$+ \lambda \left(\det \begin{bmatrix} a_{11} & a_{12} \\ a_{21} & a_{22} \end{bmatrix} + \det \begin{bmatrix} a_{11} & a_{13} \\ a_{31} & a_{33} \end{bmatrix} + \det \begin{bmatrix} a_{22} & a_{23} \\ a_{32} & a_{33} \end{bmatrix} \right) - \det A = 0.$$

6.2 SIMILARITY TO DIAGONAL MATRICES $T : V \longrightarrow V$

If T is a linear transformation from the finite-dimensional vector space V into itself, then we have seen that T can be represented relative to a given basis for V as multiplication by a matrix A. The choice of the basis for V determines the matrix A. A change in basis will change the matrix representation for T. We have also shown that all such matrix representations of T are similar, that is, $A' = P^{-1}AP$, and that similar matrices have the same eigenvalues. In this section we shall be interested in determining under what conditions a basis for V can be chosen so that the matrix A representing T is a diagonal matrix.

A square matrix A is said to be **diagonalizable** if there exists an invertible matrix P such that the matrix $D = P^{-1} AP$ is a diagonal matrix. That is, $D = (d_{ij})$, where $d_{ij} = 0$ for $i \neq j$.

It is not always possible for an $n \times n$ matrix A to be diagonalized, as shown in Example 2 below. However, if A *can* be diagonalized, then it must have n linearly independent eigenvectors, as we shall prove in the following theorem.

Theorem 6.3
An $n \times n$ matrix A is similar to a diagonal matrix D if and only if A has n linearly independent eigenvectors. Furthermore, in this case the diagonal elements of D are the common eigenvalues of A and D.

Proof. Assume that $P^{-1}AP = D$, a diagonal matrix. Then $AP = PD$. Let

$$
P = \begin{bmatrix} p_{11} & p_{12} & \cdots & p_{1n} \\ p_{21} & p_{22} & \cdots & p_{2n} \\ \vdots & \vdots & & \vdots \\ p_{n1} & p_{n2} & \cdots & p_{nn} \end{bmatrix}
\quad \text{and} \quad
D = \begin{bmatrix} d_{11} & 0 & \cdots & 0 \\ 0 & d_{22} & \cdots & 0 \\ \vdots & & & \vdots \\ 0 & 0 & \cdots & d_{nn} \end{bmatrix}.
$$

Then,

$$
AP = PD = \begin{bmatrix} d_{11}p_{11} & d_{22}p_{12} & \cdots & d_{nn}p_{1n} \\ d_{11}p_{21} & d_{22}p_{22} & \cdots & d_{nn}p_{2n} \\ \vdots & \vdots & \vdots & \vdots \\ d_{11}p_{n1} & d_{22}p_{n2} & \cdots & d_{nn}p_{nn} \end{bmatrix}.
$$

Let us denote the column vectors of the matrix P by $\mathbf{p}_i$. Then the above matrix equation can be restated in the following form:

$$
A\mathbf{p}_i = d_{ii}\mathbf{p}_i, \qquad i = 1, 2, \ldots, n. \tag{6.4}
$$

Since none of the $\mathbf{p}_i$ is the zero vector because P is invertible we see from (6.4) that the $\mathbf{p}_i$ are eigenvectors of A corresponding to the eigenvalues d_{ii}. Furthermore, since P is an invertible matrix, its column vectors must be linearly independent, as desired.

Conversely, if the matrix A has n linearly independent eigenvectors $\mathbf{p}_1, \mathbf{p}_2, \ldots, \mathbf{p}_n$ corresponding to the eigenvalues $\lambda_1, \lambda_2, \ldots, \lambda_n$, then let the matrix P be constructed with the $\mathbf{p}_i$ as column vectors:

$$
P = [\mathbf{p}_1 : \mathbf{p}_2 : \ldots : \mathbf{p}_n].
$$

Since its column vectors are linearly independent, the matrix P is invertible. Thus,

$$
AP = [A\mathbf{p}_1 : A\mathbf{p}_2 : \ldots : A\mathbf{p}_n] = [\lambda_1\mathbf{p}_1 : \lambda_2\mathbf{p}_2 : \ldots : \lambda_n\mathbf{p}_n]
$$

$$
= P \begin{bmatrix} \lambda_1 & 0 & \cdots & 0 \\ 0 & \lambda_2 & \cdots & 0 \\ \vdots & \vdots & \vdots & \vdots \\ 0 & 0 & \cdots & \lambda_n \end{bmatrix}
$$

$$
= PD.
$$

Hence, $P^{-1}AP = D$ and A is similar to a diagonal matrix with its eigenvalues on the main diagonal. This completes the proof of the theorem.

The proof gives a method for constructing the matrix P that will diagonalize A, should such be possible.

Example 1   Diagonalize, if possible, the matrix

$$A = \begin{bmatrix} 1 & -2 \\ 0 & 3 \end{bmatrix}.$$

From Example 3 of Section 6.1 we know that the eigenvalues and corresponding eigenvectors of this matrix A are

$$\lambda_1 = 1, \quad \mathbf{p}_1 = \begin{bmatrix} 1 \\ 0 \end{bmatrix} \quad \text{and} \quad \lambda_2 = 3, \quad \mathbf{p}_2 = \begin{bmatrix} 1 \\ -1 \end{bmatrix}.$$

Hence the matrix P is given by the proof of the theorem as

$$P = \begin{bmatrix} 1 & 1 \\ 0 & -1 \end{bmatrix},$$

and we compute

$$P^{-1} = \begin{bmatrix} 1 & 1 \\ 0 & -1 \end{bmatrix}.$$

Thus,

$$P^{-1}AP = \begin{bmatrix} 1 & 1 \\ 0 & -1 \end{bmatrix} \cdot \begin{bmatrix} 1 & -2 \\ 0 & 3 \end{bmatrix} \cdot \begin{bmatrix} 1 & 1 \\ 0 & -1 \end{bmatrix} = \begin{bmatrix} 1 & 0 \\ 0 & 3 \end{bmatrix} = D.$$

Example 2   Show that the matrix

$$A = \begin{bmatrix} 1 & -2 \\ 2 & -3 \end{bmatrix}$$

is not diagonalizable.

The characteristic equation for A is

$$\det(\lambda I - A) = \det \begin{bmatrix} \lambda - 1 & 2 \\ -2 & \lambda + 3 \end{bmatrix} = (\lambda + 1)^2 = 0.$$

Therefore, A has a single eigenvalue $\lambda = -1$. This fact by itself is not sufficient to show that A is not diagonalizable, since the diagonal matrix $-I_2$ has the same property and is already diagonal. In this case, however, the eigenspace of A has dimension 1. This is found in the usual way by solving the system $A\mathbf{x} = -\mathbf{x}$ or $(I + A)\mathbf{x} = \mathbf{0}$.

The augmented matrix for this homogeneous system of equations is (verify this)

$$\begin{bmatrix} 2 & -2 & \vdots & 0 \\ 2 & -2 & \vdots & 0 \end{bmatrix}.$$

The solutions therefore have the form $x_1 = x_2 = t$, and each eigenvector has the form

$$t \begin{bmatrix} 1 \\ 1 \end{bmatrix} = t\mathbf{u}.$$

Since the single vector $\mathbf{u}$ constitutes a basis for the eigenspace of A, A fails to have two linearly independent eigenvectors and cannot, by Theorem 6.3., be similar to a diagonal matrix.

Let us warn against making the *inductive leap* to the statement that A was not similar to a diagonal matrix because it had a single eigenvalue. Rather it was the fact that the dimension of its eigenspace was smaller than $n = 2$. It is easy to see that the matrix $-I$ (for any dimension) has the single eigenvalue $\lambda = -1$, yet is similar to (indeed is already) a diagonal matrix. However, its eigenspace has dimension n, with the basis for $\mathbb{R}^n$ as its linearly independent eigenvectors. Consider also the following example that illustrates each of the steps in the diagonalizing process.

Example 3   Diagonalize, if possible, the following matrix

$$A = \begin{bmatrix} 2 & 1 & 1 \\ 1 & 2 & 1 \\ 1 & 1 & 2 \end{bmatrix}.$$

Step 1. Find the eigenvalues as roots of the characteristic equation $\det(\lambda I - A) = 0$.

Here we see that

$$\det(\lambda I - A) = \det \begin{bmatrix} \lambda - 2 & -1 & -1 \\ -1 & \lambda - 2 & -1 \\ -1 & -1 & \lambda - 2 \end{bmatrix} = \lambda^3 - 6\lambda^2 + 9\lambda - 4$$

$$= (\lambda - 1)^2 (\lambda - 4).$$

Therefore, A has eigenvalues $\lambda_1 = 1$ and $\lambda_2 = 4$. Note that there are only two *distinct* eigenvalues of A, yet A is 3×3. To determine whether A is similar to a diagonal matrix, we proceed to the next step.

Step 2. Find the eigenvectors corresponding to each eigenvalue.

For the eigenvalue $\lambda_1 = 1$, solve the homogeneous system $(I - A)\mathbf{x} = \mathbf{0}$, that is,

$$\begin{bmatrix} -1 & -1 & -1 \\ -1 & -1 & -1 \\ -1 & -1 & -1 \end{bmatrix} \cdot \begin{bmatrix} x_1 \\ x_2 \\ x_3 \end{bmatrix} = \begin{bmatrix} 0 \\ 0 \\ 0 \end{bmatrix}.$$

The augmented matrix for this system reduces to the matrix (verify this)

$$\begin{bmatrix} 1 & 1 & 1 & | & 0 \\ 0 & 0 & 0 & | & 0 \\ 0 & 0 & 0 & | & 0 \end{bmatrix}.$$

Therefore, the solutions to the system are of the form $x_1 = -x_2 - x_3, x_2 = s, x_3 = t$. Two linearly independent eigenvectors correspond to λ_1. These can be found by setting $t = 0$, $s = 1$, and then $t = 1$, $s = 0$, to obtain

$$\mathbf{u} = \begin{bmatrix} -1 \\ 1 \\ 0 \end{bmatrix} \quad \text{and} \quad \mathbf{v} = \begin{bmatrix} -1 \\ 0 \\ 1 \end{bmatrix}.$$

Any eigenvector $\mathbf{x}$ corresponding to λ_1 is expressible as

$$\mathbf{x} = s\mathbf{u} + t\mathbf{v}.$$

For the eigenvalue $\lambda_2 = 4$, solve the homogeneous system $(4I - A)\mathbf{x} = \mathbf{0}$, whose augmented matrix is

$$\begin{bmatrix} 2 & -1 & -1 & | & 0 \\ -1 & 2 & -1 & | & 0 \\ -1 & -1 & 2 & | & 0 \end{bmatrix}.$$

This matrix is equivalent to the matrix (verify this)

$$\begin{bmatrix} 1 & 0 & -1 & | & 0 \\ 0 & 1 & -1 & | & 0 \\ 0 & 0 & 0 & | & 0 \end{bmatrix}.$$

Therefore solutions to the system are of the form $x_1 = x_2 = x_3 = t$; let $t = 1$, then the vector

$$\mathbf{w} = \begin{bmatrix} 1 \\ 1 \\ 1 \end{bmatrix}$$

is a basis for the eigenspace of A corresponding to $\lambda_2 = 4$.

Step 3. Compare the number of linearly independent eigenvectors with the dimension of the matrix and complete the computation of P, if this is possible.

Since our matrix is of dimension three and has three eigenvectors $\mathbf{u}, \mathbf{v}$, and $\mathbf{w}$, we must verify that they are indeed linearly independent. If this is the case, then the matrix P, whose column vectors are $\mathbf{u}$, $\mathbf{v}$, and $\mathbf{w}$, will be such that

$$P^{-1}AP = \begin{bmatrix} 1 & 0 & 0 \\ 0 & 1 & 0 \\ 0 & 0 & 4 \end{bmatrix}.$$

We already know that $\mathbf{u}$ and $\mathbf{v}$ are linearly independent. To see that all three are linearly independent we must show that $\mathbf{w}$ is not a linear combination of the other two, that is, that $\mathbf{w}$ is not in the space spanned by $\mathbf{u}$ and $\mathbf{v}$. This can be accomplished in a number of ways, as discussed in earlier chapters. Perhaps the easiest way in this case is to note that the matrix P has a nonzero determinant, where

$$P = \begin{bmatrix} -1 & -1 & 1 \\ 1 & 0 & 1 \\ 0 & 1 & 1 \end{bmatrix}.$$
$$\ \ \mathbf{u}\ \ \ \ \ \mathbf{v}\ \ \ \ \mathbf{w}$$

Then $P^{-1}AP$ is as indicated. This completes the diagonalization of A.

We conclude this section with two theorems, the first of which disposes of the problem mentioned in Step 3 of Example 3. We shall show that it is not necessary to verify each time that the vector $\mathbf{w}$ (as in that example) is linearly independent of the vectors $\mathbf{u}$ and $\mathbf{v}$. It will always be the case that eigenvectors belonging to *different* eigenvalues are linearly independent.

Theorem 6.4

Let A be an $n \times n$ matrix. Then distinct eigenvectors of A corresponding to distinct eigenvalues of A are linearly independent.

Proof. Let A have distinct eigenvalues $\lambda_1, \lambda_2, \ldots, \lambda_m$, where $m \leqslant n$ and $\lambda_i \neq \lambda_j$ when $i \neq j$. Let $\mathbf{u}_1, \mathbf{u}_2, \ldots, \mathbf{u}_m$ be eigenvectors of A corresponding, respectively, to these eigenvalues. Thus, $A\mathbf{u}_i = \lambda_i \mathbf{u}_i$ for each $i = 1, 2, \ldots, m$. Note that this may not include all of the eigenvectors of A, since a given eigenvalue may determine an eigenspace of A whose dimension is more than one. However, since $\mathbf{u}_i$ can be any nonzero vector from the eigenspace of A corresponding to the eigenvalue λ_i, these will be sufficient for our proof.

Since $\mathbf{u}_1 \neq \mathbf{0}$, the set $\{\mathbf{u}_1\}$ consisting of the single vector $\mathbf{u}_1$ is linearly independent. Let k be the *largest* of the integers $1, 2, \ldots, m$ such that the set $\{\mathbf{u}_1, \mathbf{u}_2, \ldots, \mathbf{u}_k\}$ is linearly independent. Thus, $1 \leqslant k \leqslant m$. Now if $k \neq m$, then $k < m$ and the set of vectors $\{\mathbf{u}_1, \mathbf{u}_2, \ldots, \mathbf{u}_{k+1}\}$ is linearly dependent on account of our choice of k. Hence, there exist scalars $a_1, a_2, \ldots, a_{k+1}$ (not all zero) such that

$$a_1\mathbf{u}_1 + a_2\mathbf{u}_2 + \ldots + a_k\mathbf{u}_k + a_{k+1}\mathbf{u}_{k+1} = \mathbf{0}. \tag{6.5}$$

This being the case, it must be true that

$$0 = A0 = A(a_1 \mathbf{u}_1 + a_2 \mathbf{u}_2 + \ldots + a_{k+1} \mathbf{u}_{k+1})$$
$$= a_1 A\mathbf{u}_1 + a_2 A\mathbf{u}_2 + \ldots + a_{k+1} A\mathbf{u}_{k+1}$$

or

$$0 = a_1 \lambda_1 \mathbf{u}_1 + a_2 \lambda_2 \mathbf{u}_2 + \ldots + a_{k+1} \lambda_{k+1} \mathbf{u}_{k+1}. \tag{6.6}$$

Now, take λ_{k+1} times Eq. (6.5), which yields

$$0 = a_1 \lambda_{k+1} \mathbf{u}_1 + a_2 \lambda_{k+1} \mathbf{u}_2 + \ldots + a_{k+1} \lambda_{k+1} \mathbf{u}_{k+1}. \tag{6.7}$$

Subtracting Eq. (6.7) from Eq. (6.6) results in the equation

$$0 = a_1 (\lambda_1 - \lambda_{k+1}) \mathbf{u}_1 + \ldots + a_k (\lambda_k - \lambda_{k+1}) \mathbf{u}_k + 0;$$

but the set of vectors $\{\mathbf{u}_1, \ldots, \mathbf{u}_k\}$ is linearly independent, so this equation implies that the coefficients are all zero, that is,

$$a_i (\lambda_i - \lambda_{k+1}) = 0, \qquad i = 1, 2, \ldots, k.$$

Since the eigenvalues are all distinct, this implies that

$$a_1 = a_2 = \ldots = a_k = 0.$$

But this fact together with Eq. (6.5) implies that $a_{k+1} = 0$ also. (Why?) This contradicts the fact that the a_i in (6.5) were *not* all zero. Hence, k is *not* less than m and therefore $k = m$. Thus, the eigenvectors $\mathbf{u}_1, \mathbf{u}_2, \ldots, \mathbf{u}_m$ are linearly independent.

As an immediate consequence of this theorem and Theorem 6.3 it follows that if the $n \times n$ matrix A has n *distinct* eigenvalues, then it must have n linearly independent eigenvectors corresponding to those eigenvalues. It must, therefore, be diagonalizable. We saw in Example 3 and in the matrix just preceding that example that, while distinct eigenvalues are sufficient for A to be diagonalizable, this is not a necessary condition. We state this formally as the following theorem.

Theorem 6.5
A sufficient (but not necessary) condition for the $n \times n$ matrix A to be similar to a diagonal matrix is that A have n distinct eigenvalues.

Example 4   Find, if possible, a diagonal matrix similar to the matrix

$$A = \begin{bmatrix} -1 & -2 & 3 \\ 0 & 1 & 5 \\ 0 & 0 & 2 \end{bmatrix}.$$

The characteristic equation for A is

$$\det(\lambda I - A) = (\lambda + 1)(\lambda - 1)(\lambda - 2) = 0.$$

Therefore, A has the three distinct eigenvalues -1, 1, and 2. This means that A is similar to the diagonal matrix

$$D = \begin{bmatrix} -1 & 0 & 0 \\ 0 & 1 & 0 \\ 0 & 0 & 2 \end{bmatrix}.$$

To find a matrix P so that $D = P^{-1}AP$, we must find eigenvectors of A corresponding to these distinct eigenvalues. As illustrated in Step 2 of Example 3, these are (verify this):

For $\lambda_1 = -1$:

$$\mathbf{u}_1 = \begin{bmatrix} 1 \\ 0 \\ 0 \end{bmatrix}.$$

For $\lambda_2 = 1$:

$$\mathbf{u}_2 = \begin{bmatrix} 1 \\ -1 \\ 0 \end{bmatrix}.$$

For $\lambda_3 = 2$:

$$\mathbf{u}_3 = \begin{bmatrix} -7 \\ 15 \\ 3 \end{bmatrix}.$$

Thus,

$$P = \begin{bmatrix} 1 & 1 & -7 \\ 0 & -1 & 15 \\ 0 & 0 & 3 \end{bmatrix} \quad \text{and} \quad P^{-1} = \begin{bmatrix} 1 & 1 & -\frac{8}{3} \\ 0 & -1 & 5 \\ 0 & 0 & \frac{1}{3} \end{bmatrix}.$$

Example 5   Let T be the linear transformation in $\mathbb{R}^2$ that reflects every point in $\mathbb{R}^2$ in the line $y = x$. Does there exist a basis for $\mathbb{R}^2$ such that the matrix representation for T is a diagonal matrix? The reflection is sketched in Fig. 6.2. Obviously, T takes $(1, 1)$ to itself and $(1, -1)$ to its negative, so the answer is *yes*. Here is how it works out by matrix algebra.

Since T takes each vector (x, y) in $\mathbb{R}^2$ to the vector (y, x), it can be represented relative to the standard basis for $\mathbb{R}^2$ by the matrix

$$A = \begin{bmatrix} 0 & 1 \\ 1 & 0 \end{bmatrix}.$$

Now solve the characteristic equation $\det(\lambda I - A) = \lambda^2 - 1 = 0$ to find the eigenvalues for T. These are $\lambda_1 = 1$ and $\lambda_2 = -1$. The corresponding eigenvectors are found to be (verify this)

$$\mathbf{u}_1 = \begin{bmatrix} 1 \\ 1 \end{bmatrix} \quad \text{and} \quad \mathbf{u}_2 = \begin{bmatrix} 1 \\ -1 \end{bmatrix}.$$

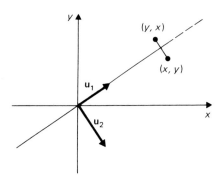

Figure 6.2

Hence, the set $\mathbf{u}_1$, $\mathbf{u}_2$ is a basis for $\mathbb{R}^2$, relative to which the matrix representation for T is the diagonal matrix

$$D = \begin{bmatrix} 1 & 0 \\ 0 & -1 \end{bmatrix}.$$

Example 6 Consider the transformation $T: \mathbb{R}^2 \to \mathbb{R}^2$ given by the equation

$$T(x, y) = (y - x, x - 3y).$$

The matrix representation for T relative to the standard basis for $\mathbb{R}^2$ is (verify this)

$$A = \begin{bmatrix} -1 & 1 \\ 1 & -3 \end{bmatrix}.$$

The characteristic equation for A, and hence for T, is $\lambda^2 + 4\lambda + 2 = 0$ (check this). Therefore, T has eigenvalues $\lambda_1 = -2 + \sqrt{2}$ and $\lambda_2 = -2 - \sqrt{2}$. Also, a basis for the eigenspaces of T consists of two linearly independent eigenvectors

$$\mathbf{u} = \begin{bmatrix} 1 + \sqrt{2} \\ 1 \end{bmatrix} \quad \text{and} \quad \mathbf{v} = \begin{bmatrix} 1 - \sqrt{2} \\ 1 \end{bmatrix}.$$

Relative to the basis $\{\mathbf{u}, \mathbf{v}\}$ of $\mathbb{R}^2$, the transformation T can be represented by the diagonal matrix

$$\begin{bmatrix} -2 + \sqrt{2} & 0 \\ 0 & -2 - \sqrt{2} \end{bmatrix} = \begin{bmatrix} \dfrac{\sqrt{2}}{4} & \dfrac{2 - \sqrt{2}}{4} \\ -\dfrac{\sqrt{2}}{4} & \dfrac{2 + \sqrt{2}}{4} \end{bmatrix} \begin{bmatrix} -1 & 1 \\ 1 & -3 \end{bmatrix} \begin{bmatrix} 1 + \sqrt{2} & 1 - \sqrt{2} \\ 1 & 1 \end{bmatrix}.$$

EXERCISES (6.2)

For each of the following matrices A, find a matrix P so that $P^{-1}AP$ is a diagonal matrix D; find D.

1. $\begin{bmatrix} 3 & -1 \\ 2 & 0 \end{bmatrix}$

2. $\begin{bmatrix} 3 & 1 \\ 1 & 3 \end{bmatrix}$

3. $\begin{bmatrix} \frac{1}{2} & \frac{1}{2} \\ \frac{1}{2} & \frac{1}{2} \end{bmatrix}$

4. $\begin{bmatrix} -1 & 0 \\ 0 & 2 \end{bmatrix}$

5. $\begin{bmatrix} 0 & 2 \\ 3 & 0 \end{bmatrix}$

6. $\begin{bmatrix} 0 & 0 \\ 0 & 0 \end{bmatrix}$

7. $\begin{bmatrix} 1 & 0 & 0 \\ 2 & -1 & 0 \\ 1 & 2 & 3 \end{bmatrix}$

8. $\begin{bmatrix} 1 & -1 & 4 \\ 0 & 2 & -2 \\ 0 & 0 & 3 \end{bmatrix}$

9. $\begin{bmatrix} 8 & 9 & 9 \\ 3 & 2 & 3 \\ -9 & -9 & -10 \end{bmatrix}$

Show that none of the following matrices is similar to a diagonal matrix.

10. $\begin{bmatrix} 1 & -1 \\ 0 & 1 \end{bmatrix}$

11. $\begin{bmatrix} 2 & -3 \\ 1 & -1 \end{bmatrix}$

12. $\begin{bmatrix} 2 & 1 & 0 \\ 0 & 2 & 0 \\ 0 & 0 & 1 \end{bmatrix}$

13. $\begin{bmatrix} -1 & 0 & 1 \\ -1 & 3 & 0 \\ -4 & 13 & -1 \end{bmatrix}$

14. $\begin{bmatrix} 3 & 1 & 0 & 0 \\ 0 & 3 & 0 & 0 \\ 0 & 0 & -1 & 1 \\ 0 & 0 & 0 & -1 \end{bmatrix}$

Determine whether the given matrix is similar to a diagonal matrix, and if it is, find a matrix P that diagonalizes it.

15. $\begin{bmatrix} 3 & 1 & 0 \\ 1 & 3 & 0 \\ 0 & 0 & 2 \end{bmatrix}$

16. $\begin{bmatrix} 3 & 11 & 3 \\ 0 & -4 & -3 \\ 2 & 6 & 1 \end{bmatrix}$

17. $\begin{bmatrix} -1 & 1 & 0 \\ 0 & -1 & 1 \\ 0 & 0 & -1 \end{bmatrix}$

18. $\begin{bmatrix} 5 & 1 & 1 \\ -3 & 1 & -3 \\ -2 & -2 & 2 \end{bmatrix}$

19. $\begin{bmatrix} 19 & -9 & -6 \\ 25 & -11 & -9 \\ 17 & -9 & -4 \end{bmatrix}$

20. $\begin{bmatrix} -1 & 2 & 0 \\ 2 & -1 & 0 \\ 0 & 0 & 3 \end{bmatrix}$

21. $\begin{bmatrix} -1 & 4 & -2 \\ -3 & 4 & 0 \\ -3 & 1 & 3 \end{bmatrix}$

22. $\begin{bmatrix} -1 & 0 & 0 & 0 \\ 0 & -1 & 0 & 0 \\ 0 & 0 & 2 & 1 \\ 0 & 0 & 1 & 2 \end{bmatrix}$

23. $\begin{bmatrix} 2 & 0 & 0 & 0 \\ 0 & 2 & -5 & 5 \\ 0 & 0 & -3 & 0 \\ 0 & 0 & 0 & -3 \end{bmatrix}$

In Exercises 24–26, let $T: \mathbb{R}^2 \to \mathbb{R}^2$ be the given transformation. Determine whether or not there is a basis for $\mathbb{R}^2$ such that the matrix representation of T relative to that basis is diagonal. If so, find the basis and the diagonal matrix representation.

24. $T(x, y) = (x + 3y, y)$

25. $T(x, y) = (x, 0)$

26. $T(x, y) = (3x + y, x + 3y)$

In Exercises 27 and 28, let T be the transformation on the vector space P_2 of quadratic polynomials defined by

$$T(c + bx + ax^2) = 5c - (2a - 3b)x + (3a - 2b)x^2.$$

27. Write a matrix representation for T relative to the standard basis $\{1, x, x^2\}$.

28. Find a basis for P_2 such that the matrix representation for T relative to that basis is a diagonal matrix.

29. Show that for $n \times n$ matrices A and P, where P is invertible, the following holds:

$$(P^{-1}AP)^2 = P^{-1}A^2P$$

and hence

$$(P^{-1}AP)^k = P^{-1}A^kP \quad \text{for any integer } k > 0.$$

In Exercises 30–32, use the results of Exercise 29 to find A^{10} for the given A.

30. $A = \begin{bmatrix} 1 & 0 \\ 1 & 2 \end{bmatrix}$ **31.** $A = \begin{bmatrix} 2 & 1 \\ 1 & 2 \end{bmatrix}$ **32.** $A = \begin{bmatrix} 2 & -1 & 1 \\ 3 & -2 & 3 \\ 3 & -1 & 0 \end{bmatrix}$

Hint. In each case find a diagonal matrix similar to A.

33. Show that if $D = \lambda I$, then, for every invertible matrix P,

$$D = \lambda I = P^{-1}DP.$$

34. Interpret Exercise 33 for matrices A that have but a single eigenvalue λ.

35. Show that if D is a diagonal matrix and $D^2 = 0$, then $D = 0$.

36. Interpret Exercise 35 for a matrix A such that $A^2 = 0$ if A is diagonalizable.

37. Show that a 90° rotation T in $\mathbb{R}^2$ is a linear transformation whose eigenvalues are not real numbers. Can a basis for $\mathbb{R}^2$ be chosen so that T can be represented by a diagonal matrix? Can the matrix representation of T be diagonalized if we assume that matrix to be a complex matrix (i.e., its entries are complex numbers)?

38. Let $A = (a_{ij})$ be an upper- or lower-triangular matrix with distinct diagonal entries. Prove that A is similar to a diagonal matrix.

39. *Cayley–Hamilton Theorem.* Let $\det(\lambda I - A) = P_A(\lambda) = 0$ be the characteristic equation of a square matrix A. Then $P_A(A) = 0$, that is, the matrix A satisfies its characteristic equation. Prove this theorem for diagonal matrices. Here, if A is $n \times n$ and

$$P_A(\lambda) = \lambda^n + a_1\lambda^{n-1} + a_2\lambda^{n-2} + \ldots + a_{n-1}\lambda + a_n,$$

then

$$P_A(A) = A^n + a_1 A^{n-1} + a_2 A^{n-2} + \ldots + a_{n-1}A + a_n I_n.$$

6.3 SYMMETRIC MATRICES

In Theorems 6.3 and 6.4 we saw that if an $n \times n$ matrix A has exactly n distinct (real) eigenvalues, it is surely similar to a diagonal matrix with these distinct eigenvalues as the diagonal entries. Therefore, if the characteristic equation $\det(\lambda I - A) = 0$ has n distinct real roots, then A is similar to a diagonal matrix. On the other hand, if $\det(\lambda I - A) = 0$ has repeated real roots, some further effort is required to determine if the various eigenspaces of A have dimensions large enough so that their sum is n. Since the determination of roots of polynomials of degree n is, in general, quite difficult, it is often necessary to use computers and special computation techniques to obtain approximations to the eigenvalues of A and hence to the diagonal matrix similar to A, if it exists.

There are, fortunately, a number of theorems assuring that in special circumstances a matrix A is diagonalizable. One such theorem was suggested in Exercise 38 of the preceding section. A deeper result concerning symmetric matrices is considered in this section.

A matrix A is called **symmetric** if $A = A^t$. Symmetric matrices arise in several contexts. One of these is the consideration of quadratic forms and their application to the study of certain classical curves and surfaces. This we will examine in the next section.

It should be fairly obvious that only a square matrix can be symmetric.

Example 1   The matrices

$$M = \begin{bmatrix} 7 & 2 & 1 \\ 2 & 7 & -1 \\ 1 & -1 & 4 \end{bmatrix} \quad \text{and} \quad N = \begin{bmatrix} -8 & 5 & 4 \\ 5 & 3 & 1 \\ 4 & 1 & 0 \end{bmatrix}$$

are symmetric, since $M = M^t$ and $N = N^t$. On the other hand, the matrix

$$K = \begin{bmatrix} 1 & 3 & 0 \\ 3 & 2 & 2 \\ -1 & 2 & 1 \end{bmatrix}$$

is not symmetric since

$$K^t = \begin{bmatrix} 1 & 3 & -1 \\ 3 & 2 & 2 \\ 0 & 2 & 1 \end{bmatrix} \neq K.$$

The following theorem is called the *spectral theorem*. We state it here without proof. Its proof would require concepts not discussed in this book; however the 2×2 case is Exercise 16. The theorem tells us that for the class of symmetric matrices diagonalization is always possible—although not necessarily easy.

Theorem 6.6

Let A be any real symmetric matrix. Then there exists a real nonsingular matrix P such that $P^{-1}AP$ is a diagonal matrix.

From the spectral theorem we also learn that every real symmetric matrix A has only real eigenvalues since these will appear as the diagonal entries in the matrix $P^{-1}AP$. (Recall that A and $P^{-1}AP$ have the same eigenvalues. Why?) Therefore the characteristic polynomial $\det(\lambda I - A)$ has only real roots. This is not to say that these roots are always rational, nor are they always easily obtainable. Here also, numerical methods and computers are often necessary to approximate the real eigenvalues of A.

Example 2   The matrix M of Example 1 is symmetric. Therefore, according to Theorem 6.6, it has real eigenvalues. Its characteristic equation is

$$\det(\lambda I - M) = \det \begin{bmatrix} \lambda-7 & -2 & -1 \\ -2 & \lambda-7 & 1 \\ -1 & 1 & \lambda-4 \end{bmatrix} = \lambda^3 - 18\lambda^2 + 99\lambda - 162$$

$$= (\lambda-3)(\lambda-6)(\lambda-9) = 0.$$

So M has three distinct eigenvalues: $\lambda_1 = 3$, $\lambda_2 = 6$, and $\lambda_3 = 9$. Each of the eigenspaces corresponding to these eigenvalues is one dimensional. According to the spectral theorem, there is a real matrix P such that $P^{-1}MP$ is diag$[3, 6, 9]$. We find the matrix P, as in the previous section, by finding the eigenvectors of M. These turn out to be

$$\mathbf{p}_1 = \begin{bmatrix} -1 \\ 1 \\ 2 \end{bmatrix}, \qquad \mathbf{p}_2 = \begin{bmatrix} 1 \\ -1 \\ 1 \end{bmatrix}, \qquad \text{and} \qquad \mathbf{p}_3 = \begin{bmatrix} 1 \\ 1 \\ 0 \end{bmatrix},$$

so the matrix

$$P = \begin{bmatrix} -1 & 1 & 1 \\ 1 & -1 & 1 \\ 2 & 1 & 0 \end{bmatrix}$$

is such that $P^{-1}MP = \text{diag}[3, 6, 9]$, as you can readily verify. A similar computation gives the matrix

$$Q = \begin{bmatrix} 1 & 1 & -3 \\ -4 & 2 & 1 \\ 7 & 1 & 1 \end{bmatrix}$$

as the matrix of eigenvectors of the symmetric matrix N of Example 1 (verify this).

Note that for each of the two symmetric matrices M and N the eigenvectors are mutually orthogonal. That is, for M

$$\langle \mathbf{p}_1, \mathbf{p}_2 \rangle = \langle \mathbf{p}_2, \mathbf{p}_3 \rangle = \langle \mathbf{p}_1, \mathbf{p}_3 \rangle = 0$$

and for N

$$\langle \mathbf{q}_1, \mathbf{q}_2 \rangle = \langle \mathbf{q}_2, \mathbf{q}_3 \rangle = \langle \mathbf{q}_1, \mathbf{q}_3 \rangle = 0.$$

This is not a coincidence. Indeed, let λ_1 and λ_2 be *distinct* eigenvalues of any *symmetric* matrix A, and let $\mathbf{v}_1$ and $\mathbf{v}_2$ be the corresponding eigenvectors considered as $n \times 1$ matrices. Then the matrix $\mathbf{v}_1^t A \mathbf{v}_2$ is also necessarily symmetric, since it is 1×1. Therefore, since $A = A^t$,

$$\mathbf{v}_1^t A \mathbf{v}_2 = (\mathbf{v}_1^t A \mathbf{v}_2)^t = \mathbf{v}_2^t A^t \mathbf{v}_1 = \mathbf{v}_2^t A \mathbf{v}_1 \qquad (6.8)$$

by the properties of transposes. Also $A\mathbf{v}_1 = \lambda_1 \mathbf{v}_1$ and $A\mathbf{v}_2 = \lambda_2 \mathbf{v}_2$, so that the Eq. (6.8) becomes

$$\mathbf{v}_1^t \lambda_2 \mathbf{v}_2 = \mathbf{v}_2^t \lambda_1 \mathbf{v}_1 \qquad \text{or} \qquad \lambda_2 \mathbf{v}_1^t \mathbf{v}_2 = \lambda_1 \mathbf{v}_2^t \mathbf{v}_1. \qquad (6.9)$$

But the product $\mathbf{v}_1^t \mathbf{v}_2$ is a 1×1 matrix and is, therefore, symmetric; hence,

$$\mathbf{v}_1^t \mathbf{v}_2 = (\mathbf{v}_1^t \mathbf{v}_2)^t = \mathbf{v}_2^t \mathbf{v}_1.$$

Substituting this in (6.9) we have

$$\lambda_2 \mathbf{v}_1^t \mathbf{v}_2 = \lambda_1 \mathbf{v}_1^t \mathbf{v}_2 \qquad \text{or} \qquad (\lambda_1 - \lambda_2)\mathbf{v}_1^t \mathbf{v}_2 = \mathbf{0}.$$

Since $\lambda_1 \neq \lambda_2$, the scalar $\lambda_1 - \lambda_2 \neq 0$. Therefore, the matrix $\mathbf{v}_1^t \mathbf{v}_2 = \mathbf{0}$. The inner product $\langle \mathbf{v}_1, \mathbf{v}_2 \rangle$ is the only entry in the 1×1 matrix $\mathbf{v}_1^t \mathbf{v}_2$. Thus $\mathbf{v}_1$ and $\mathbf{v}_2$ are orthogonal. This proves the following theorem:

Theorem 6.7

If A is any symmetric matrix, then eigenvectors corresponding to distinct eigenvalues are orthogonal.

We recall from Chapter 5 that a matrix P is said to be *orthogonal* if and only if P is nonsingular and $P^{-1} = P^t$, that is, if and only if $P^t P = I$.

An $n \times n$ matrix A is said to be **orthogonally diagonalizable** if it is possible to find an *orthogonal* matrix P such that $P^t AP = P^{-1} AP$ is a diagonal matrix.

The matrices P and Q of Example 2 are *not* orthogonal matrices, even though their column vectors are mutually orthogonal. They can, however, easily be transformed into orthogonal matrices by normalizing the column vectors, that is, by dividing each vector by its length.

Example 3 Find orthogonal matrices P_1 and Q_1 that orthogonally diagonalize the matrices M and N, respectively, of Examples 1 and 2.

The vectors

$$\mathbf{u}_1 = \frac{\mathbf{p}_1}{\|\mathbf{p}_1\|} = \begin{bmatrix} -\dfrac{1}{\sqrt{6}} \\ \dfrac{1}{\sqrt{6}} \\ \dfrac{2}{\sqrt{6}} \end{bmatrix}, \quad \mathbf{u}_2 = \frac{\mathbf{p}_2}{\|\mathbf{p}_2\|} = \begin{bmatrix} \dfrac{1}{\sqrt{3}} \\ -\dfrac{1}{\sqrt{3}} \\ \dfrac{1}{\sqrt{3}} \end{bmatrix}, \quad \mathbf{u}_3 = \frac{\mathbf{p}_3}{\|\mathbf{p}_3\|} = \begin{bmatrix} \dfrac{1}{\sqrt{2}} \\ \dfrac{1}{\sqrt{2}} \\ 0 \end{bmatrix}$$

are a set of orthonormal eigenvectors for the matrix M. The matrix

$$P_1 = \begin{bmatrix} -\dfrac{1}{\sqrt{6}} & \dfrac{1}{\sqrt{3}} & \dfrac{1}{\sqrt{2}} \\ \dfrac{1}{\sqrt{6}} & -\dfrac{1}{\sqrt{3}} & \dfrac{1}{\sqrt{2}} \\ \dfrac{2}{\sqrt{6}} & \dfrac{1}{\sqrt{3}} & 0 \end{bmatrix}$$

is orthogonal and is such that $P_1^t M P_1 = \text{diag}[3, 6, 9]$, as desired (verify this).

Similarly, you should verify that the matrix N is orthogonally diagonalized by the matrix

$$Q_1 = \begin{bmatrix} \dfrac{1}{\sqrt{66}} & \dfrac{1}{\sqrt{6}} & -\dfrac{3}{\sqrt{11}} \\ -\dfrac{4}{\sqrt{66}} & \dfrac{2}{\sqrt{6}} & \dfrac{1}{\sqrt{11}} \\ \dfrac{7}{\sqrt{66}} & \dfrac{1}{\sqrt{6}} & \dfrac{1}{\sqrt{11}} \end{bmatrix}.$$

The two matrices described so far have both had n ($n = 3$) distinct eigenvectors. As you are aware, this is not always true for a given matrix, not even for a symmetric matrix. Nevertheless, because of Theorem 6.6, it is always true that an $n \times n$ real symmetric matrix A will be diagonalizable, in fact, orthogonally diagonalizable. Therefore, every $n \times n$ real symmetric matrix A must have n linearly independent eigenvectors. The following theorem, whose proof we omit, assures us of this.

Theorem 6.8

If the eigenvalue λ of an $n \times n$ real symmetric matrix A is repeated $k \leqslant n$ times, then the eigenspace of A corresponding to λ is k-dimensional.

By using Theorems 6.6–6.8, we get the following algorithm for orthogonally diagonalizing a given real symmetric matrix A:

1. Find a basis of eigenvectors for each eigenspace of A;

2. By applying the Gram–Schmidt process where necessary to each of these bases, obtain an orthonormal basis for each eigenspace.

3. Form the orthogonal matrix P whose columns are the basis vectors obtained in Step 2.

Example 4 Find a matrix P that orthogonally diagonalizes the matrix

$$A = \begin{bmatrix} -1 & 2 & 2 \\ 2 & -1 & 2 \\ 2 & 2 & -1 \end{bmatrix}.$$

The characteristic equation for the matrix A is

$$\det(\lambda I - A) = \det \begin{bmatrix} \lambda+1 & -2 & -2 \\ -2 & \lambda+1 & -2 \\ -2 & -2 & \lambda+1 \end{bmatrix} = (\lambda+3)^2(\lambda-3) = 0.$$

Therefore A has two eigenspaces. One of these is a subspace S_1 of dimension two corresponding to the eigenvalue $\lambda = -3$. It is spanned by the two eigenvectors (verify this)

$$\mathbf{u}_1 = \begin{bmatrix} -1 \\ 0 \\ 1 \end{bmatrix} \quad \text{and} \quad \mathbf{u}_2 = \begin{bmatrix} -1 \\ 1 \\ 0 \end{bmatrix}.$$

The second eigenspace S_2 has dimension one and corresponds to the eigenvalue $\lambda = 3$; it is spanned by the eigenvector

$$\mathbf{u}_3 = \begin{bmatrix} 1 \\ 1 \\ 1 \end{bmatrix}.$$

Note that $\mathbf{u}_3$ is orthogonal to both $\mathbf{u}_1$ and $\mathbf{u}_2$, as indicated by Theorem 6.7; but $\langle \mathbf{u}_1, \mathbf{u}_2 \rangle = 1$; hence they are *not* orthogonal. By applying the Gram–Schmidt process we obtain the orthonormal basis

$$\mathbf{v}_1 = \frac{\mathbf{u}_1}{\|\mathbf{u}_1\|} = \begin{bmatrix} -\dfrac{1}{\sqrt{2}} \\ 0 \\ \dfrac{1}{\sqrt{2}} \end{bmatrix} \quad \text{and} \quad \mathbf{v}_2 = \frac{\mathbf{u}_2 - \langle \mathbf{u}_2, \mathbf{v}_1 \rangle \mathbf{v}_1}{\|\mathbf{u}_2 - \langle \mathbf{u}_2, \mathbf{v}_1 \rangle \mathbf{v}_1\|} = \begin{bmatrix} -\dfrac{1}{\sqrt{6}} \\ \dfrac{2}{\sqrt{6}} \\ -\dfrac{1}{\sqrt{6}} \end{bmatrix}$$

for S_1 and the orthonormal basis

$$\mathbf{v}_3 = \frac{\mathbf{u}_3}{||\mathbf{u}_3||} = \begin{bmatrix} \dfrac{1}{\sqrt{3}} \\[2mm] \dfrac{1}{\sqrt{3}} \\[2mm] \dfrac{1}{\sqrt{3}} \end{bmatrix}$$

for S_2. Therefore the orthogonal matrix

$$P = \begin{bmatrix} -\dfrac{1}{\sqrt{2}} & -\dfrac{1}{\sqrt{6}} & \dfrac{1}{\sqrt{3}} \\[3mm] 0 & \dfrac{2}{\sqrt{6}} & \dfrac{1}{\sqrt{3}} \\[3mm] \dfrac{1}{\sqrt{2}} & -\dfrac{1}{\sqrt{6}} & \dfrac{1}{\sqrt{3}} \end{bmatrix}$$

is such that $P'AP = \text{diag}[-3, -3, 3]$.

EXERCISES (6.3)———————————————————————————————

Find the eigenvalues and hence the dimensions of the eigenspaces of the following symmetric matrices A.

1. $\begin{bmatrix} 1 & -1 \\ -1 & 1 \end{bmatrix}$

2. $\begin{bmatrix} 2 & -1 \\ -1 & 2 \end{bmatrix}$

3. $\begin{bmatrix} \frac{1}{2} & 3 \\ 3 & -1 \end{bmatrix}$

4. $\begin{bmatrix} 1 & 2 \\ 2 & 0 \end{bmatrix}$

5. $\begin{bmatrix} 1 & 1 & 1 \\ 1 & 1 & 1 \\ 1 & 1 & 1 \end{bmatrix}$

6. $\begin{bmatrix} 6 & 0 & 0 \\ 0 & 2 & 2 \\ 0 & 2 & 2 \end{bmatrix}$

7. $\begin{bmatrix} 1 & -1 & 0 \\ -1 & 1 & 0 \\ 0 & 0 & 5 \end{bmatrix}$

8. $\begin{bmatrix} 2 & -1 & 0 & 0 \\ -1 & 2 & 0 & 0 \\ 0 & 0 & 1 & -1 \\ 0 & 0 & -1 & 1 \end{bmatrix}$

9. $\begin{bmatrix} 2 & -1 & -1 & 0 \\ -1 & 2 & -1 & 0 \\ -1 & -1 & 2 & 0 \\ 0 & 0 & 0 & 3 \end{bmatrix}$

10. Find an orthogonal matrix P so that for the matrix

$$A = \begin{bmatrix} a & b \\ b & a \end{bmatrix}$$

$b \neq 0$, $P'AP$ is diagonal.

11. Find an orthogonal matrix P and the diagonal matrix $P^{-1}AP$ for each matrix A of Exercises 1–9.

12. Show that the matrices $A^t A$, AA^t, and $A + A^t$ are symmetric for any matrix A.

13. Show that if $B = P^{-1}AP$, then $B^k = P^{-1}A^k P$ for any positive integer k.

14. Use Exercise 13 to find A^{10} if

$$A = \begin{bmatrix} 2 & -1 \\ -1 & 2 \end{bmatrix}.$$

15. Two $n \times n$ matrices A and B are called *orthogonally similar* if there is an orthogonal matrix P such that $B = P^{-1}AP = P^t AP$. Show that if A is a symmetric matrix and A and B are orthogonally similar, then B is also symmetric.

16. Prove the spectral theorem (Theorem 6.6) for the 2×2 case. (Note that Exercise 10 is a special case.)

17. Prove that any 2×2 real symmetric matrix has only real eigenvalues.

Let A be an $n \times n$ matrix with complex-number ($z = a + bi$) entries. The *conjugate* A^* of A is the matrix formed by conjugating ($\bar{z} = a - bi$) each entry of A. The *adjoint* (or *conjugate transpose*) of A is the matrix $(A^*)^t$.

18. Show that $(A^*)^t = (A^t)^*$.

19. Find A^* and $(A^*)^t$ when

$$A = \begin{bmatrix} 1-i & i \\ 3 & 1+i \end{bmatrix}.$$

A complex matrix A is called *unitary* if $(A^*)^t = A^{-1}$, *self adjoint* if $(A^*)^t = A$, and *normal* if it commutes with its adjoint. (See Exercise 18.)

20. Show that the following matrix is unitary:

$$A = \begin{bmatrix} \dfrac{i}{\sqrt{2}} & \dfrac{1}{\sqrt{2}} \\ -\dfrac{1}{\sqrt{2}} & -\dfrac{i}{\sqrt{2}} \end{bmatrix}.$$

21. Show that the following matrix is self adjoint:

$$A = \begin{bmatrix} 3 & 1-2i \\ 1+2i & 1 \end{bmatrix}.$$

22. Is the following matrix normal?

$$A = \begin{bmatrix} 0 & 1-i \\ -1-i & 1 \end{bmatrix}.$$

6.4 QUADRATIC FORMS

Symmetric matrices can be applied quite naturally to the study of analytic geometry. In this section we shall use them to study quadratic forms and their graphs—the classical curves called *conic sections*.

The most general *linear equation in two variables* x and y is, of course,

$$Ax + By + C = 0.$$

Its graph is a line in 2-space. The most general *quadratic equation in two variables* has the form

$$ax^2 + 2bxy + cy^2 + dx + ey + f = 0, \qquad (6.10)$$

where at least one of the real numbers a, b, c is not zero. (The reason for using $2b$ in (6.10) rather than simply b' will appear shortly. It loses no generality—our b is just $b'/2$—but will prove to be more convenient later on.)

The expression

$$ax^2 + 2bxy + cy^2 \qquad (6.11)$$

is called the **quadratic form** associated with equation (6.10).

Example 1   Given the quadratic equation $2b \blacktriangleright 5$

$$3x^2 + 5xy - 2y^2 - 7x + 8y - 3 = 0.$$

This is (6.10) with $a = 3$, $b = 5/2$, $c = -2$, $d = -7$, $e = 8$, $f = -3$. The quadratic form associated with it is

$$3x^2 + 5xy - 2y^2.$$

Example 2   Some quadratic equations and their associated quadratic forms are as follows:

Qudratic equation	Quadratic form
$x^2 + 3xy - y^2 - 7x + 4y - 6 = 0$	$x^2 + 3xy - y^2$
$x^2 + y^2 = 9$	$x^2 + y^2$
$xy - 7 = 0$	xy

In plane analytic geometry it is shown that the graph of the general quadratic equation is either one of the four conic sections (a circle, an ellipse, a parabola, or a hyperbola) or one of the degenerate cases. (See any text on analytic geometry.)

Example 3   The graph of the quadratic equation $x^2 + xy + y^2 - 1 = 0$ is the ellipse of Fig. 6.3. Note that this ellipse has its axes rotated $45°$ from the coordinate axes. Its equation does not have one of the standard forms for the equation of an ellipse with

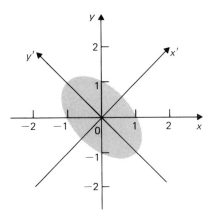

Figure 6.3

center at the origin and axes along the coordinate axes, namely

$$\frac{x^2}{u^2} + \frac{y^2}{v^2} = 1.$$

We shall develop a method here using symmetric matrices whereby the rotation of the axes can be performed. We represent the general quadratic equation

$$ax^2 + 2bxy + cy^2 + dx + ey + f = 0 \qquad (6.12)$$

in matrix notation as follows. Let

$$X = \begin{bmatrix} x \\ y \end{bmatrix}, \qquad A = \begin{bmatrix} a & b \\ b & c \end{bmatrix}, \qquad N = [d \;\; e], \qquad f = [f].$$

Then (6.12) becomes (verify this)

$$X'AX + NX + f = 0 \qquad (6.13)$$

and the quadratic form $ax^2 + 2bxy + cy^2$ associated with the equation has the form $X'AX$. The symmetric matrix A is called the *matrix of the quadratic form*.

Example 4   The ellipse of Example 3 is represented by the matrix equation $X'AX = 1$, where

$$A = \begin{bmatrix} 1 & \frac{1}{2} \\ \frac{1}{2} & 1 \end{bmatrix} \qquad \text{and} \qquad 1 = [1].$$

We adopt the convention that 1×1 matrices $[a]$ will not be distinguished from their single entry a. To rotate the axes and eliminate the xy term from the quadratic equation we proceed as follows. Consider Eq. (6.13).

Step 1. Find a matrix P that orthogonally diagonalizes A.

Step 2. Interchange the columns of P if necessary, so that det $P = 1$, assuring that P represents a rotation of the plane (see Exercise 23 of Section 5.6).

Step 3. Introduce a transformation of coordinates

$$X = PX', \qquad \text{where} \qquad X' = \begin{bmatrix} x' \\ y' \end{bmatrix}. \qquad (6.14)$$

Step 4. Substitute (6.14) into (6.13) and obtain the transformed equation

$$(PX')^t A (PX') + N(PX') + f = 0$$

or

$$X''^t P^t A P X' + N P X' + f = 0.$$

Since P orthogonally diagonalizes A, we get $P^t A P = \text{diag}[\lambda_1, \lambda_2]$, where λ_1 and λ_2 are the eigenvalues of A. Thus, the quadratic equation (6.12) becomes (verify this)

$$\lambda_1 x'^2 + \lambda_2 y'^2 + d'x' + e'y' + f = 0;$$

it contains no cross-product term $x'y'$. Note that this is a new linear-algebra proof that the graph of a quadratic equation is a conic section.

We have discussed the main ideas contained in the following theorem:

Theorem 6.9

Let the matrix form of the general quadratic equation of a conic section be

$$X^t A X + K X + f = 0.$$

Let the matrix P orthogonally diagonalize A with det $P = 1$. Then $X = PX'$ rotates the axes so that the equation of the rotated conic contains no $x'y'$ term and is

$$X''^t (P^t A P) X' + (KP) X' + f = 0.$$

Example 5   Rotate the axes to eliminate the xy term from the equation of the ellipse in Example 3.

Solution. From Example 4, we have the equation

$$X^t A X = 1, \qquad \text{where} \qquad A = \begin{bmatrix} 1 & \frac{1}{2} \\ \frac{1}{2} & 1 \end{bmatrix}.$$

Since

$$\det(\lambda I - A) = \lambda^2 - 2\lambda + \tfrac{3}{4} = (\lambda - \tfrac{3}{2})(\lambda - \tfrac{1}{2}) = 0,$$

we consider the eigenvalues $\lambda_1 = 3/2$, $\lambda_2 = 1/2$. The associated orthonormal eigenvectors are, respectively,

$$\mathbf{p}_1 = \begin{bmatrix} \dfrac{1}{\sqrt{2}} \\ \dfrac{1}{\sqrt{2}} \end{bmatrix} \quad \text{and} \quad \mathbf{p}_2 = \begin{bmatrix} -\dfrac{1}{\sqrt{2}} \\ \dfrac{1}{\sqrt{2}} \end{bmatrix},$$

so that

$$P = \begin{bmatrix} \dfrac{1}{\sqrt{2}} & -\dfrac{1}{\sqrt{2}} \\ \dfrac{1}{\sqrt{2}} & \dfrac{1}{\sqrt{2}} \end{bmatrix}.$$

The matrix P orthogonally diagonalizes A; thus $P^t A P = \text{diag}[\,3/2, 1/2\,]$. Since $\det P = 1$, this is the desired transformation matrix, so we substitute $X = PX'$ in the equation $X^t A X = 1$ to get

$$X'^t(P^t A P)X' = 1 \quad \text{or} \quad \tfrac{3}{2}x'^2 + \tfrac{1}{2}y'^2 = 1$$

which, in standard form, is

$$\frac{x'^2}{\tfrac{2}{3}} + \frac{y'^2}{2} = 1.$$

This is the equation of an ellipse with the major axis of length $2\sqrt{2}$ along the y'-axis and the minor axis of length $2\sqrt{6}/3$ along the x'-axis.

    The matrix P has the form

$$\begin{bmatrix} \cos\phi & -\sin\phi \\ \sin\phi & \cos\phi \end{bmatrix} \tag{6.15}$$

(see Exercise 20 of Section 5.6), so $\phi = 45°$, as was indicated in Fig. 6.3.

Example 6   Describe and sketch the graph of the conic section whose equation is

$$x^2 + 2xy + y^2 - x + y = 0. \tag{6.16}$$

The associated quadratic form $x^2 + 2xy + y^2$ determines the matrix

$$A = \begin{bmatrix} 1 & 1 \\ 1 & 1 \end{bmatrix}.$$

The matrix form of equation (6.16) is, therefore,

$$X^t A X + [-1, 1]X = 0.$$

The matrix A has eigenvalues $\lambda_1 = 0$ and $\lambda_2 = 2$ with associated orthonormal eigenvectors

$$\mathbf{p}_1 = \begin{bmatrix} -\dfrac{1}{\sqrt{2}} \\ \dfrac{1}{\sqrt{2}} \end{bmatrix} \quad \text{and} \quad \mathbf{p}_2 = \begin{bmatrix} \dfrac{1}{\sqrt{2}} \\ \dfrac{1}{\sqrt{2}} \end{bmatrix}.$$

Since

$$\det \begin{bmatrix} -\dfrac{1}{\sqrt{2}} & \dfrac{1}{\sqrt{2}} \\ \dfrac{1}{\sqrt{2}} & \dfrac{1}{\sqrt{2}} \end{bmatrix} = -1,$$

we interchange the columns $\mathbf{p}_1$ and $\mathbf{p}_2$, so that

$$P = \begin{bmatrix} \dfrac{1}{\sqrt{2}} & -\dfrac{1}{\sqrt{2}} \\ \dfrac{1}{\sqrt{2}} & \dfrac{1}{\sqrt{2}} \end{bmatrix} \quad \text{and} \quad P'AP = \begin{bmatrix} 2 & 0 \\ 0 & 0 \end{bmatrix}.$$

Performing the linear transformation $X = PX'$, we obtain the matrix form of (6.16):

$$X'^t \begin{bmatrix} 2 & 0 \\ 0 & 0 \end{bmatrix} X' + [-1, 1] \begin{bmatrix} \dfrac{1}{\sqrt{2}} & -\dfrac{1}{\sqrt{2}} \\ \dfrac{1}{\sqrt{2}} & \dfrac{1}{\sqrt{2}} \end{bmatrix} X' = 0$$

or

$$2x'^2 + \frac{2}{\sqrt{2}} y' = 0. \tag{6.17}$$

Equation (6.17) yields the standard form of the equation of a parabola, namely,

$$x'^2 = -\frac{1}{\sqrt{2}} y' \quad \text{or} \quad y' = -\sqrt{2} x'^2;$$

its vertex is at the origin and it opens along the negative (rotated) y'-axis. Since the transformation matrix P again has the form (6.15), we obtain $\sin \phi = 1/\sqrt{2}$ and $\cos \phi = 1/\sqrt{2}$. Thus, $\phi = 45°$. The parabola is sketched in Fig. 6.4

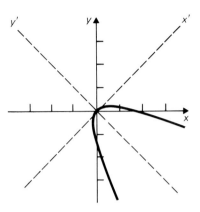

Figure 6.4

Sometimes it is necessary to translate the origin to a different point before the equation acquires the standard form of a conic. Such a translation is, of course, not a linear transformation of the plane (why?). It can, however, either be done *prior* to rotation, and a new plane considered, or it can be done *after* the rotation, as in the following example.

Example 7 Identify the conic whose equation is

$$2x^2 - 4xy - y^2 - 6x - 8y = -13.$$

The matrix A of the associated quadratic form is

$$A = \begin{bmatrix} 2 & -2 \\ -2 & -1 \end{bmatrix}.$$

It has eigenvalues $\lambda_1 = 3$ and $\lambda_2 = -2$, with corresponding associated orthonormal eigenvectors

$$\mathbf{p}_1 = \begin{bmatrix} \dfrac{2}{\sqrt{5}} \\ -\dfrac{1}{\sqrt{5}} \end{bmatrix} \quad \text{and} \quad \mathbf{p}_2 = \begin{bmatrix} \dfrac{1}{\sqrt{5}} \\ \dfrac{2}{\sqrt{5}} \end{bmatrix}.$$

The matrix P that orthogonally diagonalizes A is

$$P = \begin{bmatrix} \dfrac{2}{\sqrt{5}} & \dfrac{1}{\sqrt{5}} \\ -\dfrac{1}{\sqrt{5}} & \dfrac{2}{\sqrt{5}} \end{bmatrix}, \quad \text{so} \quad P^t A P = \begin{bmatrix} 3 & 0 \\ 0 & -2 \end{bmatrix}.$$

Therefore the rotated form of the given equation is

$$X'^t(P^t A P)X' + KPX' = -13 \quad \text{or} \quad 3x'^2 - 2y'^2 - \frac{4}{\sqrt{5}}x' - \frac{22}{\sqrt{5}}y' = -13.$$

Now it is easier to recognize the conic section and to sketch its graph if its equation is in standard form, so we shall translate the axes to a new origin. To do this, complete the square as follows:

$$3\left(x'^2 - \frac{4}{3\sqrt{5}}x'\right) - 2\left(y'^2 + \frac{11}{\sqrt{5}}y'\right) = -13.$$

So

$$3\left(x'^2 - \frac{4}{3\sqrt{5}}x' + \left(\frac{-2}{3\sqrt{5}}\right)^2\right) - 2\left(y'^2 + \frac{11}{\sqrt{5}}y' + \left(\frac{11}{2\sqrt{5}}\right)^2\right)$$

$$= -13 + 3\left(\frac{-2}{3\sqrt{5}}\right)^2 - 2\left(\frac{11}{2\sqrt{5}}\right)^2.$$

This equation simplifies to

$$3\left(x' - \frac{2}{3\sqrt{5}}\right)^2 - 2\left(y' + \frac{11}{2\sqrt{5}}\right)^2 = -\frac{149}{6},$$

which is also equivalent to

$$\frac{\left(y' + \dfrac{11}{2\sqrt{5}}\right)^2}{(149/12)} - \frac{\left(x' - \dfrac{2}{3\sqrt{5}}\right)^2}{(149/18)} = 1.$$

This is the standard form for a hyperbola with center at $(2/(3\sqrt{5}), -11(2\sqrt{5}))$ in the $x'y'$ coordinate system, whose transverse axis lies along the y'-axis, and whose conjugate axis lies along the x'-axis. The x' and y' axes are rotated through an angle ϕ such that $\cos\phi = 2/\sqrt{5}$ and $\sin\phi = -1/\sqrt{5}$; that is, about $-26.57°$.

Give the quadratic form associated with each of the following quadratic equations.

1. $xy = 2$ **2.** $8xy = 5$

3. $53x^2 - 72xy + 32y^2 = 80$ **4.** $2x^2 - 4y^2 = 7$

5. $16x^2 - 24xy + 9y^2 - 60x - 80y + 100 = 0$

6. $64x^2 - 240xy + 225y^2 + 1020x - 544y = 0$

7. $2x^2 - 3xy + 4y^2 - 7x + 2y + 7 = 0$

8. $9x^2 + 4y^2 - 36x - 24y + 36 = 0$

9–16. Write the matrix A of each of the quadratic forms of Exercises 1–8.

17–24. Express each of the equations in Exercises 1–8 in matrix form.

25–32. Name the conics that are the graphs of the equations in Exercises 1–8.

33–40. Sketch graphs for each of the conics of Exercises 1–8.

41. Show that no circle with center at the origin can have an equation with an xy term.

In Exercises 42–45, let the coefficients a, b, c, d, e, and f of the general quadratic equations be as stated in Eq. (6.10). Show that each of the following is invariant under any rotation:

42. The sum $a + c$

43. The discriminant $b^2 - ac$

44. The number $R = \det \begin{bmatrix} a & b & d \\ b & c & e \\ d & e & f \end{bmatrix}$

45. Show that the discriminant in Exercise 43 is negative, zero, or positive when the conic is an ellipse, parabola, or hyperbola, respectively.

46. Show that if the number R in Exercise 44 is zero, the conic degenerates into a point or into one or two lines; these are called *degenerate conics*.

It is possible that the general quadratic equation (6.10) cannot be satisfied by any real numbers at all; for example, $x^2 + y^2 + 1 = 0$. In this case the equation has no graph and it is called an *imaginary conic*. Determine whether the following equations represent a degenerate or an imaginary conic and sketch the graph where possible.

47. $x^2 - y^2 = 0$ **48.** $x^2 + y^2 = -3$ **49.** $9x^2 + 16y^2 = 0$

50. $16x^2 - 9y^2 = 0$ **51.** $9x^2 + 12xy + 4y^2 = 52$ **52.** $x^2 + 3y^2 + 9 = 0$

53. $x^2 - 2xy + y^2 = 0$ **54.** $x^2 + y^2 - 2x - 4y = -5$

6.5 QUADRIC SURFACES

We now extend the results of the previous section to three variables and then give an indication of the n-variable generalization.

Consider the general quadratic equation in three variables:

$$a_{11}x_1^2 + a_{22}x_2^2 + a_{33}x_3^2 + 2a_{12}x_1x_2 + 2a_{13}x_1x_3 + 2a_{23}x_2x_3$$
$$+ bx_1 + cx_2 + dx_3 + f = 0, \quad \textbf{(6.18)}$$

where not all of the coefficients a_{ij} are zero. The *associated quadratic form* is

$$a_{11}x_1^2 + a_{22}x_2^2 + a_{33}x_3^2 + 2a_{12}x_1x_2 + 2a_{13}x_1x_3 + 2a_{23}x_2x_3,$$

which has the matrix form

$$[x_1, x_2, x_3] \begin{bmatrix} a_{11} & a_{12} & a_{13} \\ a_{12} & a_{22} & a_{23} \\ a_{13} & a_{23} & a_{33} \end{bmatrix} \begin{bmatrix} x_1 \\ x_2 \\ x_3 \end{bmatrix} \quad \text{or} \quad X^tAX,$$

where

$$X = \begin{bmatrix} x_1 \\ x_2 \\ x_3 \end{bmatrix} \quad \text{and} \quad A = \begin{bmatrix} a_{11} & a_{12} & a_{13} \\ a_{12} & a_{22} & a_{23} \\ a_{13} & a_{23} & a_{33} \end{bmatrix}.$$

The symmetric matrix A is the *matrix of the quadratic form*, just as in the two-variable case considered in the previous section. It is clear that the quadratic (6.18) can be written also in matrix form as

$$X^tAX + KX + f = 0, \quad \text{where} \quad K = [b, c, d]. \quad \textbf{(6.19)}$$

Example 1   Given quadratic equation

$$3x_1^2 + 7x_3^2 + 2x_1x_2 - 3x_1x_3 + 4x_2x_3 - 3x_1 = 4,$$

the matrix form (6.19) is

$$[x_1, x_2, x_3] \begin{bmatrix} 3 & 1 & -\frac{3}{2} \\ 1 & 0 & 2 \\ -\frac{3}{2} & 2 & 7 \end{bmatrix} \begin{bmatrix} x_1 \\ x_2 \\ x_3 \end{bmatrix} + [-3, 0, 0] \begin{bmatrix} x_1 \\ x_2 \\ x_3 \end{bmatrix} - 4 = 0. \quad \textbf{(6.20)}$$

The graphs of quadratic equations in three variables are called *quadrics*, or *quadric surfaces*. In Fig. 6.5 through 6.7 we have sketched the usual nondegenerate quadrics and given the standard forms of their equations in the three variables x, y, z.

Each of these surfaces can, of course, be oriented along different axes with corresponding variations in the equations. The presence of one or more x_ix_j terms (called *cross products*) in the equation of a nondegenerate quadric indicates that the quadric has been rotated out of its standard position with respect to these axes, while the presence of *both* x_i^2 and x_i terms generally indicates that its "center" is located at some point other than the origin (a translation from the standard form).

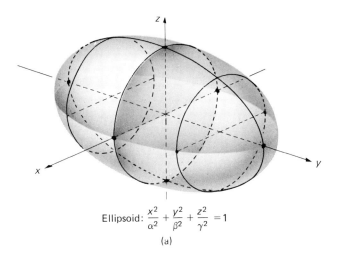

Ellipsoid: $\dfrac{x^2}{\alpha^2} + \dfrac{y^2}{\beta^2} + \dfrac{z^2}{\gamma^2} = 1$

(a)

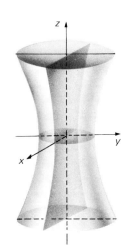

Elliptic hyperboloid of one sheet:

$$\frac{x^2}{\alpha^2} + \frac{y^2}{\beta^2} - \frac{z^2}{\gamma^2} = 1$$

(b)

Figure 6.5

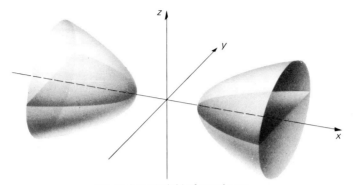

Elliptic hyperboloid of two sheets:

$$\frac{x^2}{\alpha^2} - \frac{y^2}{\beta^2} - \frac{z^2}{\gamma^2} = 1$$

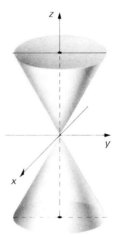

Elliptic cone

$$\frac{x^2}{\alpha^2} + \frac{y^2}{\beta^2} = \frac{z^2}{\gamma^2}$$

Figure 6.6

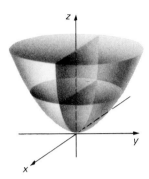

Elliptic paraboloid

$$\frac{x^2}{\alpha^2} + \frac{y^2}{\beta^2} = z$$

(a)

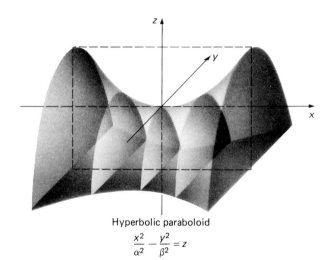

Hyperbolic paraboloid

$$\frac{x^2}{\alpha^2} - \frac{y^2}{\beta^2} = z$$

(b)

Figure 6.7

Example 2 Name and sketch the quadric surface whose matrix equation is

$$[x, y, z]\begin{bmatrix} 4 & 0 & 0 \\ 0 & -9 & 0 \\ 0 & 0 & 8 \end{bmatrix}\begin{bmatrix} x \\ y \\ z \end{bmatrix} = 72.$$

The corresponding quadratic equation in x, y, z is $4x^2 - 9y^2 + 8z^2 = 72$. Dividing by 72 we get

$$\frac{x^2}{18} - \frac{y^2}{8} + \frac{z^2}{9} = 1,$$

which is a standard form for the equation of an elliptic hyperboloid of one sheet oriented along the y-axis; this graph is sketched in Fig. 6.8.

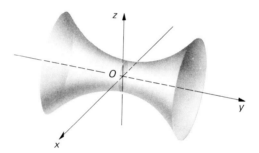

Figure 6.8

Example 3 Name and sketch the graph of the quadratic equation

$$x^2 - 4xz + 2y^2 + 4z^2 - 3x + 2y - 4z = 5.$$

The matrix form of this equation is (verify this)

$$[x, y, z]\begin{bmatrix} 1 & 0 & -2 \\ 0 & 2 & 0 \\ -2 & 0 & 4 \end{bmatrix}\begin{bmatrix} x \\ y \\ z \end{bmatrix} + [-3, 2, -4]\begin{bmatrix} x \\ y \\ z \end{bmatrix} = 5.$$

We find that the eigenvalues of the matrix

$$A = \begin{bmatrix} 1 & 0 & -2 \\ 0 & 2 & 0 \\ -2 & 0 & 4 \end{bmatrix}$$

are $\lambda_1 = 0, \lambda_2 = 2, \lambda_3 = 5$, and the corresponding orthonormal eigenvectors are

$$\mathbf{p}_1 = \begin{bmatrix} \dfrac{2}{\sqrt{5}} \\ 0 \\ \dfrac{1}{\sqrt{5}} \end{bmatrix}, \quad \mathbf{p}_2 = \begin{bmatrix} 0 \\ 1 \\ 0 \end{bmatrix}, \quad \mathbf{p}_3 = \begin{bmatrix} -\dfrac{1}{\sqrt{5}} \\ 0 \\ \dfrac{2}{\sqrt{5}} \end{bmatrix}.$$

The determinant of the matrix

$$P = \begin{bmatrix} \dfrac{2}{\sqrt{5}} & 0 & -\dfrac{1}{\sqrt{5}} \\ 0 & 1 & 0 \\ \dfrac{1}{\sqrt{5}} & 0 & \dfrac{2}{\sqrt{5}} \end{bmatrix}$$

is 1, hence there is a rotation. Furthermore, $P^t AP$ is the diagonal matrix

$$D = P^t AP = \begin{bmatrix} 0 & 0 & 0 \\ 0 & 2 & 0 \\ 0 & 0 & 5 \end{bmatrix}.$$

Therefore, making the orthogonal coordinate transformation $PX' = X$, we have the new equation

$$[x', y', z'] \begin{bmatrix} 0 & 0 & 0 \\ 0 & 2 & 0 \\ 0 & 0 & 5 \end{bmatrix} \begin{bmatrix} x' \\ y' \\ z' \end{bmatrix} + [-3, 2, -4] \begin{bmatrix} \dfrac{2}{\sqrt{5}} & 0 & -\dfrac{1}{\sqrt{5}} \\ 0 & 1 & 0 \\ \dfrac{1}{\sqrt{5}} & 0 & \dfrac{2}{\sqrt{5}} \end{bmatrix} \begin{bmatrix} x' \\ y' \\ z' \end{bmatrix} = 5,$$

which is

$$2y'^2 + 5z'^2 - 2\sqrt{5}x' + 2y' - \sqrt{5}z' = 5.$$

The presence of the first-degree terms in y' and z' indicates that the center of the surface is not at the origin, so we must translate the axes. We do this by completing the square in the equation. Thus (verify this)

$$2\left(y'^2 + y' + \dfrac{1}{4}\right) + 5\left(z'^2 - \dfrac{1}{\sqrt{5}}z' + \dfrac{1}{20}\right) = 2\sqrt{5}x' + \dfrac{23}{4}$$

or

$$2\left(y' + \dfrac{1}{2}\right)^2 + 5\left(z' - \dfrac{1}{2\sqrt{5}}\right)^2 = 2\sqrt{5}\left(x' + \dfrac{23}{8\sqrt{5}}\right).$$

This equation may also be written as

$$\frac{\left(y' + \frac{1}{2}\right)^2}{\sqrt{5}} + \frac{\left(z' - \frac{1}{2\sqrt{5}}\right)^2}{(2\sqrt{5}/5)} = \left(x' + \frac{23}{8\sqrt{5}}\right)$$

which is the equation of an elliptic paraboloid, somewhat as in Fig. 6.7 but oriented so that its axis of symmetry is the positive x''-axis (Fig. 6.9).

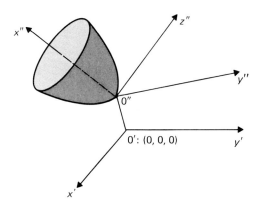

Figure 6.9

Although the problem of translating the axes to establish a new center introduces a slight complication, the results demonstrated in Examples 2 and 3 are three-dimensional illustrations of the following theorem, known as the **principal-axis** *theorem.*

Theorem 6.10

Let A be an $n \times n$ symmetric matrix. The quadratic form $X^t A X$ can be written as the sum of squares $\lambda_1 y_1^2 + \lambda_2 y_2^2 + \ldots + \lambda_n y_n^2$, where λ_i are the eigenvalues of A and $X = PY$, where P is the orthogonal matrix such that $P^t A P$ is $\text{diag}[\lambda_1, \lambda_2, \ldots, \lambda_n]$.

The proof is left for you.

Name the following quadric surfaces:

1. $x^2 + y^2 + z^2 = 9$ **2.** $x^2 - y^2 - z^2 = 25$ **3.** $16y^2 + z^2 = 16x$

4. $36x^2 + 4y^2 + 9z^2 - 36 = 0$ **5.** $x^2 + 9y^2 - 4z^2 = 0$

6. $2x^2 - 3y^2 + 6z^2 = 18$ **7.** $9x^2 - 3z^2 + y = 0$

8-14. Write the quadratic equations of Exercises 1–7 in the form $X^t AX + KX + f = 0$, that is, find the matrices A and K.

In Exercises 15–21, find an orthogonal matrix P such that $P^t AP$ is diagonal and the substitution $X = PY$ results in an equation without any cross products; name the quadric; translate where necessary.

15. $xy + z = 0$ **16.** $4x^2 + 4y^2 + 4z^2 + 4xy + 4xz + 4yz = 5$

17. $xz = 1$ **18.** $7x^2 + 8xy - 4xz + 3y^2 + 2z^2 = 1$

19. $2xy - 6xz = 1$ **20.** $144x^2 + 100y^2 + 81z^2 - 216xz - 540x - 720z = 0$

21. $2xy + 2xz + 2yz - 6x - 6y - 4z = -9$

22. Prove the principal-axis theorem (Theorem 6.10) for $\mathbb{R}^3$.

23. Sketch the proof of the principal-axis theorem for $\mathbb{R}^n$.

24. Show that a translation of axes cannot be accomplished in the plane by a linear transformation.

6.6 AN APPLICATION TO SYSTEMS OF DIFFERENTIAL EQUATIONS

This section is addressed only to those who have studied calculus. In Exercise 21 of Section 3.1 you were asked to show that the collection $D[0, 1]$ of all differentiable functions defined on the closed interval $[0, 1]$ was a real vector space. In fact, if a and b are any real numbers with $a < b$, the collection of all real-valued differentiable functions on the closed interval $[a, b]$ is a real vector space U. Let V be the subspace of U consisting of all these functions whose first derivative is differentiable. Then it can be verified that the transformation $D : V \to U$ that maps each twice-differentiable function f in V into its derivative, namely, $D(f) = f'$, is a linear transformation (see Exercise 19).

    In many applications of mathematics to physics, chemistry, economics, and so forth, the ideas considered are expressible in the form of an equation involving functions and their derivatives. Such equations are called **differential equations**. One of the simplest differential equations is

$$y' = ay, \tag{6.21}$$

where y' is the derivative of the function $y = f(x)$ and a is a constant. Expressed in familiar terms this differential equation becomes

$$D(y) = ay.$$

In other words, if a nonzero y that satisfies (6.21) exists, then a is an eigenvalue and y is an eigenvector corresponding to a for the transformation D (derivative). It can be verified that the eigenspace corresponding to the eigenvalue a is spanned by the function $y = e^{ax}$. Thus every solution to (6.21) has the form

$$y = ce^{ax}, \tag{6.22}$$

where c is an arbitrary real number. The solution (6.22) is called the *general solution* to the differential equation (6.21).

If a particular problem generating the differential equation imposes additional conditions that allow us to identify a particular vector in the eigenspace of solutions, we call it a *particular solution* of the differential equation.

Example 1 Solve the differential equation

$$y' = 3y \tag{6.23}$$

subject to the *initial condition* $y(0) = 5$.

The general solution to Eq. (6.23) is $y = ce^{3x}$. The fact that $y(0) = 5$ gives us $5 = ce^{(3)(0)} = c$, so the particular solution to (6.23) is $y = 5e^{3x}$.

While there are many ways in which linear algebra aids in the solution of more complicated differential equations than (6.21), we shall indicate only one such idea here.* Since we have tools for solving systems of linear equations, we will consider systems of linear differential equations of the form

$$
\begin{aligned}
y'_1 &= a_{11}y_1 + a_{12}y_2 + \ldots + a_{1n}y_n, \\
y'_2 &= a_{21}y_1 + a_{22}y_2 + \ldots + a_{2n}y_n, \\
&\;\;\vdots \qquad\qquad \vdots \\
y'_n &= a_{n1}y_1 + a_{n2}y_2 + \ldots + a_{nn}y_n,
\end{aligned}
\tag{6.24}
$$

where $y_i = f_i(x)$ are functions to be determined and a_{ij} $(i, j = 1, 2, \ldots, n)$ are given real numbers (constants). Let $A = (a_{ij})$ be the $n \times n$ matrix of these real-number coefficients and let

$$
Y' = \begin{bmatrix} y'_1 \\ y'_2 \\ \vdots \\ y'_n \end{bmatrix}
\qquad \text{with} \qquad
Y = \begin{bmatrix} y_1 \\ y_2 \\ \vdots \\ y_n \end{bmatrix},
$$

where $y'_i = dy_i/dx$. Then (6.24) can be written as the matrix equation $Y' = AY$.

---

* See Ross L. Finney and Donald R. Ostberg, *Elementary Differential Equations with Linear Algebra*, Reading, Mass., Addison–Wesley Publ. Co., 1976.

Example 2   Let the system of differential equations be

$$y_1' = 2y_1, \qquad y_2' = -y_2, \qquad y_3' = 7y_3. \tag{6.25}$$

Write the system in matrix form, solve it, and find the particular solution that satisfies the given initial conditions

$$y_1(0) = 1, \qquad y_2(0) = -1, \qquad y_3(0) = 4.$$

The matrix form of (6.25) is

$$Y' = \begin{bmatrix} 2 & 0 & 0 \\ 0 & -1 & 0 \\ 0 & 0 & 7 \end{bmatrix} Y.$$

Since the system (6.25) consists entirely of equations of the form (6.21) involving only a single function in each equation, we can solve them as in Example 1. Thus the general solution is

$$y_1 = c_1 e^{2x}, \qquad y_2 = c_2 e^{-x}, \qquad y_3 = c_3 e^{7x}.$$

The particular solution that satisfies the given initial conditions is obtained as follows:

$$y_1(0) = \quad 1 = c_1 e^{(2)(0)} = c_1,$$
$$y_2(0) = -1 = c_2 e^{-(0)} = c_2,$$
$$y_3(0) = \quad 4 = c_3 e^{(7)(0)} = c_3.$$

Therefore the particular solution to the system (6.25) is

$$Y = \begin{bmatrix} e^{2x} \\ -e^{-x} \\ 4e^{7x} \end{bmatrix}$$

The system (6.25) was easily solved. This was largely because the coefficient matrix A was diagonal—the system involved only one function in each equation. To handle a system $Y' = AY$ when A is *not* diagonal is, of course, more difficult. We shall try to replace such a system with another system of equations whose matrix of coefficients is diagonal. That is, we shall try to change the variable so as to obtain a diagonal-coefficient matrix. The change will have the form

$$\begin{aligned} y_1 &= p_{11} z_1 + p_{12} z_2 + \cdots + p_{1n} z_n, \\ y_2 &= p_{21} z_1 + p_{22} z_2 + \cdots + p_{2n} z_n, \\ &\vdots \qquad\qquad \vdots \\ y_n &= p_{n1} z_1 + p_{n2} z_2 + \cdots + p_{nn} z_n, \end{aligned} \tag{6.26}$$

or

$$Y = PZ.$$

For this substitution we have to determine the entries p_{ij} of the matrix P in such a way that the new system of equations in the new but unknown functions $z_1 = z_1(x)$, $z_2, \ldots, z_n$ has a diagonal matrix of coefficients. It is easy to see that by differentiating each equation in (6.26) with respect to x we obtain $Y' = PZ'$ (since the numbers p_{ij} are constant). Substituting this result into the original system $Y' = AY$, we obtain the new system $PZ' = APZ$.

If the matrix P is nonsingular, multiplying both sides of the above equation by P^{-1} gives the following new system of differential equations:

$$Z' = (P^{-1}AP)Z = DZ. \tag{6.27}$$

If $D = P^{-1}AP$ is a diagonal matrix, we have reached our goal. Therefore, it is clear that the matrix P of our substitution should be the matrix P that diagonalizes A. Hence, if the matrix A is diagonalizable, we can solve the system. We outline the procedure in the following example.

Example 3   Solve the system of differential equations

$$y_1' = 2y_1 + 3y_2,$$
$$y_2' = 7y_1 - 2y_2.$$

Step 1. In matrix form this system is $Y' = AY$, where

$$A = \begin{bmatrix} 2 & 3 \\ 7 & -2 \end{bmatrix}.$$

Step 2. Find the matrix P that diagonalizes A.

The eigenvalues of A are the roots of its characteristic equation $\lambda^2 - 25 = 0$. Thus, we can find the eigenvectors corresponding to the eigenvalues $\lambda_1 = 5$, $\lambda_2 = -5$, as indicated in earlier sections of this chapter. Two such eigenvectors corresponding to 5 and -5, respectively, are

$$\mathbf{p}_1 = \begin{bmatrix} 1 \\ 1 \end{bmatrix} \quad \text{and} \quad \mathbf{p}_2 = \begin{bmatrix} 3 \\ -7 \end{bmatrix}.$$

So A is diagonalized by the matrix

$$P = \begin{bmatrix} 1 & 3 \\ 1 & -7 \end{bmatrix}.$$

Step 3. Make the substitutions $Y = PZ$ and $Y' = PZ'$ to obtain a new diagonal system $Z' = DZ$, where $D = P^{-1}AP$.

You can verify that in this example

$$P^{-1}AP = \begin{bmatrix} 5 & 0 \\ 0 & -5 \end{bmatrix} \quad \text{so} \quad Z' = \begin{bmatrix} 5 & 0 \\ 0 & -5 \end{bmatrix} Z.$$

Step 4. Solve the system $Z' = DZ$.

In this example the system is

$$z_1' = 5z_1, \qquad z_2' = -5z_2,$$

and its general solution is $z_1 = c_1 e^{5x}, \quad z_2 = c_2 e^{-5x}$.

Step 5. Determine Y from $Y = PZ$.

In our example,

$$Y = \begin{bmatrix} 1 & 3 \\ 1 & -7 \end{bmatrix} \begin{bmatrix} c_1 e^{5x} \\ c_2 e^{-5x} \end{bmatrix}.$$

Therefore, the general solution to the original system is

$$y_1 = c_1 e^{5x} + 3c_2 e^{-5x},$$
$$y_2 = c_1 e^{5x} - 7c_2 e^{-5x}.$$

To find a particular solution one would now use whatever initial conditions are imposed to evaluate the constants c_1 and c_2.

In this discussion we have assumed that the matrix A of the given system was diagonalizable. When such is not the case, other methods are used, which would take us beyond the scope of this book. We refer the reader to more advanced sources, such as the Finney and Ostberg text previously cited.

EXERCISES (6.6)

In Exercises 1–6, find the general solution to each of the following systems of differential equations.

1. $y_1' = 3y_1 - y_2$
  $y_2' = 2y_1$

2. $y_1' = 3y_1 + y_2$
  $y_2' = y_1 + 3y_2$

3. $y_1' = y_1 + 4y_2$
  $y_2' = 2y_1 + 3y_2$

4. $y_1' = \frac{1}{2}y_1 + 3y_2$
  $y_2' = 3y_1 - y_2$

5. $y_1' = -y_1 + 2y_2 + 2y_3$
  $y_2' = 2y_1 - y_2 + 2y_3$
  $y_3' = 2y_1 + 2y_2 - y_3$

6. $y_1' = y_2' = y_3' = y_1 + y_2 + y_3$
  Hint. Write three equations

In Exercises 7–12, find the particular solution to each system of differential equations in Exercises 1–6 respectively that satisfies the following initial conditions:

7. $y_1(0) = 1, \quad y_2(0) = -1$

8. $y_1(0) = -2, \quad y_2(0) = 3$

9. $y_1(0) = -1, \quad y_2(0) = 5$

10. $y_1(0) = 4, \quad y_2(0) = -2$

11. $y_1(0) = y_3(0) = 1, y_2(0) = 0$

12. $y_1(0) = 1, \quad y_2(0) = 2, \quad y_3(0) = -5$

13. Find the general solution to the system of differential equations

$$y_1' = 8y_1 + 9y_2 + 9y_3,$$
$$y_2' = 3y_1 + 2y_2 + 3y_3,$$
$$y_3' = -9y_1 - 9y_2 - 10y_3.$$

14. Find the particular solution to the system in Exercise 13 that satisfies the initial conditions $y_1(0) = y_2(0) = 1$, $y_3(0) = 0$.

15. Solve the system of differential equations

$$y_1' = 2y_1 - y_2, \quad y_2' = -y_1 + 2y_2, \quad y_3' = y_3 - y_4, \quad y_4' = -y_3 + y_4.$$

16. Solve the differential equation $y'' - y' = 6y$. *Hint.* Set $y_1 = y$, $y_2 = y'$. Then note that

$$y_2' = 6y_1 + y_2 \quad \text{and} \quad y_1' = y_2.$$

17. Use the method of Exercise 16 to solve $y'' + 2y' - 8y = 0$.

18. Solve the differential equation $y''' + 15y'' - 17y' + y = 0$.

19. Prove that the transformation $D: V \to U$ that maps each twice-differentiable function f into its derivative $D(f) = f'$ is a linear transformation.

20. Prove that every solution of the differential equation $y' = ay$ (where $a = $ const) is of the form $y = ce^{ax}$ by letting $y = f(x)$ be any solution and showing that $f(x) = ce^{ax}$. *Hint.* Show that $f(x)e^{-ax}$ is constant.

6.7 BLOCK MATRICES—BLOCK MULTIPLICATION

Before proceeding to other applications of linear algebra we digress long enough to introduce a matrix-theory technique that will be used in the discussion and computations of the next chapter.

Example 1   Consider the matrix

$$A = \left[\begin{array}{cc:ccc} 2 & 0 & 0 & 0 & 0 \\ 0 & 2 & 0 & 0 & 0 \\ \hdashline 1 & 0 & 3 & 2 & 1 \\ 0 & 1 & 4 & 5 & 6 \end{array}\right].$$

It seems rather natural to partition A into blocks as indicated, so that

$$A = \begin{bmatrix} 2I_2 & Z \\ I_2 & A_{22} \end{bmatrix}.$$

As we shall see below, it is often very useful in applications to split a matrix into blocks. It is particularly helpful in multiplying two large matrices.

Example 2   Let

$$A = \begin{bmatrix} 2I_2 & Z \\ I_2 & A_{22} \end{bmatrix}$$

be the matrix of Example 1 and let

$$B = \begin{bmatrix} B_1 \\ B_2 \end{bmatrix},$$

where B_1 has two rows corresponding to the two columns in the first submatrix of the partition of A, while B_2 has three rows corresponding to the columns in Z and A_{22}. Then

$$AB = \begin{bmatrix} 2I_2 B_1 + ZB_2 \\ I_2 B_1 + A_{22} B_2 \end{bmatrix} = \begin{bmatrix} 2B_1 \\ B_1 + A_{22} B_2 \end{bmatrix}.$$

Thus, the only really nontrivial computation required to find AB is the much smaller matrix product $A_{22} B_2$. In particular, if

$$B = \begin{bmatrix} 3 & 1 & 5 \\ 2 & 0 & 6 \\ \hline 1 & -4 & 1 \\ 0 & 1 & 2 \\ -1 & 1 & -1 \end{bmatrix},$$

then, as can be readily verified,

$$A_{22} B_2 = \begin{bmatrix} 2 & -9 & 6 \\ -2 & -5 & 8 \end{bmatrix}, \quad \text{and} \quad AB = \begin{bmatrix} 6 & 2 & 10 \\ 4 & 0 & 12 \\ \hline 5 & -8 & 11 \\ 0 & -5 & 14 \end{bmatrix}.$$

   In the general case, let A be any $m \times n$ matrix and let $n = n_1 + n_2 + \ldots + n_k$ and $m = m_1 + m_2 + \ldots + m_l$. Then the matrix A can be partitioned into kl submatrices A_{st}, $s = 1, 2, \ldots, k$, $t = 1, 2, \ldots, l$, where each submatrix is $m_t \times n_s$.

   We say that the matrix $A = (a_{ij})$ is **partitioned in blocks** as

$$A = \begin{bmatrix} A_{11} & A_{12} & \cdots & A_{1l} \\ A_{21} & A_{22} & \cdots & A_{2l} \\ \vdots & & & \vdots \\ A_{k1} & A_{k2} & \cdots & A_{kl} \end{bmatrix}.$$

Several specialized examples of this sort of partitioning into blocks have already been met in previous chapters as we discussed (among other things) the augmented matrix $[A:B]$ of a system of linear equations $AX = B$; the matrix-inversion algorithm that begins with $[I:A]$ and ends with $[A^{-1}:I]$; and the standard matrix of a linear transformation $[T]_E = [T(e_1):T(e_2):\ldots:T(e_n)]$, etc.

Let A and B be two matrices such that A is $m \times n$ and B is $n \times p$. If $n = n_1 + n_2 + \ldots + n_k$ and the *columns* of A and the *rows* of B are partitioned in the same way, so that A_{si} is $m_s \times n_i$ and B_{it} is $n_i \times p_t$, then with the rows of A and the columns of B partitioned in any manner whatsoever, we have A and B partitioned into blocks as

$$A = \begin{bmatrix} A_{11} & A_{12} & \cdots & A_{1k} \\ A_{21} & A_{22} & \cdots & A_{2k} \\ \vdots & \vdots & \vdots & \vdots \\ A_{s1} & A_{s2} & \cdots & A_{sk} \end{bmatrix}, \quad B = \begin{bmatrix} B_{11} & B_{12} & \cdots & B_{1t} \\ B_{21} & B_{22} & \cdots & B_{2t} \\ \vdots & \vdots & \vdots & \vdots \\ B_{k1} & B_{k2} & \cdots & B_{kt} \end{bmatrix}.$$

The product AB can be verified to be the matrix

$$C = \begin{bmatrix} C_{11} & C_{12} & \cdots & C_{1t} \\ C_{21} & C_{22} & \cdots & C_{2t} \\ \vdots & \vdots & \vdots & \vdots \\ C_{s1} & C_{s2} & \cdots & C_{st} \end{bmatrix}, \quad \text{where} \quad C_{ij} = \sum_{r=1}^{k} A_{ir} B_{rj}.$$

This is the same form as that taken by the *element-by-element multiplication* of A and B, but is in some cases much easier to calculate, as Example 2 and the following example illustrate.

Example 3 Compute A^3 for the matrix

$$A = \begin{bmatrix} 1 & 0 & 0 & 0 & 0 & 0 \\ 0 & 1 & 0 & 0 & 0 & 0 \\ 0 & 0 & 1 & 0 & 0 & 0 \\ 0 & 0 & 0 & \frac{1}{2} & 0 & \frac{1}{2} \\ 0 & 0 & 0 & 0 & 1 & 0 \\ 0 & 0 & 0 & 0 & 0 & 1 \end{bmatrix}.$$

Solution: By partitioning A into the indicated blocks we have

$$A = \begin{bmatrix} I_3 & Z \\ Z & A_{22} \end{bmatrix},$$

so that

$$A^3 = \begin{bmatrix} I_3 & Z \\ Z & A_{22}^3 \end{bmatrix}.$$

Therefore we need only compute A_{22}^3, where

$$A_{22} = \left[\begin{array}{c|cc} \frac{1}{2} & 0 & \frac{1}{2} \\ \hline 0 & 1 & 0 \\ 0 & 0 & 1 \end{array}\right].$$

Let us partition A_{22} as indicated. Then

$$A_{22} = \left[\begin{array}{cc} \frac{1}{2}I & A' \\ Z & I_2 \end{array}\right],$$

$$A_{22}^2 = \left[\begin{array}{cc} (\frac{1}{2}I)^2 & \frac{1}{2}IA' + A'I_2 \\ Z & I_2^2 \end{array}\right] = \left[\begin{array}{c|cc} \frac{1}{4} & 0 & \frac{3}{4} \\ \hline 0 & 1 & 0 \\ 0 & 0 & 1 \end{array}\right] = \left[\begin{array}{cc} \frac{1}{4}I & A'' \\ Z & I_2 \end{array}\right],$$

$$A_{22}^3 = \left[\begin{array}{cc} \frac{1}{8}I & \frac{1}{2}A'' + A' \\ Z & I_2 \end{array}\right] = \left[\begin{array}{c|cc} \frac{1}{8} & 0 & \frac{7}{8} \\ \hline 0 & 1 & 0 \\ 0 & 0 & 1 \end{array}\right].$$

Hence

$$A^3 = \left[\begin{array}{cc} I_3 & Z \\ Z & A_{22}^3 \end{array}\right] = \left[\begin{array}{cccccc} 1 & 0 & 0 & 0 & 0 & 0 \\ 0 & 1 & 0 & 0 & 0 & 0 \\ 0 & 0 & 1 & 0 & 0 & 0 \\ 0 & 0 & 0 & \frac{1}{8} & 0 & \frac{7}{8} \\ 0 & 0 & 0 & 0 & 1 & 0 \\ 0 & 0 & 0 & 0 & 0 & 1 \end{array}\right],$$

which you can verify by direct calculation.

EXERCISES (6.7)————————————————————————————

1. Use block multiplication to find AB and A^2, if

$$A = \left[\begin{array}{cc|cc|c} 3 & 0 & 1 & 2 & -1 \\ 0 & 3 & 0 & 1 & 2 \\ \hline 0 & 0 & 1 & 0 & 0 \\ 0 & 0 & 0 & 1 & 0 \\ \hline 0 & 0 & 0 & 0 & 1 \end{array}\right], \quad B = \left[\begin{array}{ccc|cc|c} 1 & 2 & 4 & 1 & 5 & 1 \\ 1 & -1 & 3 & 0 & -2 & 0 \\ \hline 4 & 1 & -1 & 0 & 1 & 0 \\ 0 & 0 & 1 & 1 & 0 & 0 \\ \hline 1 & 0 & 1 & 0 & 1 & 0 \end{array}\right]$$

Let A and B be the following matrices:

$$A = \left[\begin{array}{rr:r:rr} 2 & 3 & 1 & 0 & 0 \\ 3 & -1 & 0 & 0 & 0 \\ \hdashline 1 & 0 & -2 & 0 & 1 \\ \hdashline -1 & 0 & 0 & 1 & 0 \\ 0 & -1 & 1 & 0 & 1 \end{array}\right], \quad B = \left[\begin{array}{r:rr} 1 & 0 & 0 \\ -2 & 0 & 0 \\ \hdashline 0 & 3 & -1 \\ \hdashline -1 & 0 & 0 \\ 1 & 0 & 0 \end{array}\right].$$

2. Compute AB using block multiplication with the indicated blocks.

3. Partition A and B in a different way and compute AB.

4. Compute A^2 and A^3.

5. Show that if $A = (A_1 : A_2 : A_3 : \ldots : A_k)$ and

$$B = \left[\begin{array}{c} B_1 \\ B_2 \\ \cdot \\ \cdot \\ B_k \end{array}\right],$$

then $AB = A_1 B_1 + A_2 B_2 + \ldots + A_k B_k$.

6. Write the standard matrix $[T]_E$ for T in block form if $T: \mathbb{R}^7 \to \mathbb{R}^5$ is given by $T(x_1, x_2, \ldots, x_7) = (x_2, x_1, x_4, x_7, x_6)$.

7

OTHER APPLICATIONS

The applications of linear algebra are many and varied. All of the sciences (biological, management, behavioral, and physical) make use of matrix and vector algebra, as a glance at the literature in these fields will reveal. In this chapter we shall look at only two general classes of applications; we should recognize that in each case only a brief introduction can be given. Other applications were indicated in previous chapters. In the appendix, we list a few additional applications.

7.1 DIRECTED GRAPHS

In this section, and the next, we shall illustrate how some simple linear-algebra techniques are used in a branch of mathematics called *graph theory*. Although it is several hundreds of years old, graph theory has just recently been found to be very helpful in interpreting many situations arising in the behavioral and management sciences that are essentially combinatorial in nature.

The term *graph* in the context of *graph theory* is not used in quite the same sense as it is in other branches of mathematics.

A **graph** is a nonempty collection of a finite number of points $P_1, P_2, \ldots, P_n$, called **vertices**, together with a finite number of **edges** $P_i P_j$ connecting some of the vertices in pairs.

Example 1   Some graphs are illustrated in Fig. 7.1.

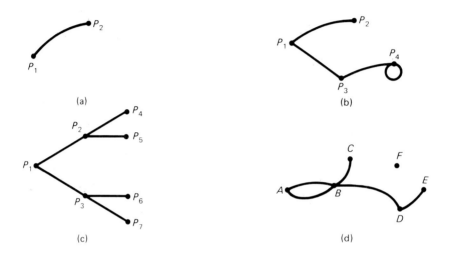

Figure 7.1

Note that graph (b) has an edge from vertex P_4 back to P_4; such an edge is called a **loop**. Note also that in graph (d) vertex F has no edge connecting it to any other vertex, while vertices A and B are connected by two distinct edges. This is possible in a graph. In these examples the edge $P_i P_j$ for each graph is considered to be the same as the edge $P_j P_i$; *the order in which they are mentioned is immaterial*. This exactly mirrors many applications. Several cities connected by highways or air routes are examples of graphs in which the order of the endpoints is unimportant (see Fig. 7.2).

In other applications, however, the order of the vertices may indeed be important. We see examples of this in hierarchical structures and in many communications models. These instances lead to the concept of a directed graph.

An **oriented graph** is a nonempty collection of a finite number of vertices P_i together with a finite number of directed edges $P_i P_j$ joining some or all of these. An oriented graph is called a **directed graph** or a **digraph** if it contains no loops and has at most one edge from P_i to P_j for each i and j. (A second edge connecting P_i and P_j must go from P_j to P_i.)

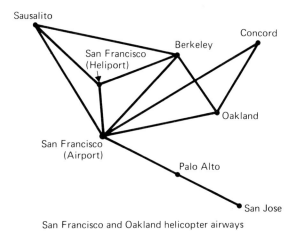

San Francisco and Oakland helicopter airways

Figure 7.2

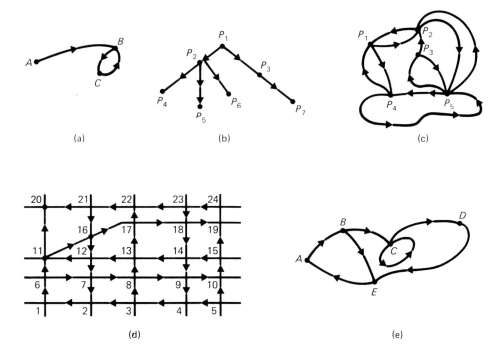

(a)

(b)

(c)

(d)

(e)

Figure 7.3

Example 2   The graphs in Fig. 7.3 illustrate oriented graphs. Note that (e) fails to be a digraph because it contains a loop; note also that (d) could be a grid of one-way streets in a downtown area.

It is often convenient to be able to represent an oriented graph by a matrix. This has the advantage of allowing computations to be performed more readily. A **matrix representation** $A = (a_{ij})$ for a given oriented graph has the same number of rows and columns as there are vertices in the graph. The entries a_{ij} in the matrix are the number of *directed* edges *from* the vertex P_i *to* the vertex P_j. If the graph is a digraph, then all of the entries in its matrix representation are either zero or one; such a matrix is called the **incidence matrix** for the digraph. The matrix representations for four of the graphs of Fig. 7.3 are as follows:

$$
\begin{array}{c}
\begin{array}{ccc}
A & B & C
\end{array} \\
\begin{array}{c}
A \\ B \\ C
\end{array}
\begin{bmatrix}
0 & 1 & 0 \\
0 & 0 & 1 \\
0 & 1 & 0
\end{bmatrix}
\end{array}
$$

(a)

$$
\begin{array}{c}
\begin{array}{ccccccc}
1 & 2 & 3 & 4 & 5 & 6 & 7
\end{array} \\
\begin{array}{c}
1 \\ 2 \\ 3 \\ 4 \\ 5 \\ 6 \\ 7
\end{array}
\begin{bmatrix}
0 & 1 & 1 & 0 & 0 & 0 & 0 \\
0 & 0 & 0 & 1 & 1 & 1 & 0 \\
0 & 0 & 0 & 0 & 0 & 0 & 1 \\
0 & 0 & 0 & 0 & 0 & 0 & 0 \\
0 & 0 & 0 & 0 & 0 & 0 & 0 \\
0 & 0 & 0 & 0 & 0 & 0 & 0 \\
0 & 0 & 0 & 0 & 0 & 0 & 0
\end{bmatrix}
\end{array}
$$

(b)

$$
\begin{array}{c}
\begin{array}{ccccc}
1 & 2 & 3 & 4 & 5
\end{array} \\
\begin{array}{c}
1 \\ 2 \\ 3 \\ 4 \\ 5
\end{array}
\begin{bmatrix}
0 & 1 & 0 & 1 & 0 \\
1 & 0 & 0 & 0 & 1 \\
0 & 1 & 0 & 0 & 1 \\
1 & 0 & 0 & 0 & 1 \\
0 & 1 & 1 & 1 & 0
\end{bmatrix}
\end{array}
$$

(c)

$$
\begin{array}{c}
\begin{array}{ccccc}
A & B & C & D & E
\end{array} \\
\begin{array}{c}
A \\ B \\ C \\ D \\ E
\end{array}
\begin{bmatrix}
0 & 1 & 0 & 0 & 0 \\
0 & 0 & 1 & 0 & 1 \\
0 & 0 & 1 & 1 & 0 \\
0 & 0 & 0 & 0 & 1 \\
1 & 0 & 0 & 0 & 0
\end{bmatrix}
\end{array}
$$

(e)

The incidence matrix for the grid in Fig. 7.3 (d) will be 24 × 24. You may wish to write out the matrix. Note that matrix (e) is not an incidence matrix, because the graph has a loop. Any incidence matrix for a digraph will have zeros on its main diagonal. (Why?)

Let us examine how a certain community problem might be modeled by a digraph.

Example 3   Consider the following interrelated statements.

1. The gross national product (GNP) rises.
2. Automobile sales increase.
3. Employment rates increase.
4. People take more vacations in the country.
5. Air-pollution levels rise in the cities.

There are, of course, many possible cause-and-effect relationships between these statements. One set of these is illustrated by the digraph of Fig. 7.4, where the arrow points from the cause to the effect.

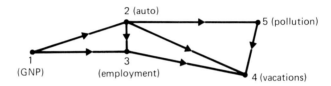

Figure 7.4

Using the numbers attached to the statements as row and column numbers, we can write the incidence matrix for this digraph:

$$
\begin{array}{c}
\begin{array}{ccccc} \ \ 1 & 2 & 3 & 4 & 5 \end{array} \\
\begin{array}{c} 1 \\ 2 \\ 3 \\ 4 \\ 5 \end{array}
\begin{bmatrix}
0 & 1 & 1 & 0 & 0 \\
0 & 0 & 1 & 1 & 1 \\
0 & 0 & 0 & 1 & 0 \\
0 & 0 & 0 & 0 & 0 \\
0 & 0 & 0 & 1 & 0
\end{bmatrix}.
\end{array}
$$

Several other concepts are required before we can analyze the above problem or use graph theory to gain insights into other problems of this type. In applying graph theory to the study of organizations, for example, it is often important to consider the question of *dominance*. Usually this sort of situation arises when, with any two people or groups, one dominates or influences the other. One may model this type of situation with a digraph in which the vertices represent the people in the organization, while the directed edges flow from the person with influence to the person being influenced.

Example 4   A juvenile gang consisting of five members *H, J, K, L,* and *M* is interviewed by a social worker, who interviews all possible pairs of members of the gang and observes which member of the pair is more influential. As a result, the following digraph is formed (Fig. 7.5), together with its incidence matrix.

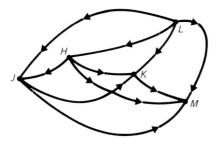

Figure 7.5

$$
\begin{array}{c}
\begin{array}{ccccc} H & J & K & L & M \end{array} \\
A = \begin{array}{c} H \\ J \\ K \\ L \\ M \end{array}
\begin{bmatrix}
0 & 1 & 1 & 0 & 1 \\
0 & 0 & 1 & 0 & 1 \\
0 & 0 & 0 & 0 & 1 \\
1 & 1 & 1 & 0 & 1 \\
0 & 0 & 0 & 0 & 0
\end{bmatrix}
\end{array}
$$

By adding the row entries of the matrix A we find that in one stage H dominates three people, J dominates two people, K dominates one person, L dominates all four of the other members of the gang, and M dominates none of them. Since L dominates everyone else, he is called the *consensus leader*.

To determine the leader of the organization in cases where there is no consensus leader, we introduce the concept of *n-stage dominance*. We shall illustrate this with the following example in which vertices of the digraph are athletic teams rather than individuals. Note, however, that the concept of dominance is still present.

Example 5 Consider the following results of football competition in a conference:

Team	Beat	Lost to
a	d, e, f	b, c
b	a, c, d	e, f
c	a, d, f	b, e
d	e, f	a, b, c
e	b, c	a, d, f
f	b, e	a, c, d

Who should represent the conference in a postseason bowl game? Teams a, b, and c could draw straws or have a play-off. Another alternative is given by the idea of n-stage dominance.

Rather than draw the dominance digraph, we set up the incidence matrix directly. Let us order the rows and columns the same as in the above list:

$$M = \begin{array}{c} \\ a \\ b \\ c \\ d \\ e \\ f \end{array} \begin{array}{cccccc} a & b & c & d & e & f \\ \left[\begin{array}{cccccc} 0 & 0 & 0 & 1 & 1 & 1 \\ 1 & 0 & 1 & 1 & 0 & 0 \\ 1 & 0 & 0 & 1 & 0 & 1 \\ 0 & 0 & 0 & 0 & 1 & 1 \\ 0 & 1 & 1 & 0 & 0 & 0 \\ 0 & 1 & 0 & 0 & 1 & 0 \end{array}\right] \end{array}.$$

The number of games won by each team is clearly the sum of the entries in its row. What about the number of games lost? From this example it is fairly clear that there is, in general, no transitivity in dominance. Thus even though team b beat team c, and team c beat team f, team b lost to team f. However, because b beat c, and c beat f, we can say that team b has *two-stage dominance* over team f. We could use the concept of two-stage dominance to select the conference representative. It turns out that the square of the incidence matrix is the matrix that represents the two-stage dominance. Note that in Example 5 the two-stage matrix is

$$M' = M^2 = \begin{array}{c} \\ a \\ b \\ c \\ d \\ e \\ f \end{array} \begin{array}{ccccccc} a & b & c & d & e & f \\ \left[\begin{array}{cccccc|c} 0 & 2 & 1 & 0 & 2 & 1 & 6 \\ 1 & 0 & 0 & 2 & 2 & 3 & 8 \\ 0 & 1 & 0 & 1 & 3 & 2 & 7 \\ 0 & 2 & 1 & 0 & 1 & 0 & 4 \\ 2 & 0 & 1 & 2 & 0 & 1 & 6 \\ 1 & 1 & 2 & 1 & 0 & 0 & 5 \end{array}\right] \end{array}.$$

From M we saw that a dominated e, and e dominated c, so that although a did not dominate c, it has two-stage dominance over c, as indicated by the fact that $m'_{13} = 1$. The fact that $m'_{12} = 2$ means that a has two-stage dominance over b via two different paths,

$$a \to e \to b \quad \text{and} \quad a \to f \to b.$$

You can sketch the digraph of the situation and note that the entries in M^2 give the number of two-edge paths from P_i to P_j, that is, those passing through an intermediate vertex. In general we give the following definition.

Let M be the incidence matrix for a dominance digraph, M^k be the kth power of M and $M^k = (a_{ij})$. The entries a_{ij} indicate the number of k-stage dominances of individual i over individual j (in the digraph).

If we so choose, this analysis can be used to send team b of Example 5 to the bowl game as the conference representative because its number of two-stage dominances, 8, is larger than that of any of the other teams in the conference. It is the "leader" at stage two. Probably a more accurate determination could be made by taking the *sum* of the first- and second-stage dominances for each individual (team). This number is often called the *power* of the individual in the dominance digraph. This is given by the matrix sum $M + M^2$. For the situation of Example 5 this is

$$M + M^2 = \begin{array}{c} \\ a \\ b \\ c \\ d \\ e \\ f \end{array} \begin{array}{cccccc} a & b & c & d & e & f \\ \left[\begin{array}{cccccc} 0 & 2 & 1 & 1 & 3 & 2 \\ 2 & 0 & 1 & 3 & 2 & 3 \\ 1 & 1 & 0 & 2 & 3 & 3 \\ 0 & 2 & 1 & 0 & 2 & 1 \\ 2 & 1 & 2 & 2 & 0 & 1 \\ 1 & 2 & 2 & 1 & 1 & 0 \end{array} \right] \end{array} \begin{array}{c} \text{Power} \\ 9 \\ 11 \\ 10 \\ 6 \\ 8 \\ 7 \end{array} .$$

This idea can, of course, be generalized to the sum $M + M^2 + \cdots + M^k$ for dominance through k stages, a sort of k-*power*.

These examples suggest some simple ways in which matrix algebra can be applied. The exercises below develop these ideas a little further.

EXERCISES (7.1)

1. Examine the situation in Example 3 for dominance. Is there a concensus leader for this situation?

2. What are the two-stage dominances in the situation of Exercise 1?

Determine which of the following matrices could be incidence matrices for digraphs of a situation with dominance.

3. $\begin{bmatrix} 1 & 0 & 0 \\ 0 & 1 & 0 \\ 0 & 0 & 1 \end{bmatrix}$ 4. $\begin{bmatrix} 0 & 0 & 0 \\ 1 & 0 & 1 \\ 1 & 1 & 0 \end{bmatrix}$ 5. $\begin{bmatrix} 0 & 1 & 0 \\ 0 & 0 & 1 \\ 1 & 1 & 0 \end{bmatrix}$

6. $\begin{bmatrix} 0 & 1 & 0 \\ 1 & 0 & 1 \\ 0 & 1 & 0 \end{bmatrix}$ 7. $\begin{bmatrix} 0 & 0 & 1 \\ 1 & 0 & 0 \\ 0 & 1 & 0 \end{bmatrix}$ 8. $\begin{bmatrix} 0 & 0 & 1 & 1 \\ 1 & 0 & 1 & 0 \\ 0 & 1 & 0 & 1 \\ 1 & 1 & 0 & 0 \end{bmatrix}$

9–14. For the incidence matrices of Exercises 3–8 find all the two-stage dominances and the total dominances in one and two stages (power) for each individual. Is there a leader?

In Exercises 15–18, we are given the dominance digraph indicated in Fig. 7.6.

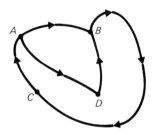

Figure 7.6

15. Write the incidence matrix.

16. Is there a consensus leader?

17. Find the sum of one- and two-stage dominances (power).

18. Is there a leader?

19. A tennis match between four people ends with the following result: Kelly has beaten both O'Brien and Thompson; Thompson has beaten O'Brien; Carter has beaten Kelly, O'Brien, and Thompson. Find the power of each player and rank them accordingly.

20. Draw a reasonable digraph and compute the power of each vertex when the vertices represent the following statements:
a) Tensions increase in the Mid-East.
b) Oil prices increase.
c) Money spent in search of geothermal energy increases.
d) Coal generation of electricity increases.
e) Air pollution increases.

21. Sketch the digraph of Example 5 and compare the paths $P_i P_k P_j$ through two vertices with the entries (m'_{ij}) of M^2.

22. In an interest survey given to student Tom Jones, the concept of paired comparisons was used. It was discovered that he preferred playing golf to fishing, watching sports on TV, playing chess, or boating. He prefers playing basketball to boating, TV sports, chess, golf, and fishing. He prefers boating to watching TV sports, and he prefers watching TV sports to playing chess. He prefers to play chess rather than go boating. What is his favorite pastime? What is the power of each pastime?

23. Use a digraph to model the authority structure of your family. Compute the power of each member.

24. Use a digraph to model the authority structure in your home town.

7.2 COMMUNICATION NETWORKS

As a second example from the behavioral and management sciences of how graph theory and matrices may be used to model ideas, let us consider communication networks.

A **communication network** consists of a finite set $A_1, A_2, \ldots, A_n$ of individuals (people, cities, etc.) such that between some pairs of individuals there is a one- or two-way communication link.

Examples of two-way communication links are two-way radio, telephone, highways, airlines, etc. A one-way link could be a messenger, a signal light, one-way radio, or television. Such a communication network can be represented by an oriented graph. A good example is the airways link of Fig. 7.2 in the previous section. Consider also the following example.

Example 1 The four cities Liddville, Jacobtown, Cooperton, and Spring City are connected by direct telephone lines, as indicated in the oriented graph in Fig. 7.7.

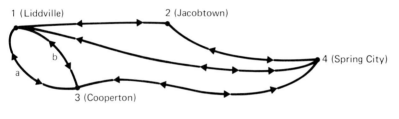

1 (Liddville)   2 (Jacobtown)

b

a

3 (Cooperton)

4 (Spring City)

Figure 7.7

The double arrows indicate two-way communication and are the equivalent to two edges each, one each way. This oriented graph is not a digraph (why?).

The matrix representation of this graph is called a **communication matrix**. In it the value of each entry m_{ij} is the number of direct-communication links (one-way) from individual A_i to individual A_j, in that direction. The value of m_{ij} is zero otherwise, including, for convenience, the values of m_{ii} (even though an individual can surely communicate with himself). The communication matrix for Example 1 is

$$M = \begin{array}{c} \\ \\ \\ \\ \\ \end{array} \begin{array}{cccc} L & J & C & S \\ \end{array}$$

$$M = \begin{bmatrix} 0 & 1 & 2 & 1 \\ 1 & 0 & 0 & 1 \\ 2 & 0 & 0 & 1 \\ 1 & 1 & 1 & 0 \end{bmatrix} \begin{array}{l} \text{Liddville} \\ \text{Jacobtown} \\ \text{Cooperton} \\ \text{Spring City} \end{array}$$

Note that M is not an incidence matrix since its entries are other than just 0 and 1. Even so (just as with the case of dominance) the square of the communication matrix gives two-stage communication links. That is, it tells us the number of communication links between two individuals (cities) that pass through exactly one other individual (city). Thus, the matrix

$$M^2 = \begin{array}{c} \\ L \\ J \\ C \\ S \end{array} \begin{array}{cccc} L & J & C & S \\ \begin{bmatrix} 6 & 1 & 1 & 3 \\ 1 & 2 & 3 & 1 \\ 1 & 3 & 5 & 2 \\ 3 & 1 & 2 & 3 \end{bmatrix} \end{array}$$

indicates that Jacobtown (J) has three communication links with Cooperton (C) that pass through one other city. These are

$$\text{Jacobtown} \rightarrow \text{Spring City} \rightarrow \text{Cooperton,}$$
$$\text{Jacobtown} \rightarrow \text{Liddville (a)} \rightarrow \text{Cooperton,}$$
$$\text{Jacobtown} \rightarrow \text{Liddville (b)} \rightarrow \text{Cooperton.}$$

What do you suppose the '6' in the $(1,1)$ position of M^2 indicates with respect to Liddville?

The cube M^3 of the communication matrix M would indicate the number of communication links between two individuals (cities) that pass through exactly two other individuals (cities), and so on.

A communication network where every link is two-way (A communicates with B *and* B communicates with A) is called a **perfect communication network**. Example 1 illustrates a perfect communication network. The matrix representation for a perfect communication network is always symmetric (why?). Note the matrix M of Example 1. We need an additional concept.

An oriented graph is called **connected** if between any two vertices there is a path consisting of a finite number of edges. If such a path does not exist between every pair of vertices, the graph is **disconnected**.

To be effective, any communication network should have a connected graph. Any individual in a communication graph is called a *liaison* if the removal of this individual from the graph (together with the edges to and from him) disconnects the graph.

Example 2 Consider the perfect communication network in a company's executive council depicted in Fig. 7.8. Note that individual C is a liaison, since removal of C from the network disconnects it. How about individual B?

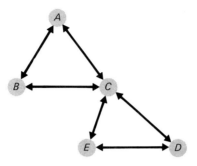

Figure 7.8

The matrix representation for the graph of Fig. 7.8 is

$$M = \begin{array}{c} \\ A \\ B \\ C \\ D \\ E \end{array} \begin{array}{ccccc} A & B & C & D & E \\ \begin{bmatrix} 0 & 1 & 1 & 0 & 0 \\ 1 & 0 & 1 & 0 & 0 \\ 1 & 1 & 0 & 1 & 1 \\ 0 & 0 & 1 & 0 & 1 \\ 0 & 0 & 1 & 1 & 0 \end{bmatrix} \end{array}.$$

It is obvious that in general (not necessarily perfect) communication networks, different individuals could play roles of varying importance. Some individuals may only send messages, while others only receive messages, and still others may both send and receive. To analyze these situations, we first examine subsets of communication networks. We shall be interested in dividing a communication network into subsystems, so that within the given subsystem *every individual has a two-way communication link*, not necessarily direct, *with every other individual in the subsystem*. We also want the subsystems having this property to be as large as possible. We shall show that such subsystems form *equivalence classes* within the large network in the sense that every individual in the network belongs to exactly one class and that between classes there is at most a one-way communication link.

Let $\mathscr{C} = \{A_1, A_2, \ldots, A_n\}$ be a communication network with individuals A_i, $i = 1, 2, \ldots, n$. We define a relation @ on $\mathscr{C}$ as follows:

A_i @ A_j if and only if there is a two-way communication link (not necessarily in one step) between A_i and A_j, or else $i = j$.

We shall leave it as an exercise to show that the relation @ has the following properties:

> *Reflexive:* A_i @ A_i for every $i = 1, 2, \ldots, n$;
>
> *Symmetric:* if A_i @ A_j, then A_j @ A_i;
>
> *Transitive:* if A_i @ A_j and A_j @ A_k, then A_i @ A_k.

Recall that in Section 5.5, in connection with similarity of matrices, we remarked that a relation that was reflexive, symmetric, and transitive was called an *equivalence relation*. Hence, @ is indeed an equivalence relation on $\mathscr{C}$. You will remember that all equivalence relations partition the set on which they are defined into disjoint *equivalence classes*. Such is the case with the communication network $\mathscr{C}$. We shall show this explicitly for the given relation @ on $\mathscr{C}$.

Let $[A_i]$ denote the collection of all those individuals A_j in $\mathscr{C}$ such that A_j @ A_i; that is, those A who have a two-way communication link with A_i. Since A_i @ A_i, the set $[A_i]$ is not empty, and each member of $\mathscr{C}$ belongs to some equivalence class. Suppose then that $[A_i]$ and $[A_j]$ are two of these classes and suppose further that $[A_i] \cap [A_j] \neq \varnothing$. Then there is some individual A who has a two-way communication link with both A_i and A_j, that is, A @ A_i *and* A @ A_j. Hence A_j @ A and A @ A_i, which implies (by transitivity) that A_j @ A_i, so A_j is in $[A_i]$. Furthermore, if X is in $[A_j]$, hence X @ A_j, then X @ A_j and A_j @ A_i imply (by transitivity again) that X @ A_i, so X is in $[A_i]$. Therefore, $[A_j] \subseteq [A_i]$. A similar argument gives $[A_i] \subseteq [A_j]$, so $[A_i] = [A_j]$. Thus, two equivalence classes are either equal or else disjoint. This proves the following:

The equivalence relation @ partitions the communications network $\mathscr{C}$ into disjoint classes in which each individual has a two-way communication link with every other individual in its class.

To complete our task we must show that there is at most a one-way link between classes. To see that this is so, suppose that there are two equivalence classes $[A_i] \neq [A_j]$ such that some individual X in $[A_i]$ can send a message to some individual Y in $[A_j]$, and that some member U of $[A_j]$ can send a message to some individual Z in $[A_i]$. Since U and Y are in $[A_j]$, two-way communication is possible between them. This is also true of X and Z in $[A_i]$. Therefore the following communication link would exist:

$$X \to Y \to U \to Z \to X,$$

which is a two-way link between Y and X. Hence Y and X are in the same class, contrary to what we proved above. Thus no such link can exist and at most one-way communication between classes is possible.

The value of splitting the communication network in a large organization into equivalence classes is fairly obvious, since once these classes are identified, the flow of information in the organization can be optimized. Let us illustrate this with a small-scale example.

Example 3   The network of intelligence agents in Platonia has six key members who need to be given certain information. The agency's director does not know where they all are. Instead he has information of the form: Hanks knows where Jacobson is, Kimball knows where Scarlati is, and so on. The director sets up the following communication matrix M that summarizes the information he has:

$$
\begin{array}{c}
\\
\text{Hanks} \\
\text{Jacobson} \\
\text{Kimball} \\
\text{Scarlati} \\
\text{Russell} \\
\text{Le Bouf}
\end{array}
\begin{array}{c}
\begin{array}{cccccc}
H & J & K & S & R & L
\end{array} \\
\left[\begin{array}{cccccc}
0 & 1 & 0 & 0 & 0 & 0 \\
0 & 0 & 0 & 0 & 1 & 0 \\
0 & 0 & 0 & 1 & 0 & 0 \\
1 & 0 & 0 & 0 & 0 & 1 \\
0 & 0 & 0 & 0 & 0 & 0 \\
0 & 0 & 1 & 0 & 0 & 0
\end{array}\right] = M.
\end{array}
$$

Here $m_{ij} = 1$ means that $i \neq j$ and person i knows where person j is and can send him a message.

We next try to identify all those individuals to whom each of the individuals can send messages. This information is obtained from the matrices M, M^2, M^3, ..., that detail the one-, two-, and three-link communication connections. We construct the lists by adding to it in successive steps until no new individual can be added to the list or until at least one individual can in successive stages send a message to *all* of his colleagues. We also presume that an individual can communicate with himself. The lists and the stages at which contact can be made are listed in the following table:

Agent	Stage 0 or 1	Stage 2	Stage 3	Final
Hanks	H, L	H, J, R	H, J, R	H, J, R
Jacobson	J, R	J, R	J, R	J, R
Kimball	K, S	H, K, S, L	H, J, K, S, L	H, J, K, S, R, L
Scarlati	H, S, L	H, J, K, S, L	H, J, K, S, R, L	H, J, K, S, R, L
Russell	R	R	R	R
Le Bouf	K, L	K, S, L	H, K, S, L	H, J, K, S, R, L

The information in the table is obtained from the matrices

$$
M^2 =
\begin{array}{c}
\begin{array}{cccccc}
H & J & K & S & R & L
\end{array} \\
\left[\begin{array}{cccccc}
0 & 0 & 0 & 0 & 1 & 0 \\
0 & 0 & 0 & 0 & 0 & 0 \\
1 & 0 & 0 & 0 & 0 & 1 \\
0 & 1 & 1 & 0 & 0 & 0 \\
0 & 0 & 0 & 0 & 0 & 0 \\
0 & 0 & 0 & 1 & 0 & 0
\end{array}\right],
\end{array}
\qquad
M^3 =
\begin{array}{c}
\begin{array}{cccccc}
H & J & K & S & R & L
\end{array} \\
\left[\begin{array}{cccccc}
0 & 0 & 0 & 0 & 0 & 0 \\
0 & 0 & 0 & 0 & 0 & 0 \\
0 & 1 & 1 & 0 & 0 & 0 \\
0 & 0 & 0 & 1 & 1 & 0 \\
0 & 0 & 0 & 0 & 0 & 0 \\
1 & 0 & 0 & 0 & 0 & 1
\end{array}\right].
\end{array}
$$

After three stages we see that a message sent to Scarlati will be relayed to everyone, so it is only necessary to contact him. After four stages a message sent to Kimball will reach everyone, and after five stages a message sent to Le Bouf will have been relayed to everyone. (Verify this.)

Let us continue our analysis further by assuming that we need a list of those from whom the agents can *receive* messages and, finally, the equivalence classes of this network. The *receive-from lists* can be computed by again constructing a communication matrix or by merely reading the *send list* backwards. That is, if A_j is on A_i's send list, put A_i on A_j's receive-from list. The equivalence classes are then the intersection of the two lists (receive and send). This is given in the following table:

Agent	Send to	Receive from	Equivalence class
Hanks	H, J, R	H, K, S, L	$\{H\}$
Jacobson	J, R	H, J, K, S, L	$\{J\}$
Kimball	H, J, K, S, R, L	K, S, L	$\{K, S, L\}$
Scarlati	H, J, K, S, R, L	K, S, L	$\{K, S, L\}$
Russell	R	H, J, K, S, R, L	$\{R\}$
Le Bouf	H, J, K, S, R, L	K, S, L	$\{K, S, L\}$

Let us use this data to sketch the oriented graph of the network of equivalence classes (see Fig. 7.9).

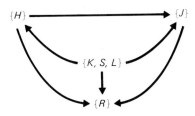

Figure 7.9

This graph, which is a digraph, gives a fairly accurate picture of the intercommunication within this intelligence network.

EXERCISES (7.2)

1. Sketch a digraph corresponding to the following communication matrix:

$$M = \begin{bmatrix} 0 & 1 & 0 & 1 \\ 1 & 0 & 1 & 0 \\ 0 & 1 & 0 & 1 \\ 1 & 0 & 1 & 0 \end{bmatrix}.$$

Is this a perfect communication network?

2. Construct the communication matrix for the business communication network in Fig. 7.10. Is this a perfect communication network?

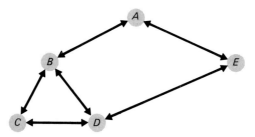

Figure 7.10

3. Identify any liaison individuals in the network of Exercise 2. Are there any liaison individuals in the network of Exercise 1?

4. Consider five people who gossip with each other. The incidence matrix representing this situation is as follows:

$$\begin{bmatrix} 0 & 1 & 1 & 0 & 1 \\ 1 & 0 & 0 & 1 & 0 \\ 0 & 0 & 1 & 0 & 1 \\ 1 & 1 & 1 & 0 & 1 \\ 1 & 0 & 1 & 1 & 0 \end{bmatrix}.$$

Sketch the communication network. If the fourth person moves out of the neighborhood, is it still possible for a rumor to spread among the remaining neighbors?

5. Sketch the one-way communication digraph for Example 3. Is this a connected graph? Are there any liaison individuals?

The oriented graph in Fig. 7.11 indicates the possible helicopter flights in the San Francisco Bay area (see Fig. 7.2 for the names of the stops).

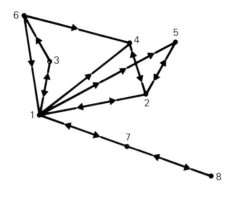

Figure 7.11

6. Write the matrix representation of this graph.

7. Write the incidence matrix for the fly-to digraph.

8. Write the incidence matrix for the fly-from digraph.

9. How many stages are necessary to fly from (4) to (6)? From (8) to (5)?

10. Is the graph of Fig. 7.11 connected?

11. Identify any liaison cities.

12. Show that the relation $@$ defined in this section for the communication network $\mathscr{C}$ is indeed reflexive, symmetric, and transitive.

13. Show that if $\mathscr{C}$ is a communication network of n individuals and if A_i can communicate at all with A_j, then this can be done in not more than $n-1$ stages.

7.3 REGULAR MARKOV CHAINS

This section and the next require a minimal understanding of the concepts of probability, such as you would study in college algebra, finite mathematics, or elementary probability.

The study of a finite sequence of experiments (or events) in which the outcome of a given experiment depends only upon the outcome of the experiment that immediately precedes it in the sequence but not on the other experiments of the sequence, gives rise to the study of *Markov processes*, or *chains*. We shall give a precise definition of a Markov process after we look at a simple example.

Example 1 Suppose that a maze is constructed in the form illustrated in Fig. 7.12. The maze consists of three chambers (numbered 1, 2, and 3 for convenience), each painted a different color, as indicated in the figure. The experimenter places a mouse into one of these chambers and then at periodic intervals observes where the mouse is. Since the experimenter does not watch the mouse constantly, it is not possible to determine the exact movements of the mouse; therefore, the movements are given as probabilities. Some notation is helpful at this point.

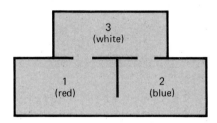

Figure 7.12

The situation, or condition, in a Markov process at which the experiment begins (the chamber in which the mouse is first placed) is called the **initial state** of the process. If the initial state is chosen by a chance device that selects the state or condition (chamber) j with probability p_j^0, the initial probability distribution is given by a vector

$$\mathbf{p}^0 = (p_1^0, p_2^0, \ldots, p_n^0).$$

Hence in our example, if the mouse is always placed in chamber 1, the initial state is always chamber 1 and the initial probability distribution would be

$$\mathbf{p}^0 = (1, 0, 0).$$

On the other hand, if the mouse had an equal chance of being placed in any one of the three chambers, the initial probability distribution would be

$$\mathbf{p}^0 = (\tfrac{1}{3}, \tfrac{1}{3}, \tfrac{1}{3}).$$

Let us denote the probability that the mouse will move from chamber i to chamber j by p_{ij}. Because the mouse has an affinity for colors of a certain hue, the probability that it moves from chamber 2 to chamber 3 might be, for example, $p_{23} = \tfrac{1}{2}$, while the probability that it moves from chamber 2 to chamber 1 might be $p_{21} = \tfrac{1}{4}$. Suppose also that it remains in chamber 2 with probability $\tfrac{1}{4}$, so $p_{22} = \tfrac{1}{4}$.

We can display all the **transition probabilities**, as the p_{ij} are called, in a matrix $A = (p_{ij})$ called the **transition matrix**. A possible transition matrix for this example could be the following:

$$P = \begin{array}{c} \\ 1 \\ 2 \\ 3 \end{array} \begin{array}{ccc} 1 & 2 & 3 \\ \left[\begin{array}{ccc} 0 & \tfrac{1}{3} & \tfrac{2}{3} \\ \tfrac{1}{4} & \tfrac{1}{4} & \tfrac{1}{2} \\ \tfrac{1}{6} & \tfrac{1}{2} & \tfrac{1}{3} \end{array} \right]. \end{array}$$

In this example, the number $p_{23} = 1/2$ in the matrix indicates the probability that the mouse will move from state (chamber) 2 to state (chamber) 3.

Let us now interrupt this example for a few formal definitions.

A **Markov chain** is a sequence of n experiments in which each experiment has m possible outcomes $a_1, a_2, \ldots, a_m$ called **states** and the probability p_{ij} that a particular state occurs depends only on the outcome of the preceding experiment.

We assume that these probabilities are nonnegative numbers p_{ij} between 0 and 1, that is, $0 \leqslant p_{ij} \leqslant 1$, which represent the probability that the outcome (state) a_j occurs on any given experiment, provided that state a_i occurred on the preceding experiment. Thus, $p_{i1} + p_{i2} + \ldots + p_{im} = 1$.

A row vector $\mathbf{p}$ is called a **probability vector** if it has nonnegative components whose sum is 1.

The vectors $\mathbf{p}^0$ in Example 1 are probability vectors, as are the row vectors of the matrix P given there.

A matrix A is called a **transition matrix** if it is square and its row vectors are probability vectors, that is, they *are nonnegative and their sum is* 1.

The transition matrix P above is an example.

Example 2   Determine which of the following are transition matrices:

$$A = \begin{bmatrix} 1 & 0 \\ 0 & 1 \end{bmatrix} \qquad B = \begin{bmatrix} 1/2 & 1/4 \\ 1/2 & 3/4 \end{bmatrix} \qquad C = \begin{bmatrix} 0.1 & 0.7 & 0.2 \\ 0.3 & 0.4 & 0.3 \\ 0.6 & 0.2 & 0.2 \end{bmatrix}.$$

Note that the row sum for each row in A and C is 1, while in B it is not. Thus A and C are transition matrices, but B is not. Is the matrix B^t a transition matrix?

Let us return to Example 1 and our mouse. Let us denote by $p_j^{(n)}$ the probability that after n observations the mouse is in chamber j. Then the probability vector

$$\mathbf{p}^{(n)} = (p_1^{(n)}, p_2^{(n)}, p_3^{(n)})$$

indicates the distribution for this situation. It can be shown that for $j = 1, 2, 3$ these probabilities satisfy,

$$p_j^{(n)} = p_1^{(n-1)} p_{1j} + p_2^{(n-1)} p_{2j} + p_3^{(n-1)} p_{3j}.$$

Thus the probability of being in chamber j after n steps is the sum of three terms composed of the probability of being in any of the three chambers after $n - 1$ steps multiplied by the probability of moving from that chamber to chamber j at the nth step. Note that these equations can be written in matrix form as

$$\mathbf{p}^{(n)} = \mathbf{p}^{(n-1)}A,$$

where A is the transition matrix. (Verify this for the above example.) Let us iterate this process by letting n take on the values $1, 2, \ldots$. We get

$$\mathbf{p}^{(1)} = \mathbf{p}^{(0)}A,$$
$$\mathbf{p}^{(2)} = \mathbf{p}^{(1)}A = (\mathbf{p}^{(0)}A)A = \mathbf{p}^{(0)}A^2,$$
$$\mathbf{p}^{(3)} = \mathbf{p}^{(2)}A = (\mathbf{p}^{(0)}A^2)A = \mathbf{p}^{(0)}A^3,$$
$$\vdots \qquad \vdots \qquad \vdots \qquad \vdots$$

We have the following theorem for all Markov chains.

Theorem 7.1

Let A be the transition matrix for a Markov chain. The probability distribution $\mathbf{p}^{(k)}$ after k steps is given by $\mathbf{p}^{(k)} = \mathbf{p}^{(0)}A^{(k)}$, where $\mathbf{p}^{(0)}$ is the initial distribution.

Let us refer again to Example 1 assuming this time that the mouse has an equal chance of being initially placed in any one of the three chambers of Fig. 7.12. Thus,

$$\mathbf{p}^{(0)} = (\tfrac{1}{3}, \tfrac{1}{3}, \tfrac{1}{3}).$$

Let us further suppose that the transition matrix is as follows:

$$T = \begin{bmatrix} 0.1 & 0.7 & 0.2 \\ 0.3 & 0.4 & 0.3 \\ 0.5 & 0.2 & 0.3 \end{bmatrix}.$$

Then, after three observations, the position of the mouse is given by

$$\mathbf{p}^{(0)}T^3 = (\tfrac{1}{3}, \tfrac{1}{3}, \tfrac{1}{3}) \begin{bmatrix} 0.1 & 0.7 & 0.2 \\ 0.3 & 0.4 & 0.3 \\ 0.5 & 0.2 & 0.3 \end{bmatrix}^3$$

$$= (\tfrac{1}{3}, \tfrac{1}{3}, \tfrac{1}{3}) \begin{bmatrix} 0.294 & 0.438 & 0.268 \\ 0.294 & 0.436 & 0.270 \\ 0.298 & 0.428 & 0.274 \end{bmatrix}$$

$$= (0.295, 0.434, 0.271).$$

This last vector expresses the probability distribution after three observations.

Suppose that we begin the mouse–maze experiments by placing the mouse in the first chamber every time. In this case the initial state is given by the vector

$$\mathbf{p}^{(0)} = (1, 0, 0).$$

Therefore, after three observations, the position of the mouse is given by the following probability distribution:

$$(1, 0, 0) \begin{bmatrix} 0.294 & 0.438 & 0.268 \\ 0.294 & 0.436 & 0.270 \\ 0.298 & 0.428 & 0.274 \end{bmatrix} = (0.294, 0.438, 0.268).$$

This result is the first row of T^3. Of course, this is not a coincidence since the entries $p_{ij}^{(k)}$ of the transition matrix A^k of a Markov chain give the probabilities of passing from state a_i to state a_j after k stages (for all i and j).

Example 3 Consider the transition matrix

$$R = \begin{bmatrix} 0.5 & 0.5 \\ 0.7 & 0.3 \end{bmatrix}.$$

Let us construct successive powers of R; these are:

$$R^2 = \begin{bmatrix} 0.6 & 0.4 \\ 0.56 & 0.44 \end{bmatrix}, \qquad R^3 = \begin{bmatrix} 0.58 & 0.42 \\ 0.588 & 0.412 \end{bmatrix}, \qquad R^4 = \begin{bmatrix} 0.584 & 0.416 \\ 0.5824 & 0.4176 \end{bmatrix}.$$

If we continue in this way we shall see that the powers of R approach the matrix

$$\begin{bmatrix} \frac{7}{12} & \frac{5}{12} \\ \frac{7}{12} & \frac{5}{12} \end{bmatrix} = \begin{bmatrix} 0.5867 & 0.4167 \\ 0.5867 & 0.4167 \end{bmatrix} \text{ (approximately)}.$$

It is interesting to note that if $\mathbf{u} = (7/12, 5/12)$ then $\mathbf{u}R = \mathbf{u}$. Such a vector is called a *fixed-point* of the matrix R.

A probability vector $\mathbf{u}$ is a **fixed-point** of the matrix A if and only if $\mathbf{u} = \mathbf{u}A$.

In Example 3 we noted that, as n increased, the powers R^n of the transition matrix R became more and more like a matrix W whose rows are equal to the fixed-point vector for R. This was not a coincidence. For certain transition matrices such will always be the case.

A transition matrix A of a Markov chain is called **regular** if some power A^n of A has only positive entries.

The matrix R of Example 3 is regular since $R = R^1$ has only positive entries, while the matrix

$$B = \begin{bmatrix} 1 & 0 \\ 0.4 & 0.6 \end{bmatrix}$$

is not regular since, for every power $B^n = (b_{ij})$ of B, $b_{12} = 0$. The identity matrix I_n is also an example of a transition matrix that is not regular. Other examples of transition matrices that *are* regular can be found in the exercises at the end of this section. We have the following theorem, whose proof we omit since it requires concepts from the theory of limits.

Theorem 7.2

If A is a regular transition matrix of a Markov chain, then

i) *A has a unique fixed-point probability vector* **w** *whose components are positive;*
ii) *The powers A^n of A (where n is a positive integer) approach a matrix W whose row vectors are each equal to* **w**.

In many experiments the researcher hopes that, no matter how the process begins, it will settle down to some stable predictable behavior. Such is not always the case; but, as the above theorem states, when a regular Markov chain is involved, stable long-range behavior is predictable. The mouse–maze experiment of Example 1 is just such a case. While it might appear at first that the mouse exhibited a preference for some chambers because of having been released in a particular place, after a long number of observations the transition probabilities will stabilize at values independent of the particular chamber into which the mouse is first put. This is because the transition matrix T is regular.

The following example is classical.

Example 4 *The spread of a rumor* Assume that a given piece of information is passed to individual a_1 who in turn passes it on to individual a_2 who passes it on to a_3, and so on. Each time the information is passed to a new individual, we shall assume that there is probability p that the information will be reversed. Thus, if individual a_i receives the message as true, there is probability p that it will be passed on as false; hence the probability that it will be passed on as true is equal to $1 - p$.

This gives us an example of a regular Markov chain with the transition matrix

$$P = \begin{matrix} & \text{False} & \text{True} \\ \text{False} \\ \text{True} \end{matrix} \begin{bmatrix} 1-p & p \\ p & 1-p \end{bmatrix}.$$

We are, of course, interested in successive powers of the matrix P, since the probability distribution for the nth individual will be $\mathbf{u}P^n$, where $\mathbf{u}$ is the initial distribution.

We show that the fixed-point probability vector **w** for P is

$$\mathbf{w} = (\tfrac{1}{2}, \tfrac{1}{2})$$

by demonstrating a general formula for the fixed-point of any positive 2×2 transition matrix. Let a and b be real numbers with $0 < a < 1$ and $0 < b < 1$. Then any positive 2×2 transition matrix will have the form

$$P = \begin{bmatrix} 1-a & a \\ b & 1-b \end{bmatrix}.$$

Since P is regular, it must have a fixed-point vector $\mathbf{w} = (w_1, w_2)$ such that $\mathbf{w}P = \mathbf{w}$. Hence,

$$\mathbf{w}P = (w_1, w_2) \begin{bmatrix} 1-a & a \\ b & 1-b \end{bmatrix} = (w_1(1-a) + w_2 b, \; w_1 a + w_2(1-b)),$$

so that

$$w_1 = w_1(1-a) + w_2 b,$$
$$w_2 = w_1 a + w_2(1-b).$$

This becomes $w_1 a = w_2 b$. Since $\mathbf{w}$ is a probability vector, we also have $w_1 + w_2 = 1$. This gives us the 2×2 system

$$w_1 a - w_2 b = 0,$$
$$w_1 + w_2 = 1.$$

Thus, the fixed-point vector for P is

$$\mathbf{w} = \left(\frac{b}{a+b}, \frac{a}{a+b} \right).$$

In the case of Example 4, where $a = b = p$, this becomes $\mathbf{w} = (\frac{1}{2}, \frac{1}{2})$.

EXERCISES (7.3) ——————————————————————————————

Decide which of the following matrices are regular transition matrices:

1. $\begin{bmatrix} \frac{1}{2} & \frac{1}{2} \\ \frac{1}{3} & \frac{2}{3} \end{bmatrix}$
2. $\begin{bmatrix} 0 & 1 \\ 1 & 0 \end{bmatrix}$
3. $\begin{bmatrix} \frac{1}{2} & \frac{1}{2} \\ 1 & 0 \end{bmatrix}$
4. $\begin{bmatrix} 0.2 & 0.4 & 0.4 \\ 0.3 & 0.3 & 0.4 \\ 0.1 & 0.5 & 0.4 \end{bmatrix}$

5. $\begin{bmatrix} \frac{1}{2} & \frac{1}{2} \\ 0 & 1 \end{bmatrix}$
6. $\begin{bmatrix} \frac{1}{2} & \frac{1}{2} & 0 \\ 0 & \frac{1}{2} & \frac{1}{2} \\ \frac{1}{3} & \frac{1}{3} & \frac{1}{3} \end{bmatrix}$
7. $\begin{bmatrix} 0 & 1 \\ \frac{1}{3} & \frac{2}{3} \end{bmatrix}$

8. $\begin{bmatrix} \frac{1}{2} & 0 & \frac{1}{2} \\ 0 & \frac{1}{2} & \frac{1}{2} \\ \frac{1}{2} & \frac{1}{2} & 0 \end{bmatrix}$
9. $\begin{bmatrix} \frac{1}{2} & \frac{1}{3} \\ \frac{1}{4} & \frac{1}{6} \end{bmatrix}$
10. $\begin{bmatrix} \frac{1}{3} & \frac{1}{3} & \frac{1}{3} \\ 0 & 1 & 0 \\ \frac{2}{3} & \frac{1}{6} & \frac{1}{6} \end{bmatrix}$

11. Suppose that the quality of air in Midtown is checked every day to see whether it is within acceptable standards (C—clean) or not (D—Dirty) with respect to a certain particulate. Assume that if a given day is C, the probability it will be C the next day is $\frac{2}{3}$, while if it is D, the probability it will be C the next day is $\frac{1}{5}$. What is the probability that it will be D three days later if on day one it is D?

12. A certain sales representative visits three cities: Springfield, Portland, and Middletown. To avoid being bored he doesn't cover them in the same order but conducts a Markov chain of transitions from one city to another. His matrix is as follows:

$$
T = \begin{array}{c} \\ S \\ P \\ M \end{array}
\begin{array}{ccc} S & P & M \end{array}
\begin{bmatrix} 0 & 0.6 & 0.4 \\ 0.5 & 0 & 0.5 \\ 0.3 & 0.7 & 0 \end{bmatrix}.
$$

Assuming that he starts at Springfield, what is the probability he will return to Springfield after three transitions?

13. What are the various probabilities for the salesman in Exercise 12 to be in each city after four transitions?

14. Immediately after inauguration the President is faced with a serious economic slump and must choose a set of economic advisors from two conflicting philosophical persuasions. The policies of Group I will produce a boom year in the next year with probability 0.7, but the probability of a recession the following year is 0.6. The policies of Group II will bring a boom year following a recession with probability 0.5, and will follow a boom year with one of recession with probability 0.3. The president's concern is to have a boom year three years hence, during the next Presidential campaign. Which philosophy (if consistently followed) will give the greatest likelihood of producing this favourable turn of events? (Set up transition matrices for each group.)

15. Find the fixed-point probability vector for each regular transition matrix in Exercises 1–10.

16. Find the fixed-point for the regular transition matrix

$$
\begin{bmatrix} p & q & 1-p-q \\ q & 1-p-q & p \\ 1-p-q & p & q \end{bmatrix},
$$

where $0 < p < \frac{1}{2}, 0 < q < \frac{1}{2}$.

17. Show that if a, b, c, and d are in the open interval $(0, 1)$, then the following matrix is regular:

$$
\begin{bmatrix} 1-a & 0 & a & 0 \\ b & 0 & 1-b & 0 \\ 0 & 1-c & 0 & c \\ 0 & d & 0 & 1-d \end{bmatrix}
$$

18. Find the fixed–point vector for the matrix of Exercise 17.

Given the following regular matrices A. In each case find the matrix W approached by the powers A^n of A as n becomes large.

19.
$$A = \begin{bmatrix} \frac{1}{2} & \frac{1}{2} \\ \frac{1}{3} & \frac{2}{3} \end{bmatrix}$$

20.
$$A = \begin{bmatrix} \frac{5}{8} & \frac{3}{8} \\ \frac{3}{8} & \frac{5}{8} \end{bmatrix}$$

21.
$$A = \begin{bmatrix} 0.8 & 0.2 \\ 0.6 & 0.4 \end{bmatrix}$$

22.
$$A = \begin{bmatrix} 0.8 & 0.2 \\ 0.2 & 0.8 \end{bmatrix}$$

23.
$$A = \begin{bmatrix} \frac{2}{3} & \frac{1}{3} \\ 1 & 0 \end{bmatrix}$$

24.
$$A = \begin{bmatrix} 0.6 & 0.4 \\ 1 & 0 \end{bmatrix}$$

25.
$$A = \begin{bmatrix} 0 & 1 & 0 \\ 0 & 0 & 1 \\ 0.5 & 0.5 & 0 \end{bmatrix}$$

26.
$$A = \begin{bmatrix} \frac{1}{4} & \frac{1}{2} & \frac{1}{4} \\ \frac{3}{5} & \frac{2}{5} & 0 \\ 0 & \frac{2}{3} & \frac{1}{3} \end{bmatrix}$$

27. Consider the salesman in Exercise 12. In the long run, will his policy allow him to visit each city equally often?

28. Solve the mouse–maze problem of Example 1 using the first transition matrix P given in that example (you will need a calculator).

29. Show that the three-state Markov chain with transition matrix

$$T = \begin{bmatrix} 0.25 & 0.50 & 0.25 \\ 0.40 & 0.60 & 0 \\ 1 & 0 & 0 \end{bmatrix}$$

has a unique fixed-probability vector $(0.4, 0.5, 0.1)$.

30. Apply the spread-of-a-rumour example (Example 4) to the following case. The Governor tells a person a_1 his intentions with respect to speculation that he will resign and seek a U.S. Senate seat at the next election. The first hearer a_1 relays the news to person a_2 who relays it to a_3, etc. Let the probability that any one person will reverse the message when he passes it on be $p = 0.2$. What is the probability for the nth person to be told that the Governor will indeed seek the senate seat? (Use a two-state Markov chain.)

31. Which of the transition matrices of Exercises 11, 12, and 14 are regular? Find the fixed-point probability vector for each of those that is regular.

32. In England, sons of members of the Labor Party vote Labor with probability 0.5, vote Conservative with probability 0.4, and vote Liberal with probability 0.1. The probabilities for sons of Conservative Party members are 0.7 Conservative, 0.2 Labor, and 0.1 Liberal. For the sons of Liberals the probabilities are 0.2 Conservative, 0.4 Labor, and 0.4 Liberal. Given these statistics, what is the probability that the grandson of a liberal will vote labor? What is the long-range voting pattern for offspring of each party affiliation?

7.4 ABSORBING MARKOV CHAINS

We turn our attention now to a type of Markov chain that is quite different from the regular chains studied in Section 7.3. To introduce these chains let us look at a modification of the mouse–maze example of that section.

Example 1 Suppose that a mouse is put into the maze of Fig. 7.13. Suppose also that the mouse moves from compartment to compartment, but when he arrives in compartment 4, he remains in it (since there is food there) and does not move on to any other.

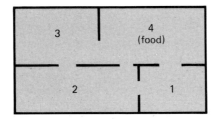

Figure 7.13

Suppose also that the transition matrix for this Markov chain is

$$T = \begin{array}{c} \\ 1 \\ 2 \\ 3 \\ 4 \end{array} \begin{array}{cccc} 1 & 2 & 3 & 4 \\ \begin{bmatrix} 0.3 & 0.3 & 0 & 0.4 \\ 0.2 & 0.3 & 0.2 & 0.3 \\ 0 & 0.3 & 0.3 & 0.4 \\ 0 & 0 & 0 & 1 \end{bmatrix} \end{array}.$$

The last row of T indicates that, if the mouse is in chamber (state) 4, he will remain there.

A state in a Markov chain is called an **absorbing state** if it is impossible to leave it. A Markov chain is called an **absorbing chain** if it has at least one absorbing state and it is possible to reach some absorbing state from every nonabsorbing state in the chain (not necessarily in one step).

Thus, assuming that the mouse likes food, we conclude that the Markov chain of Example 1 is an absorbing chain since chamber 4 is an absorbing state and it is possible to reach chamber 4 from any other chamber (in this case, in one step).

Example 2 The transition matrix

$$A = \begin{array}{c} \\ a_1 \\ a_2 \\ a_3 \end{array} \begin{array}{ccc} a_1 & a_2 & a_3 \\ \begin{bmatrix} 1 & 0 & 0 \\ 0 & \frac{1}{3} & \frac{2}{3} \\ 0 & \frac{1}{2} & \frac{1}{2} \end{bmatrix} \end{array}$$

fails to be the transition matrix for an absorbing Markov chain because, even though state a_1 is an absorbing state, it is not possible to reach it from the nonabsorbing state a_2: from a_2 one can move only to a_3 or remain in a_2, and from a_3 one can only move to a_2 or remain in a_3.

Let us examine a third example. This is an example of an absorbing chain of the type often referred to as the *random walk with absorbing barriers.*

Example 3 Consider a game with two players, each starting with two marbles. On each play of the game player A has probability p of winning a marble from his opponent (player B) and a probability $1 - p$ of losing a marble to him. The game ends when one of the players has gambled away all of his marbles.

As a Markov chain, this game has five states a_0, a_1, a_2, a_3, a_4 corresponding to player A having 0, 1, 2, 3, 4 marbles. States a_0 and a_4 are absorbing states. (Why?) State a_0 corresponds to player A losing all his marbles (player B wins) and state a_4 corresponds to player A winning all of the marbles (and the game). The transition matrix for this game is

$$T = \begin{array}{c} \\ a_0 \\ a_1 \\ a_2 \\ a_3 \\ a_4 \end{array} \begin{array}{ccccc} a_0 & a_1 & a_2 & a_3 & a_4 \\ \left[\begin{array}{ccccc} 1 & 0 & 0 & 0 & 0 \\ 1-p & 0 & p & 0 & 0 \\ 0 & 1-p & 0 & p & 0 \\ 0 & 0 & 1-p & 0 & p \\ 0 & 0 & 0 & 0 & 1 \end{array}\right]. \end{array}$$

Note that, for example, $p_{24} = 0$; it is impossible for player A to have one marble and after one play of the game to have three marbles. He may win or lose only one marble at a time.

The matrix T is a transition matrix for an absorbing Markov chain. This example raises three questions typical of such chains:

1. What is the probability that player A will win? In general, what is the probability that the process will end in a given absorbing state?
2. On the average, how long will it require for the game to end (for the process to be absorbed)?
3. On the average, how many times will player A hold 1, 2, or 3 marbles? (How many times will the process be in each nonabsorbing state?)

To answer these questions we develop a general technique for handling absorbing Markov chains.

First, let us renumber the states of an arbitrary absorbing Markov chain so that the absorbing states come first and reformulate the transition matrix accordingly. Thus, in our example matrix T becomes:

$$
T' = \begin{array}{c} \\ a_0 \\ a_4 \\ a_1 \\ a_2 \\ a_3 \end{array}
\begin{array}{ccccc}
a_0 & a_4 & a_1 & a_2 & a_3 \\
\begin{bmatrix} 1 & 0 & 0 & 0 & 0 \\ 0 & 1 & 0 & 0 & 0 \\ 1-p & 0 & 0 & p & 0 \\ 0 & 0 & 1-p & 0 & p \\ 0 & p & 0 & 1-p & 0 \end{bmatrix}
\end{array} .
$$

Now we are able to partition T' into blocks (see Chapter 6) as follows:

$$
T' = \left[\begin{array}{c|c} I_2 & 0 \\ \hline R & S \end{array} \right] ,
$$

where I_2 is the 2×2 identity matrix, 0 is the 2×3 zero matrix,

$$
R = \begin{bmatrix} 1-p & 0 \\ 0 & 0 \\ 0 & p \end{bmatrix}, \quad \text{and} \quad S = \begin{bmatrix} 0 & p & 0 \\ 1-p & 0 & p \\ 0 & 1-p & 0 \end{bmatrix} .
$$

In general, if there are r absorbing states and $s = n - r$ nonabsorbing states, the $n \times n$ transition matrix T for an absorbing Markov chain can be written in block form as

$$
T = \left[\begin{array}{c|c} I_r & 0 \\ \hline R & S \end{array} \right] , \tag{7.1}
$$

where 0 is an $r \times s$ zero matrix, R is an $s \times r$ matrix, and S is an $s \times s$ matrix. This is the *canonical form for the transition matrix of an absorbing Markov chain with r absorbing states and s nonabsorbing states.*

It is at least intuitively clear that, in any absorbing Markov chain, the probability that the process will eventually be absorbed is one. In the previous section we showed that the entries p_{ij} of the matrix T^n gave the probability of being in state j after n steps (plays of the game) in the chain if we began in state i. It is an exercise in block multiplication to show that from (7.1) we obtain

$$
T^n = \left[\begin{array}{c|c} I_r & 0 \\ \hline Q & S^n \end{array} \right] , \tag{7.2}
$$

where we do not bother to compute the $s \times r$ matrix Q. The form of T^n indicates that the matrix S^n gives the probabilities of being in each of the s nonabsorbing states of the process after n steps, for each possible nonabsorbing initial state. But this must approach zero as n increases, that is, S^n approaches the zero matrix 0_s.

The matrix $F = (I - S)^{-1}$ is called the **fundamental matrix** for an absorbing Markov chain.

The fundamental matrix for the marble game of Example 3 is

$$F = \left\{ \begin{bmatrix} 1 & 0 & 0 \\ 0 & 1 & 0 \\ 0 & 0 & 1 \end{bmatrix} - \begin{bmatrix} 0 & p & 0 \\ 1-p & 0 & p \\ 0 & 1-p & 0 \end{bmatrix} \right\}^{-1} = \begin{bmatrix} 1 & -p & 0 \\ p-1 & 1 & -p \\ 0 & p-1 & 1 \end{bmatrix}^{-1}.$$

With $q = 1 - p$, this becomes (verify this)

$$F = \frac{1}{1-2pq} \begin{bmatrix} 1-pq & p & p^2 \\ q & 1 & p \\ q^2 & q & 1-pq \end{bmatrix}.$$

We shall see how this fundamental matrix F helps answer the questions posed above. To answer question 3 we have the following theorem, which we state without proof.

Theorem 7.3
The entries in the fundamental matrix $F = (I - S)^{-1}$ of an absorbing Markov chain give the average (mean) number of times in each nonabsorbing state of the chain for each possible nonabsorbing initial state.

Example 3 (continued) We have already calculated F for the marble game. Since the game begins in state a_2 (each player has two marbles), the second row of F

$$\frac{q}{1-2pq}, \qquad \frac{1}{1-2pq}, \qquad \frac{p}{1-2pq}$$

gives the average number of times that player A will have one marble, two marbles, and three marbles, respectively. Now if we add these numbers together we obtain the total average number of times that player A can play the game, that is,

$$\frac{p+q+1}{1-2pq} = \frac{2}{1-2pq}.$$

This is the answer to question 2. In general, we have the following theorem to answer question 2.

Theorem 7.4
Let F be the fundamental matrix of an absorbing Markov chain with r absorbing and $s = n - r$ nonabsorbing states. Let C be the $s \times 1$ matrix $[1, 1, \ldots, 1]^t$. Then, the $s \times 1$ matrix $N = FC$ has as its entries the average (mean) number of steps before being absorbed, for each possible nonabsorbing initial state.

Thus, $N = (n_i)$, where n_i is the average number of steps (beginning in state a_i) before the chain is absorbed (ends in an absorbing state).

Example 4 Let us return to the mouse–maze chain of Example 1. We have the matrix

$$T' = \begin{bmatrix} I_1 & 0 \\ \hline R & S \end{bmatrix}, \quad \text{where } S = \begin{bmatrix} 0.3 & 0.3 & 0 \\ 0.2 & 0.3 & 0.2 \\ 0 & 0.3 & 0.3 \end{bmatrix},$$

so that

$$I - S = \begin{bmatrix} 0.7 & -0.3 & 0 \\ -0.2 & 0.7 & -0.2 \\ 0 & -0.3 & 0.7 \end{bmatrix}$$

and the fundamental matrix is

$$F = (I - S)^{-1} = \begin{bmatrix} 1.66 & 0.81 & 0.23 \\ 0.54 & 1.89 & 0.54 \\ 0.23 & 0.81 & 1.66 \end{bmatrix}.$$

Hence,

$$N = F \begin{bmatrix} 1 \\ 1 \\ 1 \end{bmatrix} = \begin{bmatrix} 2.7 \\ 2.97 \\ 2.7 \end{bmatrix}.$$

The mouse will always reach the food after three steps in the chain. The average number of observations necessary to find it in chamber 4 with the food is 2.7 if it is initially placed in chamber 1 or chamber 3, and 2.97 if it is initially placed in chamber 2.

The answer to the first of our three questions is contained in the following theorem.

Theorem 7.5

Let b_{ij} be the probability that an absorbing Markov chain with r absorbing and $n - r = s$ nonabsorbing states will be absorbed (end) in state a_j if it begins in the nonabsorbing state a_i; also let $B = (b_{ij})$. Then $B = FR$, where F is the fundamental matrix and R is the $s \times r$ matrix in the lower left block of the canonical form (7.1).

Example 5 For the mouse–maze chain of Example 1 the canonical form of the transition matrix is

$$T = \begin{bmatrix} 1 & 0 & 0 & 0 \\ \hline 0.4 & 0.3 & 0.3 & 0 \\ 0.3 & 0.2 & 0.3 & 0.2 \\ 0.4 & 0 & 0.3 & 0.3 \end{bmatrix};$$

whence,

$$R = \begin{bmatrix} 0.4 \\ 0.3 \\ 0.4 \end{bmatrix}.$$

We have already found the fundamental matrix F in Example 4 to be

$$F = \begin{bmatrix} 1.66 & 0.81 & 0.23 \\ 0.54 & 1.89 & 0.54 \\ 0.23 & 0.81 & 1.66 \end{bmatrix}; \quad \text{thus,} \quad B = FR = \begin{bmatrix} 0.999 \\ 0.999 \\ 0.999 \end{bmatrix}.$$

The probability that the mouse will end up in chamber 4 with the food when it begins initially in any of the other three chambers is 0.999, or nearly one.

Example 6 For the marble game of Example 3 we have the following (remember that $q = 1 - p$):

$$B = \frac{1}{1-2pq}\begin{bmatrix} 1-pq & p & p^2 \\ q & 1 & p \\ q^2 & q & 1-pq \end{bmatrix}\begin{bmatrix} q & 0 \\ 0 & 0 \\ 0 & p \end{bmatrix} = \frac{1}{1-2pq}\begin{bmatrix} q-pq^2 & p^3 \\ q^2 & p^2 \\ q^3 & p-p^2q \end{bmatrix}.$$

Hence, the probability that player A (who began with two marbles) will win, is $p^2/(1-2pq)$, and the probability that he will lose (player B wins) is $q^2/(1-2pq)$. Substituting $q = (1-p)$, we confirm our intuition, namely,

$$\frac{q^2}{1-2pq} + \frac{p^2}{1-2pq} = \frac{(1-p)^2 + p^2}{1-2p(1-p)} = \frac{1-2p+2p^2}{1-2p+2p^2} = 1.$$

EXERCISES (7.4) ————————————————————————————————

Which of the following transition matrices are from absorbing Markov chains, which are from regular chains, and which are from neither?

1. $\begin{bmatrix} \frac{1}{3} & \frac{2}{3} \\ 0 & 1 \end{bmatrix}$ **2.** $\begin{bmatrix} \frac{1}{3} & \frac{2}{3} \\ 1 & 0 \end{bmatrix}$ **3.** $\begin{bmatrix} 1 & 0 \\ 0.3 & 0.7 \end{bmatrix}$ **4.** $\begin{bmatrix} 0 & 1 \\ 0.3 & 0.7 \end{bmatrix}$

5. $\begin{bmatrix} 1 & 0 \\ 0 & 1 \end{bmatrix}$ **6.** $\begin{bmatrix} 0 & 1 \\ 1 & 0 \end{bmatrix}$ **7.** $\begin{bmatrix} 1 & 0 & 0 & 0 \\ 0 & 1 & 0 & 0 \\ 0 & 0 & \frac{1}{2} & \frac{1}{2} \\ 0 & 0 & \frac{3}{4} & \frac{1}{4} \end{bmatrix}$ **8.** $\begin{bmatrix} \frac{1}{3} & 0 & \frac{2}{3} \\ 0 & 1 & 0 \\ \frac{2}{3} & 0 & \frac{1}{3} \end{bmatrix}$

9. $\begin{bmatrix} 0.7 & 0.1 & 0.2 \\ 0.4 & 0.3 & 0.3 \\ 0 & 1 & 0 \end{bmatrix}$
 10. $\begin{bmatrix} \frac{1}{3} & \frac{1}{3} & \frac{1}{3} & 0 & 0 \\ 0 & \frac{1}{5} & \frac{1}{5} & \frac{2}{5} & \frac{1}{5} \\ 1 & 0 & 0 & 0 & 0 \\ 0 & \frac{1}{2} & 0 & \frac{1}{2} & 0 \\ 0 & 1 & 0 & 0 & 0 \end{bmatrix}$

11. $\begin{bmatrix} 0 & 0.1 & 0.2 & 0.3 & 0.4 \\ 1 & 0 & 0 & 0 & 0 \\ 0.1 & 0.2 & 0.3 & 0.4 & 0 \\ 0 & 0 & 1 & 1 & 1 \\ 0.2 & 0.3 & 0.4 & 0 & 0.1 \end{bmatrix}$
 12. $\begin{bmatrix} 1 & 0 & 0 & 0 & 0 \\ 0 & 1 & 0 & 0 & 0 \\ 0 & 0 & 1 & 0 & 0 \\ 0.1 & 0.1 & 0.2 & 0.2 & 0.4 \\ 0.2 & 0.2 & 0.2 & 0.2 & 0.2 \end{bmatrix}$

Each of the following matrices is the transition matrix for an absorbing Markov chain. Find the fundamental matrix F for each.

13. $\begin{bmatrix} 1 & 0 \\ \frac{1}{2} & \frac{1}{2} \end{bmatrix}$
 14. $\begin{bmatrix} \frac{3}{5} & \frac{2}{5} \\ 0 & 1 \end{bmatrix}$
 15. $\begin{bmatrix} \frac{1}{5} & \frac{2}{5} & \frac{2}{5} \\ 0 & 1 & 0 \\ \frac{2}{5} & \frac{1}{5} & \frac{2}{5} \end{bmatrix}$

16. $\begin{bmatrix} \frac{1}{2} & 0 & \frac{1}{2} & 0 & 0 \\ 1 & 0 & 0 & 0 & 0 \\ 0 & \frac{1}{2} & 0 & \frac{1}{2} & 0 \\ 0 & 0 & \frac{1}{2} & 0 & \frac{1}{2} \\ 0 & 0 & 0 & 0 & 1 \end{bmatrix}$
 17. $\begin{bmatrix} 1 & 0 & 0 & 0 & 0 \\ \frac{1}{3} & 0 & \frac{1}{3} & 0 & \frac{1}{3} \\ 0 & \frac{1}{3} & 0 & \frac{1}{3} & \frac{1}{3} \\ 0 & 1 & 0 & 0 & 0 \\ 0 & 0 & 0 & 0 & 1 \end{bmatrix}$

18–22. Find the matrix $N = FC$ of Theorem 7.4 for each of the chains of Exercises 13–17.

23–27. Find the matrix $B = FR$ of Theorem 7.5 for each of the chains of Exercises 13–17.

28. Work out the probabilities for the marble game of Example 3 if $p = q = \frac{1}{2}$.

29. Write the canonical forms

$$\left[\begin{array}{c|c} I_r & 0 \\ \hline R & S \end{array} \right]$$

for those matrices of Exercises 1–12 that come from absorbing Markov chains.

30. Find the fundamental matrix F for each of the absorbing Markov chains occurring in Exercises 1–12.

In Exercises 31–34, suppose that we play a coin-flipping game using a fair coin. Player A has \$3 and player B has \$2. The coin is flipped; if it is a head, A pays B a dollar; if it is a tail, B pays A a dollar.

31. Show that this game can be modeled with an absorbing Markov chain. Write the transition matrix in canonical form.

32. Find the matrices F, N, and B.

33. How long is the game likely to last?

34. What are the probabilities of winning for each player?

The annual sales convention is held in Boston. When attending the convention, Barry Brown has a choice of four moderately expensive hotels. Hotels M and N are, however, less expensive than the more luxurious hotels K and L. The following array lists the probabilities that if Barry stays in one of the hotels the first year he will go to a given hotel the next year:

$$
\begin{array}{c c}
 & \begin{array}{cccc} M & N & K & L \end{array} \\
\begin{array}{c} M \\ N \\ K \\ L \end{array} &
\left[\begin{array}{cccc}
\frac{1}{3} & 0 & \frac{2}{3} & 0 \\
0 & 1 & 0 & 0 \\
0 & \frac{1}{2} & 0 & \frac{1}{2} \\
\frac{1}{3} & \frac{1}{3} & \frac{1}{3} & 0
\end{array}\right]
\end{array}
$$

35. If he stays in hotel M the first year, what is the probability he will stay in a luxury hotel (K or L) during the following two years?

36. Show that this can be modeled as an absorbing Markov chain. Find the matrices F, N, and B and interpret them.

In a certain sociological experiment it was discovered that the educational level of children depended upon the educational level of their parents. The people were classified into three groups: those with no higher than an eighth-grade education (E), those who had at least one year of secondary school (S) beginning with grade nine, and those who had at least one term of college (C). If a parent is in one of these groups, the probabilities that a child will belong to any of these groups are given in the following table:

$$
\begin{array}{cc}
 & \begin{array}{c} \text{Child} \\ \begin{array}{ccc} E & S & C \end{array} \end{array} \\
\text{Parent} \begin{array}{c} E \\ S \\ C \end{array} &
\left[\begin{array}{ccc}
0.7 & 0.2 & 0.1 \\
0.4 & 0.4 & 0.2 \\
0.1 & 0.2 & 0.7
\end{array}\right]
\end{array}
$$

37. What is the probability that the grandson of a parent in group S will attend college

38. Suppose that a different experimenter finds that, if the parent has some college education (C), the child always attends some college. Modify the transition matrix accordingly.

39. Given the situation in Problem 38, what is the average number of generations before the offspring of each class will attend some college?

40. Prove Theorem 7.5. ($Hint$. Compute b_{ij}, remembering that a_i is a nonabsorbing state and a_j is an absorbing state.)

APPENDIX

In this Appendix we have gathered together several algorithms discussed in the text. They are presented here in simplified form for convenient reference. You should consult the appropriate sections of the text for full explanation of the procedures given here.

THE GAUSS–JORDAN REDUCTION OF A MATRIX

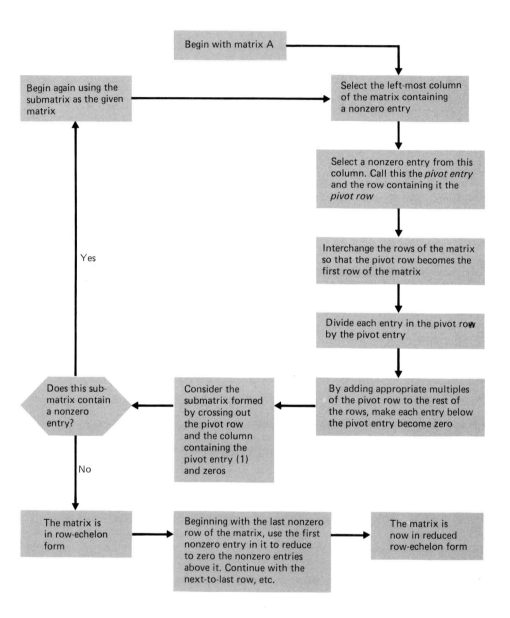

Chart 1
(see Section 1.2)

THE MATRIX-INVERSION ALGORITHM

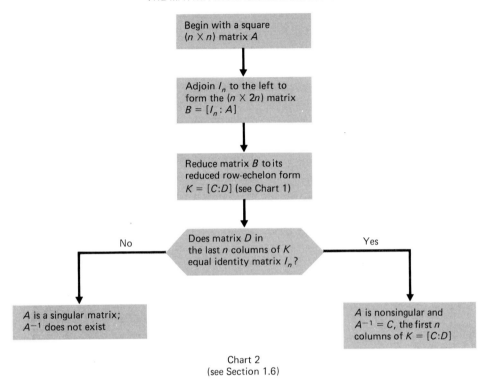

Chart 2
(see Section 1.6)

PROPERTIES OF DETERMINANTS
(See Section 2.3)

Let A and B be $n \times n$ matrices and A^t the transpose of A. The following are true:

$$\det A^t = \det A, \quad \text{(Theorem 2.1)}$$
$$\det (AB) = (\det A)(\det B) \quad \text{(Eq. (2.22))}$$

1. If B is obtained from A by interchanging any two rows (columns) of A, then

$$\det B = -\det A.$$

2. If B is obtained from A by multiplying any row (column) of A by the nonzero constant k, then

$$\det B = k (\det A).$$

3. If B is obtained from A by adding to any row (column) of A a multiple of any other row (column) of A then

$$\det B = \det A.$$

4. If two rows (columns) of A are identical, then

$$\det A = 0.$$

5. If A has a zero row (column), then

$$\det A = 0.$$

If A is nonsingular, then $\det A \neq 0$ and

$$\det (A^{-1}) = \frac{1}{\det A} \quad \text{(Exercise 29, p. 91)}.$$

If A is nonsingular, then

$$A^{-1} = \frac{1}{\det A} \ (\text{adj } A) \quad \text{(Theorem 2.5)},$$

where adj A is the transpose of the cofactor matrix of A.

TEST FOR LINEAR INDEPENDENCE OR DEPENDENCE
(See Sections 3.2 and 3.4)

Given a set $S = \{v_1, v_2, \ldots, v_n\}$ of vectors from the vector space V. (If necessary change these to n-tuples in $\mathbb{R}^n$, as in Section 5.3.)

1. *Form the linear combination* (with unknown scalars)

$$c_1 v_1 + c_2 v_2 + \ldots + c_n v_n = 0.$$

2. *Consider the scalars c_i by examining the resulting homogeneous system of equations in one of the following ways:*

   a) *Reduce the coefficient matrix A to row-echelon form.*

   i) If this is I_n, then the system has only the trivial solution and the set S of vectors is *linearly independent*.

   ii) If this is not I_n, the system has nontrivial solutions and the set S is *linearly dependent*.

   b) *Use the determinant of the matrix A.*

   i) If $\det A \neq 0$, the system has only the trivial solution and S *is linearly independent*.

   ii) If $\det A = 0$, the system has nontrivial solutions and the set S is *linearly dependent*.

Example Let S be the set of vectors $\{(1, 2, 1), (0, -1, 3), (1, 6, 2)\}$ from $\mathbb{R}^3$.
1. *Form*:

$$c_1(1, 2, 1) + c_2(0, -1, 3) + c_3(1, 6, 2) = (c_1 + c_3, 2c_1 - c_2 + 6c_3, c_1 + 3c_2 + 2c_3)$$
$$= (0, 0, 0).$$

2. *Consider:*

$$c_1 \qquad + c_3 = 0,$$
$$2c_1 - c_2 + 6c_3 = 0,$$
$$c_1 + 3c_2 + 2c_3 = 0.$$

The coefficient matrix A is

$$A = \begin{bmatrix} 1 & 0 & 1 \\ 2 & -1 & 6 \\ 1 & 3 & 2 \end{bmatrix}.$$

(Note that the columns of A are the vectors in S.)
Matrix A is row-equivalent to I_n, so S is linearly independent.
   Also, det $A = -13 \neq 0$, so S is linearly independent.

PROPERTIES OF A REAL INNER PRODUCT
(See Sections 4.2–4.4)

1. $\langle \mathbf{u}, \mathbf{v} \rangle = \langle \mathbf{v}, \mathbf{u} \rangle$ (a real number)
2. $\langle a\mathbf{u} + b\mathbf{v}, \mathbf{w} \rangle = a\langle \mathbf{u}, \mathbf{w} \rangle + b\langle \mathbf{v}, \mathbf{w} \rangle$
3. $\langle \mathbf{u}, \mathbf{u} \rangle \geqslant 0$
4. $\langle \mathbf{u}, \mathbf{u} \rangle = 0$ if and only if $\mathbf{u} = \mathbf{0}$
5. $\langle \mathbf{u}, a\mathbf{v} + b\mathbf{w} \rangle = a\langle \mathbf{u}, \mathbf{v} \rangle + b\langle \mathbf{u}, \mathbf{w} \rangle$ (Theorem 4.2)

Length in an inner-product space:

$$\|\mathbf{u}\| = \langle \mathbf{u}, \mathbf{u} \rangle^{1/2}, \quad \|a\mathbf{u}\| = |a|\,\|\mathbf{u}\|.$$

Angle between two vectors:

$$\cos \theta = \frac{\langle \mathbf{u}, \mathbf{v} \rangle}{\|\mathbf{u}\|\,\|\mathbf{v}\|}.$$

The Cauchy–Schwarz inequality   (Theorem 4.5):

$$|\langle \mathbf{u}, \mathbf{v} \rangle| \leqslant \|\mathbf{u}\|\,\|\mathbf{v}\|.$$

Orthonormal set of vectors:

$S = \{\mathbf{v}_1, \mathbf{v}_2, \ldots, \mathbf{v}_n\}$ is an orthonormal set of vectors if and only if

$$\langle \mathbf{v}_i, \mathbf{v}_j \rangle = \begin{cases} 1 & \text{when } i = j, \\ 0 & \text{when } i \neq j. \end{cases}$$

The Gram–Schmidt Process in $\mathbb{R}^3$ (see Section 4.4):
   Given the vectors $\mathbf{v}_1$, $\mathbf{v}_2$, and $\mathbf{v}_3$, form the orthonormal set $\{\mathbf{w}_1, \mathbf{w}_2, \mathbf{w}_3\}$ as follows:

$$\mathbf{w}_1 = \frac{\mathbf{v}_1}{\|\mathbf{v}_1\|},$$

$$\mathbf{w}_2 = \frac{\mathbf{v}_2 - \langle \mathbf{w}_1, \mathbf{v}_2 \rangle \mathbf{w}_1}{\|\mathbf{v}_2 - \langle \mathbf{w}_1, \mathbf{v}_2 \rangle \mathbf{w}_1\|},$$

$$\mathbf{w}_3 = \frac{\mathbf{v}_3 - \langle \mathbf{w}_1, \mathbf{v}_3 \rangle \mathbf{w}_1 - \langle \mathbf{w}_2, \mathbf{v}_3 \rangle \mathbf{w}_2}{\|\mathbf{v}_3 - \langle \mathbf{w}_1, \mathbf{v}_3 \rangle \mathbf{w}_1 - \langle \mathbf{w}_2, \mathbf{v}_3 \rangle \mathbf{w}_2\|}.$$

THE MATRIX REPRESENTATION $[T]_H^G$ OF A LINEAR TRANSFORMATION
(See Section 5.3)

Let $G = \{\mathbf{u}_1, \mathbf{u}_2, \ldots, \mathbf{u}_n\}$ and $H = \{\mathbf{v}_1, \mathbf{v}_2, \ldots, \mathbf{v}_m\}$ be bases for $\mathbb{R}^n$ and $\mathbb{R}^m$, respectively. Let $T: \mathbb{R}^n \to \mathbb{R}^m$ be a linear transformation.

To find the matrix representation $[T]_H^G$ of T proceed as follows:

1. Use the defining condition for T to find the image vectors $T(\mathbf{u}_1)$, $T(\mathbf{u}_2)$, $\ldots$, $T(\mathbf{u}_n)$ for each basis vector in G.

2. Form the $m \times n$ matrix K whose ith column vector is the column vector $[T(\mathbf{u}_i)]$, $i = 1, 2, \ldots, n$.

3. Form the $m \times m$ matrix L whose jth column vector is the column vector $[\mathbf{v}_j]$, $j = 1, 2, \ldots, m$.

4. Adjoin the two matrices L and K as follows:

$$\begin{bmatrix} L & \vdots & K \end{bmatrix}$$
$$\mathbf{v}_1 \ldots \mathbf{v}_m \quad T(\mathbf{u}_1) \ldots T(\mathbf{u}_n)$$

5. By a Gauss–Jordan reduction reduce $[L:K]$ to $[I_m:A]$. Then $A = [T]_H^G$.

CHANGE OF BASIS AND SIMILARITY
(See Section 5.5)

Let $G = \{\mathbf{u}_1, \mathbf{u}_2, \ldots, \mathbf{u}_n\}$ and $H = \{\mathbf{w}_1, \mathbf{w}_2, \ldots, \mathbf{w}_n\}$ be two bases for $\mathbb{R}^n$. Then the matrix

$$S = \begin{bmatrix} [\mathbf{u}_1]_H [\mathbf{u}_2]_H \ldots [\mathbf{u}_n]_H \end{bmatrix},$$

whose ith column is the column vector $[\mathbf{u}_i]_H$, is the *transition matrix from the basis G to the basis H*. Thus,

$$[\mathbf{v}]_H = S[\mathbf{v}]_G.$$

Matrix S is nonsingular and its inverse S^{-1} is the *transition matrix from the basis H to* *the basis G.* Thus, for any vector v in $\mathbb{R}^n$,

$$[\mathbf{v}]_G = S^{-1}[\mathbf{v}]_H.$$

Algorithm for computing S:
Represent each of the basis vectors in G and in H with respect to the *standard basis*
E for $\mathbb{R}^n$. Denote these matrix representations by $[\mathbf{u}_i]$ and $[\mathbf{w}_i]$, respectively
$(i = 1, 2, \ldots, n)$. Form the matrix

$$M = \left[\; [\mathbf{w}_1] \ldots [\mathbf{w}_n] \; \vdots \; [\mathbf{u}_1] \ldots [\mathbf{u}_n] \; \right].$$

Perform a Gauss–Jordan reduction on M to arrive at $[I_n:S]$. Then S is the desired
transition matrix from G to H.

Note that S is the matrix representation of the identity transformation
$I: \mathbb{R}^n \to \mathbb{R}^n$ in the sense that $S = [I]_H^G$.

Example Let

$$G = \{\mathbf{v}_1 = (1, 0, 1), \mathbf{v}_2 = (1, -1, 0), \mathbf{v}_3 = (0, 0, -1)\},$$
$$H = \{\mathbf{u}_1 = (1, 1, 1), \mathbf{u}_2 = (1, -1, -1), \mathbf{u}_3 = (1, 0, 1)\}$$

be bases for $\mathbb{R}^3$. Find the transition matrix (change-of-basis matrix) from G to H.
Using the algorithm above we seek $[I]_H^G$, so we have the augmented matrix

$$\begin{bmatrix} 1 & 1 & 1 & \vdots & 1 & 1 & 0 \\ 1 & -1 & 0 & \vdots & 0 & -1 & 0 \\ 1 & -1 & 1 & \vdots & 1 & 0 & -1 \end{bmatrix}$$

$$\mathbf{u}_1 \quad \mathbf{u}_2 \quad \mathbf{u}_3 \quad \mathbf{v}_1 \quad \mathbf{v}_2 \quad \mathbf{v}_3$$

which is row-equivalent to

$$\begin{bmatrix} 1 & 0 & 0 & \vdots & 0 & -\frac{1}{2} & \frac{1}{2} \\ 0 & 1 & 0 & \vdots & 0 & \frac{1}{2} & \frac{1}{2} \\ 0 & 0 & 1 & \vdots & 1 & 1 & -1 \end{bmatrix}.$$

So the matrix

$$S = [I]_H^G = \begin{bmatrix} 0 & -\frac{1}{2} & \frac{1}{2} \\ 0 & \frac{1}{2} & \frac{1}{2} \\ 1 & 1 & -1 \end{bmatrix}$$

is the desired transition matrix. We note that

$$S^{-1} = \begin{bmatrix} 2 & 0 & 1 \\ -1 & 1 & 0 \\ 1 & 1 & 0 \end{bmatrix} = [I]_G^H.$$

Algorithm for the representation of a linear transformation $T: \mathbb{R}^n \to \mathbb{R}^n$ (Theorem 5.9):

Let $A = [T]_G$ and $B = [T]_H$ be the matrix representations of T in the G and H bases, respectively, while S is the transition matrix from the basis H to the basis G:

$$S = [I]_G^H.$$

Then A and B are similar and $A = SBS^{-1}$.

The diagram illustrates what happens to a given vector $\mathbf{v}$ from $\mathbb{R}^n$.

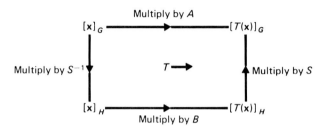

EIGENVALUES, EIGENVECTORS, AND DIAGONALIZATION
(See Sections 6.1–6.3)

To compute the *eigenvalues* for a matrix A (or for the transformation it represents), find the roots λ_i of the *characteristic equation*

$$\det(\lambda I - A) = 0.$$

To compute the *eigenvectors* $\mathbf{p}_i$ associated with these eigenvalues, solve the homogeneous system

$$(\lambda I - A)X = 0.$$

Note that similar matrices have the same eigenvalues.

If A is $n \times n$ and has n linearly independent eigenvectors

$$\mathbf{p}_1, \mathbf{p}_2, \ldots, \mathbf{p}_n$$

and

$$P = \left[[\mathbf{p}_1][\mathbf{p}_2] \cdots [\mathbf{p}_n] \right],$$

then

$$P^{-1}AP = \text{Diag}[\lambda_1, \lambda_2, \ldots, \lambda_n],$$

where λ_i are the (not necessarily distinct) eigenvalues of A corresponding to the eigenvectors $\mathbf{p}_i$, $i = 1, 2, \ldots, n$ respectively.

Note that real symmetric matrices $A = A^t$ are always similar to diagonal matrices (see Section 6.3).

REFERENCES

Additional examples of applications of linear algebra including discussions of linear programming and mathematical modeling can be found in the following works.

Anton, H. and C. Rorres, *Applications of Linear Algebra*. New York: Wiley, 1977.

Coleman, J. S., *Introduction to Mathematical Sociology*. New York: The Free Press, 1964.

Cooper, L., and D. Steinberg, *Methods and Applications of Linear Programming*. Philadelphia: Saunders, 1974.

Dantzig, G. B., *Linear Programming and Extensions*, Princeton, N.J.: Princeton University Press, 1963.

Flament, C., *Applications of Graph Theory to Group Structures*. Englewood Cliffs, N.J.: Prentice-Hall, 1963.

Gale, D., *The Theory of Linear Economic Models*. New York: McGraw-Hill, 1960.

Grossman, S. I., and J. E. Turner, *Mathematics for the Biological Sciences*. New York: Macmillan, 1974.

Kemeny, J. G., and J. L. Snell, *Finite Markov Chains*. Princeton, N.J.: D. Van Nostrand and Co., 1960.

Keyfitz, N., *Introduction to the Mathematics of Populations*. Reading, Mass.: Addition–Wesley, 1968.

Lancaster P., *Mathematics Models of the Real World*. Englewood Cliffs, N.J.: Prentice-Hall, 1976.

Lazersfeld, P. F., and N. W. Henry, *Latent Structure Analysis*. Boston, Mass.: Houghton Mifflin, 1968.

Luce, R. D., and H. Raiffa, *Games and Decisions*. New York: John Wiley and Sons, 1957.

Malkevitch, J., and W. Meyer, *Graphs, Models and Finite Mathematics*. Englewood Cliffs, N.J.: Prentice Hall, 1974.

Roberts, F. S., *Discrete Mathematical Models*. Englewood Cliffs, N.J.: Prentice-Hall, 1976.

Rubinstein, M. F., *Patterns of Problem Solving*. Englewood Cliffs, N.J.: Prentice-Hall, 1975.

Singleton, R. R., and W. F. Tyndall, *Games and Programming*. San Francisco: Freeman, 1974.

Smythe, W. R., and L. A. Johnson, *Introduction to Linear Programming with Applications*. Englewood Cliffs, N.J.: Prentice-Hall, 1966.

Vajda, S. *An Introduction to Linear Programming and the Theory of Games*. London/New York: Methuen/Wiley, 1960.

White, H. C., *An Anatomy of Kinship*. Englewood Cliffs, N.J.: Prentice-Hall, 1963.

ANSWERS

CHAPTER 1

Exercises 1.1 (page 11)

1.

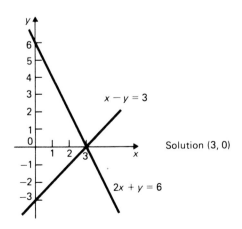

$$x - y = 3$$

Solution (3, 0)

$$2x + y = 6$$

3.

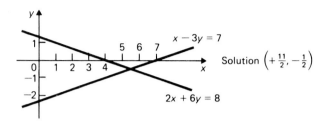

5.

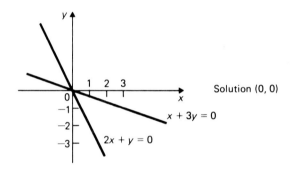

7. $(5, -1)$ **9.** $(-8, 6)$ **11.** $\left(\dfrac{1 \pm 2\sqrt{19}}{5}, \dfrac{-2 \pm \sqrt{19}}{5}\right)$

13. $(4, -1)$ **15.** $(1, -2)$ **17.** $(\frac{3}{2}, \frac{3}{4}, \frac{1}{4})$ **19.** $(1, 1, -1)$

21. $(-\frac{2}{7}, -1, -\frac{5}{7})$ **23.** $(0, 1, -1, 2)$ **25.** $(1, -t, t, -1)$ for any real number t.

27. \$6000 at 5% and \$4000 at 6%.

29. Mix $\frac{2}{3}$ tons of 10% and $\frac{4}{3}$ tons of 25%.

31. 50 lbs. of each, 20% carbohydrate.

33. Watch \$75.00, necklace \$25.00, ring \$125.00.

35. Substitute $\sqrt{x} = r,\ \sqrt{y} = s,\ \sqrt{z} = t$. Solve the resulting linear system. Hence, $x = 4$, $y = 9$, $z = 16$.

37. Substitute $r = \sqrt{x^2 - 1}$; $r = \sqrt{3}$, so $x = \pm 2$, $y = \sqrt{3}$.

39. Substitute $r = \dfrac{1}{3x - y}$, $s = \dfrac{1}{x + 3y}$; therefore, $x = \dfrac{2059}{4160}$, $y = \dfrac{2407}{4160}$.

41. If $a_1 b_2 - a_2 b_1 = 0$, there can be infinitely many solutions. For example, the system

$$\begin{cases} 2x + 3y = 0 \\ 6x + 9y = 0 \end{cases}$$

has solutions of the form $x = -3t/2$, $y = t$, for any real number t.

43. For each $i = 1, 2, \ldots, m$,

$$a_{i1}(r_1 + s_1) + a_{i2}(r_2 + s_2) + \cdots + a_{in}(r_n + s_n)$$

$$= a_{i1}r_1 + a_{i1}s_1 + a_{i2}r_2 + a_{i2}s_2 + \cdots + a_{in}r_n + a_{in}s_n$$

$$= a_{i1}r_1 + a_{i2}r + \cdots + a_{in}r_n + a_{i1}s_1 + a_{i2}s_2 + \cdots + a_{in}s_n = b_i + c_i.$$

So the system has $(r_1 + s_1, r_2 + s_2, \ldots, r_n + s_n)$ as a solution.

Exercises 1.2 (page 21)

1. The matrix B results from interchanging rows 1 and 2 of A (Theorem 1.2(i)); C results by adding (-1) times row one of B to row two of B (Theorem 1.2(iii)); D comes from C by multiplying row two of C by -1 and by making a new third row, the result of adding (-2) times row one of C to row three of C; E results from interchanging rows two and three of D, multiplying the new row two by -1, and then forming a new row three by adding (-3) times the changed row two to row three; the matrix F results from dividing row three of E by 12, and then adding 4 times the result to row two of E.

3. $(1, -1)$ **5.** $(\frac{27}{15}, \frac{1}{15}, \frac{25}{15})$ **7.** $(4, 5, -6)$ **9.** $(1, -1, 0)$

11. $(1, 1, -1)$ **13.** $(1, -1, \frac{3}{2})$ **15.** $(1, 0, -1, 2)$ **17.** $(1, -1, 1, -1, 1, -1)$

19–26. See same Exercises in Section 1.1.

27. No; $y = -\frac{5}{6}x^3 + 3x^2 - \frac{7}{6}x + 1$.

29. $\begin{bmatrix} 1 & 0 & -1 & -2 & -3 \\ 0 & 1 & 2 & 3 & 4 \\ 0 & 0 & 0 & 0 & 0 \\ 0 & 0 & 0 & 0 & 0 \\ 0 & 0 & 0 & 0 & 0 \end{bmatrix}$

31. I_4 **33.** 24 nickels, 8 dimes, 18 quarters.

35. 6 grams of X, 2 grams of Y, and 2 grams of Z yield 10 grams of the desired alloy.

Exercises 1.3 (page 31)

1. For any real number t the solution is $(t, 0, -t)$.

3. $\left(\dfrac{2t}{5}, \dfrac{7t}{5}, t\right)$

5. $x = 0$, $y = w = t$, $z = -t$

7. $(1, 0, 1)$

9. $x_1 = \dfrac{11 - t}{4}$, $x_2 = \dfrac{1 + 5t}{4}$, $x_3 = t$

11. Inconsistent

13. $u = x = 0$, $v = w = t$

15. Substitute the given n-tuples and simplify as indicated in Exercise 43 of Section 1.1.

17. When the augmented matrix is reduced, the last $m - n$ rows are all zero.

19. Substitute the given n-tuple and simplify as indicated in Exercise 43 of Section 1.1.

Exercises 1.4 (page 40)

1. $a = 1, b = 2, c = 6$

3. $\begin{bmatrix} -4 & -2 & 2 \\ -6 & -2 & -8 \end{bmatrix}$

5. $\begin{bmatrix} 1 & -\frac{1}{2} \\ 2 & \frac{1}{2} \\ 3 & 0 \end{bmatrix}$

7. $\begin{bmatrix} 0 & 1 \\ -\frac{1}{2} & 0 \end{bmatrix}$

9. $\begin{bmatrix} 4 & 1 & -3 \\ 2 & 0 & 10 \\ 1 & 2 & 2 \end{bmatrix}$

11. Not defined.

13. F

15. $[-3, 5]$

17. $\begin{bmatrix} -3 & 5 \\ -7 & 9 \end{bmatrix}$

19. $\begin{bmatrix} 10 \\ 3 \\ -13 \end{bmatrix}$

21. $\begin{bmatrix} 1 & 1 \\ 2 & 17 \end{bmatrix}$

23. $\begin{bmatrix} 1 & 1 & -6 \\ 11 & 5 & 0 \\ 12 & 6 & -6 \end{bmatrix}$

25. $\begin{bmatrix} 12 & 4 & 16 \\ -4 & -2 & 2 \end{bmatrix}$

27. $\begin{bmatrix} 2 & -1 \\ 5 & 23 \\ -1 & 8 \end{bmatrix}$

29. Not defined.

31. $\begin{bmatrix} -1 & -1 & 0 \\ 13 & 6 & -7 \\ 0 & 3 & 3 \end{bmatrix}$

33. $\begin{bmatrix} 0 & -1 & -1 \\ -1 & 4 & 5 \\ -1 & 1 & 2 \end{bmatrix}$

35. $\begin{bmatrix} 0 & -32 \\ 16 & 0 \end{bmatrix}$

37. $\begin{bmatrix} 39 & 10 & -32 \\ 72 & -5 & 66 \\ 16 & 14 & 21 \end{bmatrix}$

39. Not defined.

41. $\begin{bmatrix} 1005 & 348 & 1197 \\ 1830 & 633 & 2187 \\ 2835 & 981 & 3384 \end{bmatrix}$

43. $\begin{bmatrix} 39 & 309 \\ 618 & 4983 \end{bmatrix}$

45. Show that both are $\begin{bmatrix} 4 & 5 & 1 \\ 11 & 10 & -1 \\ 15 & 15 & 0 \end{bmatrix}$

47. This follows from the definition of multiplication of matrices.

49. Apply the definition of $\sum$ and factor out r.

51. Reorder the terms; when you add by rows and by columns, you get the same answer.

53. When you interchange the rows and columns of A^t, you get back A itself.

55. Apply the definitions of matrix addition and transpose.

57. Suppose A and B are symmetric; then $A^t = A$ and $B^t = B$. According to Exercise 55, $(A + B)^t = A^t + B^t = A + B$.

59. Apply the definition of matrix addition.

61. In particular, let A be the zero matrix.

63. Apply the definitions of scalar multiplication and matrix addition.

65. Apply the definition of scalar multiplication.

Exercises 1.5 (page 48)

1. $\begin{bmatrix} a & b & c \\ 0 & 0 & 0 \\ 0 & 0 & 0 \end{bmatrix}$

3. $\begin{bmatrix} g & h & i \\ 0 & 0 & 0 \\ 0 & 0 & 0 \end{bmatrix}$

5. $\begin{bmatrix} a & b & c \\ d & e & f \\ 0 & 0 & 0 \end{bmatrix}$

7. Both equal to $\begin{bmatrix} 2 & -2 \\ 6 & 3 \\ 12 & 12 \end{bmatrix}$

9. $AB = I_2$, but $BA = \begin{bmatrix} -5 & 2 & -4 \\ 9 & -2 & 6 \\ 12 & -4 & 9 \end{bmatrix}$

11. AI_2 is not defined.

13. Note that $I = (\delta_{ij})$, where $\delta_{ij} = \begin{cases} 1 & \text{if } i = j \\ 0 & \text{if } i \neq j \end{cases}$, $A = (a_{sk})$. Now write out the products as defined in this section.

15. Apply the definitions of matrix addition and matrix multiplication to compare the (i, j) entries of both sides of the given identity.

17. Apply the definitions of matrix multiplication and scalar multiplication. The scalar r is a common factor to all the entries of the matrices on all sides of the given identity.

19. The (i, j) entry of $-(-A)$ is $-(-a_{ij}) = a_{ij} = (i, j)$ entry of A.

21. $A(B - C) = A(B + (-1)C)) = AB + A((-1)C) = AB + (-1)AC = AB - AC$. The second equality follows from Theorem 1.5(ii).

23. $(r - s)A = (r + (-s))A = rA + (-s)A = rA - sA$. The second equality follows from Theorem 1.4(ii).

25. Tom \$19.35; Dick \$14.15; Harry \$26.85.

27. Apply the definitions of lower triangular matrix and matrix addition.

29. Suppose $A = (a_{ij})$, $B = (b_{ij})$, and $i < j$. Note that the (i, j) entry of AB is a sum of terms of the form $a_{it}b_{tj}$. If $i < t$, then $a_{it} = 0$ (since A is lower triangular). If $t \leqslant i$, then $t < j$ (since $i < j$), and hence $b_{tj} = 0$ (since B is lower triangular). So in any case $a_{it}b_{tj} = 0$, and hence AB is lower triangular.

31. $(A^t)^3 = A^t A^t A^t = (AAA)^t = (A^3)^t = 0^t = 0$ (see Exercise 30).

33. Let k be the *least* positive integer such that $N^k = 0$. If $NB = I_n$, then $N^k B = N^{k-1}NB = N^{k-1}I_n = N^{k-1}$. But $N^k = 0$ and hence $N^k B = 0$. Thus, $N^{k-1} = 0$, which contradicts the *minimal* choice of k. (Note that k *cannot* be 1 here. Why?)

35. The ith entry of CU is the number of persons whom i likes.

36–39. The answers depend on your choice of the matrix B.

Exercises 1.6 (page 62)

1. $\begin{bmatrix} 0 & 1 \\ 1 & 0 \end{bmatrix}$

3. $\begin{bmatrix} 1 & 0 \\ 0 & -\frac{1}{5} \end{bmatrix}$

5. $\begin{bmatrix} 1 & 0 & 0 \\ 0 & \frac{1}{7} & 0 \\ 0 & 0 & 1 \end{bmatrix}$

7. $\begin{bmatrix} 0 & 0 & 1 & 0 \\ 0 & 1 & 0 & 0 \\ 1 & 0 & 0 & 0 \\ 0 & 0 & 0 & 1 \end{bmatrix}$ **9.** $\begin{bmatrix} \frac{1}{7} & 0 & 0 \\ 0 & -\frac{1}{3} & 0 \\ 0 & 0 & \frac{1}{4} \end{bmatrix}$ **11.** $\begin{bmatrix} \frac{1}{4} & 0 & 0 \\ \frac{1}{6} & \frac{1}{3} & 0 \\ -\frac{4}{15} & \frac{1}{15} & \frac{1}{5} \end{bmatrix}$

13. $\begin{bmatrix} 0 & -1 & 0 & 1 \\ -1 & 0 & 0 & 1 \\ 0 & 1 & 1 & -1 \\ 1 & 1 & 0 & -1 \end{bmatrix}$

15. $\begin{bmatrix} 2 & -1 & 3 \\ 0 & 1 & -4 \\ 2 & -1 & -2 \end{bmatrix} X = \begin{bmatrix} 2 \\ 5 \\ 7 \end{bmatrix}$, so $X = \begin{bmatrix} \frac{3}{5} & \frac{1}{2} & -\frac{1}{10} \\ \frac{4}{5} & 1 & -\frac{4}{5} \\ \frac{1}{5} & 0 & -\frac{1}{5} \end{bmatrix} \begin{bmatrix} 2 \\ 5 \\ 7 \end{bmatrix} = \begin{bmatrix} 3 \\ 1 \\ -1 \end{bmatrix}$.

17. Argue as in Exercise 15 to get $X = \begin{bmatrix} 1 \\ 0 \\ -3 \end{bmatrix}$.

19. $\begin{bmatrix} -48 & 18 & 9 & -7 \\ 82 & -31 & -15 & 12 \\ 49 & -18 & -9 & 7 \\ 27 & -10 & -5 & 4 \end{bmatrix}$ **21.** $\begin{bmatrix} \frac{7}{3} & -\frac{1}{3} & -\frac{1}{3} & -\frac{2}{3} \\ \frac{4}{9} & -\frac{1}{9} & -\frac{4}{9} & \frac{1}{9} \\ -\frac{1}{9} & -\frac{2}{9} & \frac{1}{9} & \frac{2}{9} \\ -\frac{5}{3} & \frac{2}{3} & \frac{2}{3} & \frac{1}{3} \end{bmatrix}$

23. $(CA)B = C(AB) = CI = C$, and also $(CA)B = IB = B$. Hence, $B = C = A^{-1}$.

25. *Hint*: If A^{-1} exists, then $A^{-1}(AX) = 0$, so $X = 0$. Conversely, if A is singular, use the ideas of Section 1.3.

27. *Hint*: Suppose that $A^k = 0$ for minimal k and that A^{-1} exists. What can you say about A^{k-1}?

29. *Hint*: Recall that $AA^{-1} = I_3$.

31. Let $A = I$ and $B = -I$. Is $A + B$ singular or nonsingular?

33. Use the matrix inversion algorithm to compute A^{-1}.

35. \$9847, \$9431, \$33 842, approximately.

37. Compute $E_n(ci)E_n\left(\dfrac{1}{-i}\right)$.

CHAPTER 2

Exercises 2.1 (page 72)

1. 10   **3.** 6   **5.** $a^2 + b^2$ **7.** 72

9. -6 **11.** Write out both, rearrange and compare.

13. $x_1 = \frac{1}{23}$, $x_2 = -\frac{7}{23}$

15. $x_1 = \dfrac{25}{10} = 2.5, \; x_2 = \dfrac{50}{10} = 5, \; x_3 = \dfrac{30}{10} = 3$

17. $a = \frac{10}{23}, b = \frac{5}{6}, c = \frac{5}{2}.$ **19.** 12 nickels, 6 dimes, 9 quarters.

21. \$2400 in A, \$1700 in B, \$3100 in C. Total interest is \$353.

23. For $a = 0$: $x_1 = t, x_2 = x_3 = 0$ for any real number t.

  For $a = 1$: $x_1 = -3t, x_2 = -2t, x_3 = t$.

  For $a = -1$: $x_1 = -2t, x_2 = t, x_3 = 0$.

25. 6 cups and 3 plates.

27. $y = 4.9x + 1.5$ (see Exercise 26). The 1977 point $(2, 12.3)$ is not on this line.

29. Projection from the line is \$260 000 and from the parabola \$360 000. The parabola covers more of the known data.

31. Subtract row two from row three, and row one from row two. Then expand the determinant of the resulting matrix.

Exercises 2.2 (page 82)

1. 1   **3.** 1   **5.** 0   **7.** 0   **9.** -2

11. 32   **13.** $5^3 = 125$ **15.** 384   **17.** -1 **19.** -3

21. $\frac{1}{6}$ **23.** 1   **25.** $\det A = -4$

26. $M = \begin{bmatrix} 1 & 3 & 1 \\ 0 & 1 & \frac{1}{6} \\ 0 & 0 & 1 \end{bmatrix}$ **29.** $x = 1, y = -1, z = 2, w = -2$

31. $\det \begin{bmatrix} a_{11} & a_{12} \\ a_{21} & a_{22} \end{bmatrix} = a_{11}a_{22} - a_{21}a_{12} = a_{11}a_{22} - a_{12}a_{21} = \det \begin{bmatrix} a_{11} & a_{21} \\ a_{12} & a_{22} \end{bmatrix}$

Exercises 2.3 (page 89)

1. Rows one and three are interchanged; property 1.

3. Property 3 used twice.

5. Property 5   **7.** Theorem 2.2

9. Reduce it to row-echelon form and use Theorem 2.2 along with Properties 1, 2, and 3.

11. 48   **13.** 18   **15.** $-1 - \tan^2 \alpha = -\sec^2 \alpha$

17. $x^2 + y^2$ **19.** 4

21. Since interchanging the two identical rows (columns) of A gives A itself, we have $-\det A = \det A$, and hence $\det A = 0$.

23. Let $A = I_2$, $B = -I_2$. Then $\det(A + B) = \det 0 = 0 \neq \det A + \det B$.

25. Let M be a matrix in which both rows i and j are the same as row i of A, while all other rows of M are exactly as the corresponding rows of A. Expand $\det M$ along the jth row.

27. $x = 5$ **29.** $AA^{-1} = I$, so $\det(AA^{-1}) = \det A \det A^{-1} = 1$.

31. $-\sqrt{2}/2$ **33.** 8

Exercises 2.4 (page 95)

1. 14, $\begin{bmatrix} \frac{1}{7} & -\frac{3}{14} \\ \frac{2}{7} & \frac{1}{14} \end{bmatrix}$ 3. No; det $A = 0$.

5. det $A = aehj \neq 0$ 7. det $A = a^3 = 0$; $A^2 = \begin{bmatrix} 0 & 0 & bd \\ 0 & 0 & 0 \\ 0 & 0 & 0 \end{bmatrix}$, so $A^3 = A \cdot A^2 = 0$.

9. det $A' = \det A \neq 0$; apply Theorem 2.5.

11. No. Suppose A and B are nonsingular, then det $(AB) = \det A \det B \neq 0$ (by Theorem 2.5). So, by Theorem 2.5, AB is nonsingular.

13. See Exercise 11. If A is singular and B is nonsingular, then det $(AB) = 0$. For both A and B singular, AB is singular (see Exercise 12).

15. If A is nonsingular, then $B = A^{-1}(AB) = A^{-1}(AC) = C$.

17. *Hint:* A (adj A) = (det $A)I_n$.

CHAPTER 3

Exercises 3.1 (page 106)

1. Draw the lines suggested by the hint (see figure below).

$$\triangle OAP_1 \cong \triangle P_2CP_3$$

$$\triangle P_1BP_3 \cong \triangle ODP_2$$

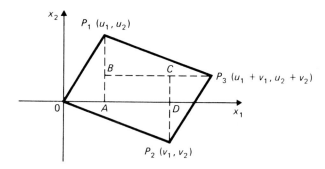

Note that $|OA| = u_1$, $|CP_3| = u_1 + v_1 - v_1 = u_1$, so $OA \cong CP_3$. Similarly, $|P_1A| = u_2$, $|CP_2| = u_2 + v_2 - v_2 = u_2$, so $P_1A \cong CP_2$. Since angles OAP_1 and P_2CP_3 are right angles, the triangles OAP_1 and P_2CP_3 are congruent. Therefore, $OP_1 \cong P_2P_3$. One similarly demonstrates the congruence of triangles ODP_2 and P_1BP_3, so P_1P_3 is congruent to OP_2. Therefore, the quadrilateral $OP_1P_3P_2$ is a parallelogram.

3.

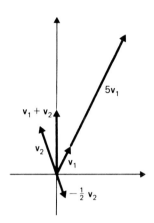

5. Check each axiom using the usual rules for polynomial addition and for multiplying a polynomial by a constant.

7. If $3x_1 - x_2 + 3x_3 = c$ and $3x_1' - x_2' + 3x_3' = c$, then $3(x_1 + x_1') - (x_2 + x_2') + 3(x_3 + x_3') = 2c = c$ implies $c = 0$.

9. Note that this is the content of Theorems 1.3 and 1.4.

11. Not a vector space; no zero vector (Axiom V4).

13. Not a vector space; let $\frac{1}{2}$ be a scalar. Then $\frac{1}{2} \cdot 3$ is not an integer (Axiom S1).

15. Vector space (check each axiom).   **17.** Vector space.   **19.** Vector space.

21. Refer to the appropriate differentiation theorems.

23. Suppose that there are two zero vectors $\mathbf{0}_1$ and $\mathbf{0}_2$. Then

$$\mathbf{0}_1 = \mathbf{0}_1 + \mathbf{0}_2 = \mathbf{0}_2 + \mathbf{0}_1 = \mathbf{0}_2.$$

25. Do part (iv) first: $0\mathbf{v} + 0\mathbf{v} = 0\mathbf{v}$, so $0\mathbf{v} = \mathbf{0}$. For (i) note that $\mathbf{v} = 1 \cdot \mathbf{v}$, so $\mathbf{v} + (-1)\mathbf{v} = 1\mathbf{v} + (-1)\mathbf{v} = (1 + (-1))\mathbf{v} = 0\mathbf{v} = \mathbf{0}$. Part (ii) follows from the uniqueness of the additive inverse. Part (iii) follows from $(\mathbf{u} - \mathbf{v}) + (\mathbf{v} - \mathbf{u}) = \mathbf{0}$ and the uniqueness of the additive inverse. For part (v), use part (iv) and observe that $\alpha \cdot \mathbf{0}_v = \alpha \cdot 0_s \mathbf{v}$ for any $\mathbf{v}$. Thus, $\alpha \cdot \mathbf{0}_v = 0_s \mathbf{v} = \mathbf{0}_v$. For (vi), if $\alpha \neq 0$ and $\alpha\mathbf{v} = \mathbf{0}$, then $\frac{1}{\alpha}\alpha\mathbf{v} = 1\mathbf{v} = \mathbf{v} = \mathbf{0}$. For (vii), use (i) and axiom S3, noting that $-\beta = \beta(-1)$. For (viii), use (i) and axiom S2.

Exercises 3.2 (page 114)

1. If $c_1(1, 0) + c_2(0, 1) = (0, 0)$, then $(c_1, c_2) = (0, 0)$, so $c_1 = c_2 = 0$.

3. $c_1(1, 0, 0, 0) + c_2(0, 1, 0, 0) + c_3(0, 0, 1, 0) = (c_1, c_2, c_3, 0) = (0, 0, 0, 0)$ implies $c_1 = c_2 = c_3 = 0$.

5. $c_1(1, 1, 1) + c_2(1, -1, 1) = (c_1 + c_2, c_1 - c_2, c_1 + c_2) = (0, 0, 0)$ implies $c_1 + c_2 = 0$ and $c_1 - c_2 = 0$. So $c_1 = c_2 = 0$.

7. $c_1(1-x)+c_2(1+x) = (c_1+c_2)+(-c_1+c_2)x = 0+0x$, so $c_1 = c_2 = 0$.

9. $c_1\begin{bmatrix} 1 & 0 \\ 0 & 0 \end{bmatrix} + c_2\begin{bmatrix} 0 & 1 \\ 0 & 0 \end{bmatrix} + c_3\begin{bmatrix} 0 & 0 \\ 0 & 1 \end{bmatrix} = \begin{bmatrix} c_1 & c_2 \\ 0 & c_3 \end{bmatrix} = \begin{bmatrix} 0 & 0 \\ 0 & 0 \end{bmatrix}$ implies $c_1 = c_2 = c_3 = 0$.

11. Dependent: $1(2, 2)+(-2)(1, 1) = (0, 0)$.

13. Independent.   **15.** Independent.

17. Dependent: $75(0, 0)+0(1, 1) = (0, 0)$.

19. Dependent: $\begin{bmatrix} 1 & 0 \\ 0 & 1 \end{bmatrix} - \begin{bmatrix} 1 & 2 \\ 0 & 1 \end{bmatrix} + 2\begin{bmatrix} 0 & 1 \\ 0 & 0 \end{bmatrix} = \begin{bmatrix} 0 & 0 \\ 0 & 0 \end{bmatrix}$.

21. $c_1\mathbf{v}_1 + c_2\mathbf{v}_2 = \mathbf{0}$ implies $c_1\mathbf{v}_1 = -c_2\mathbf{v}_2$. Therefore, since at least one of the coefficients, say c_1, is not zero, we have

$$\mathbf{v}_1 = \frac{-c_2}{c_1}\mathbf{v}_2 = k\mathbf{v}_2.$$

23. $c_1\mathbf{u}+c_2\mathbf{w} = c_1(3, 2)+c_2(-2, -2) = (3c_1-2c_2, 2c_1-2c_2) = (0, 0)$ implies that $c_1 = c_2 = 0$.

25. Let $(u_1, u_2), (v_1, v_2), (w_1, w_2)$ be vectors in $\mathbb{R}^2$. The linear system

$$c_1 u_1 + c_2 v_1 + c_3 w_1 = 0,$$
$$c_1 u_2 + c_2 v_2 + c_3 w_2 = 0$$

always has nontrivial solutions, e.g., if $c_3 = 1$, then

$$c_1 = \frac{\det\begin{bmatrix} -w_1 & v_1 \\ -w_2 & v_2 \end{bmatrix}}{\det\begin{bmatrix} u_1 & v_1 \\ u_2 & v_2 \end{bmatrix}}, \quad c_2 = \frac{\det\begin{bmatrix} u_1 & -w_1 \\ u_2 & -w_2 \end{bmatrix}}{\det\begin{bmatrix} u_1 & v_1 \\ u_2 & v_2 \end{bmatrix}}, \quad \text{when } \det\begin{bmatrix} u_1 & v_1 \\ u_2 & v_2 \end{bmatrix} \neq 0.$$

27. Let us illustrate the proof for $n = 4$, $S = \{\mathbf{v}_1, \mathbf{v}_2, \mathbf{v}_3\}$. Suppose $\alpha_1\mathbf{v}_1 + \alpha_2\mathbf{v}_2 + \alpha_3\mathbf{v}_3 = \mathbf{0}$. Then $\alpha_1\mathbf{v}_1 + \alpha_2\mathbf{v}_2 + \alpha_3\mathbf{v}_3 + 0\mathbf{v}_4 = \mathbf{0}$ and hence $\alpha_1 = 0, \alpha_2 = 0, \alpha_3 = 0$ (since $\mathbf{v}_1, \ldots, \mathbf{v}_4$ are independent). Thus $\mathbf{v}_1, \mathbf{v}_2, \mathbf{v}_3$ are independent.

29. $w(x) = \det\begin{bmatrix} e^x & e^{-x} & e^{2x} \\ e^x & -e^{-x} & 2e^{2x} \\ e^x & e^{-x} & 4e^{2x} \end{bmatrix} = -6e^{2x} \neq 0$. So they are independent.

Exercises 3.3 (page 123)

1. Is   **3.** Is   **5.** Is   **7.** Is   **9.** Is

11. Is not; e.g., $\begin{bmatrix} 1 & 2 \\ 0 & 0 \end{bmatrix}$ and $\begin{bmatrix} 0 & 0 \\ -1 & 1 \end{bmatrix}$ both have zero determinant but their sum does not.

13. Is.

15. $c_1(1, 1, 0) + c_2(0, 1, 1) = (-1, 2, 3)$ implies $c_1 = -1, c_2 = 3$, and $c_1 + c_2 = 2$. This being the case, $\mathbf{x}$ is in $L(S)$; $\mathbf{x} = -1(1, 1, 0) + 3(0, 1, 1)$.

17. See Exercise 15; $\mathbf{x} = -1(1, -1, 3) + 1(2, 4, 0)$, so $\mathbf{x}$ is in $L(S)$.

19 and **21.** $\mathbf{x}$ is not in $L(S)$; it is independent of the vectors in S.

23. $\mathbf{x}$ is in $L(S)$, since $x = 1\begin{bmatrix} 2 & 4 \\ 0 & 1 \end{bmatrix} - 1\begin{bmatrix} 1 & 2 \\ 0 & 2 \end{bmatrix}$.

25. Yes; $(a, b, c) = (a + b - c)(1, 0, 0) + b(0, 1, 1) + (c - b)(1, 0, 1)$.

27. Yes.

29. Let $\mathbf{w}$ be any vector in W. Then $-\mathbf{w} = (-1)\mathbf{w}$ is in W and hence $\mathbf{0} = \mathbf{w} + (-\mathbf{w})$ is in W. All equational laws hold in W (since they already hold in V).

31. Show that they fail to be closed under vector addition.

33. All pairs of the form (z, iz), where z is a complex number.

35. These functions clearly satisfy Theorem 3.3.

Exercises 3.4 (page 132)

1. No; they are not linearly independent:
$$-1(3, 4, -5) + 3(1, 0, 0) + 4(0, 1, 0) - 5(0, 0, 1) = \mathbf{0}.$$

3. (a) Yes (b) No; linearly dependent. (c) $\{(1, 2), (3, 4)\}, \{(1, 2), (5, 6)\}, \{(3, 4), (5, 6)\}$.

5. $c_1(0, 1, 1) + c_2(1, 0, 1) + c_3(1, 1, 0) = (0, 0, 0)$ implies $c_1 = c_2 = c_3 = 0$. (Use a matrix.)

7. Let $\mathbf{u} = (u_1, u_2, u_3)$, $\mathbf{v} = (v_1, v_2, v_3)$. Then $\mathbf{u} + \mathbf{v} = (u_1 + v_1, u_2 + v_2, u_3 + v_3)$ and $(u_1 + v_1) - (u_2 + v_2) - (u_3 + v_3) = (u_1 - u_2 - u_3) + (v_1 - v_2 - v_3) = 0$, when $\mathbf{u}, \mathbf{v}$ are in W. Also $k\mathbf{u} \in W$ because $ku_1 - ku_2 - ku_3 = k(u_1 - u_2 - u_3) = k0 = 0$. (Use Theorem 3.3.)

9. See Exercise 7. The second condition follows as did the first.

11. Since $(0, 0, 0)$ is in W, $2(0) - 0 + 3(0) = c$, and hence $c = 0$; W has dimension 2 because $(x_1, x_2, x_3) = x_2(\frac{1}{2}, 1, 0) + x_3(-\frac{3}{2}, 0, 1,)$, so $\{(\frac{1}{2}, 1, 0), (-\frac{3}{2}, 0, 1)\}$ is a basis for W.

13. Both the zero subspace and all of V satisfy Theorem 3.3.

15. Suppose that V has two vectors $\mathbf{v}$ and $\mathbf{u}$ such that $\mathbf{u}$ is not a scalar multiple of $\mathbf{v}$. Then $S = \{\mathbf{u}, \mathbf{v}\}$ is linearly independent and $L(S)$ is a two-dimensional subspace of V, while $L(\mathbf{u})$ and $L(\mathbf{v})$ are distinct one-dimensional subspaces. This is too many subspaces. Therefore, every vector in V is a scalar multiple of a single vector in V, and thus dim $V = 1$.

17. 3; $\{(1 - x), (1 - x^2), (1 + x)\}$ is a basis.

19. By Lemma 3.4, any set of $n + 1$ vectors is dependent. Let $\mathbf{u} \in V$, $\mathbf{u} \notin S$. Then there exist scalars $k, c_1, \ldots, c_n$, not all zero, such that $k\mathbf{u} + c_1\mathbf{v}_1 + \cdots + c_n\mathbf{v}_n = \mathbf{0}$. In fact, $k \neq 0$.
(Why?) Therefore, $\mathbf{u} = -\dfrac{c_1}{k}\mathbf{v}_1 - \cdots - \dfrac{c_n}{k}\mathbf{v}_n$ is in $L(S)$. So $L(S) = V$.

21. Hint: Let $\mathbf{u} \in V$, $\mathbf{u} \notin L(S)$. Why does such an $\mathbf{u}$ exist? Let $\mathbf{v}_{k+1} = \mathbf{u}$ and $S' = S \cup \{\mathbf{v}_{k+1}\}$. Repeat the process with S' taking the place of S until $L(S)$ has dimension n. Why does the process stop?

23. Let $L(S) = V$. If S is not linearly independent, one vector in S can be written as a linear combination of the other members of S. (Show this.) Delete this vector from S. The remaining set of vectors still spans V. (Why?) Continue the process until such deletion is no longer possible. The remaining vectors are linearly independent. Conversely, if S is linearly independent, no fewer vectors can span V. (Why?)

Exercises 3.5 (page 140)

1. 1   **3.** 2   **5.** 3   **7.** $\{(1, \frac{1}{3})\}$

9. $\{(1, 3, 7, 1), (0, 1, 2, \frac{1}{5})\}$ **11.** $\{(1, -1, 0, 2), (0, 1, 1, \frac{1}{3}), (0, 0, 1, 0)\}$.

13. Row rank $\leqslant m$; Column rank $\leqslant n$; but Column rank $=$ Row rank $=$ Rank. Therefore, Rank $\leqslant \min\{m, n\}$.

15. No. If it has n linearly independent rows, it is invertible. (See Theorem 3.13.)

17. If rank of A is n, then (by Theorem 3.13) A^{-1} exists. Since $A^k = 0$ and A^{-1} exists, repeated left multiplication by A^{-1} gives $A = 0$, a contradiction.

19. Rank $A = 3$, Rank (adj A) $= 1$.

21. The row space of A^t is the column space of A.

23. If rank $A = n$, A^{-1} exists, so $X = A^{-1}0 = 0$.

25. See Exercise 23 for one direction. Conversely, if Rank $A < n$, then the column vectors of A are linearly dependent. The system of equations $AX = 0$ can be viewed as the following linear combination of the column vectors of A: $x_1 A_1 + x_2 A_2 + \cdots + x_n A_n = 0$. Linear dependence implies that not all of the x_i need to be zero.

27. $\{(1, 1, 0, 1, 1), (0, 1, 1, -3, -2), (0, 0, 1, -\frac{7}{3}, -\frac{5}{3}), (0, 0, 0, 1, 3)\}$

CHAPTER 4

Exercises 4.1 (page 151)

1. 11   **3.** 0   **5.** -12 **7.** Yes, their inner product is zero.

9. $\sqrt{3}, \sqrt{2}$ **11.** $\cos\theta = \frac{10}{21}$

13. $\mathbf{v} = \mathbf{0}$. For, let $\mathbf{v} = (x_1, x_2)$; then $0 = \langle \mathbf{v}, \mathbf{v} \rangle = x_1^2 + x_2^2$ implies that $x_1 = x_2 = 0$.

15. The inner product of $(0, 0, 0)$ and (x_1, x_2, x_3) is $0x_1 + 0x_2 + 0x_3 = 0$.

17. $(x_1 x_2 + y_1 y_2)^2 = (x_1^2 + y_1^2)(x_2^2 + y_2^2) - (x_1^2 y_2^2 + y_1^2 x_2^2 - 2x_1 y_2 y_1 x_2)$
$= (x_1^2 + y_1^2)(x_2^2 + y_2^2) - (x_1 y_2 - y_1 x_2)^2 \leqslant (x_1^2 + y_1^2)(x_2^2 + y_2^2)$

19. Imitate the proof in the 2-dimensional case.

21. Let $\mathbf{u} = (x_1, x_2)$, $\mathbf{v} = (y_1, y_2)$, $\mathbf{w} = (z_1, z_2)$. Then
$$\langle \mathbf{u} + \mathbf{v}, \mathbf{w} \rangle = (x_1 + y_1)z_1 + (x_2 + y_2)z_2 = \langle \mathbf{u}, \mathbf{w} \rangle + \langle \mathbf{v}, \mathbf{w} \rangle.$$

23. Imitate the calculations in Exercise 21.

25. Put $k_1 = k_2 = 1$; then put $k_2 = 0$.

27. Compute the inner products and lengths of the vectors involved.

29. Compare the squares of both sides of the inequality and imitate the proof in Exercise 17.

Exercises 4.2 (page 158)

1. -23 3. 3   5. -7 7. 0   9. 6

11. No. Compare $\langle(1+1, 2+3), (1, 4)\rangle$ with $\langle(1, 2), (1, 4)\rangle + \langle(1, 3), (1, 4)\rangle$.

13. Not an inner product. Note that $\langle 1, 1 \rangle = 0$.

15. Imitate the calculations in Example 1.

17. 4   19. 28   21. 0   23. 27   25. -1 27. -1

29. Use the properties of transpose given in Exercises 53–56 of Section 1.4 and the fact that the trace of a sum is the sum of the traces as well as the fact that A and A^t have the same trace.

31. Those in Exercises 21 and 22.

33. Note that $\langle 0 + 0, v \rangle = \langle 0, v \rangle + \langle 0, v \rangle$.

35. Use properties 2 and 1 in the definition of inner product.

37. Use property 2 in the definition of inner product and Theorem 4.2.

39. Proof is essentially the same as that given in Example 3.

41. $-\frac{3}{4}$ 43. $-\frac{21}{4}$ 45. $\frac{3}{2}$ 47. $e - 1$

Exercises 4.3 (page 167)

1. $\sqrt{10}$ 3. $\sqrt{3}$ 5. 1   7. 2

9. $\sqrt{10}$ 11. $\dfrac{1}{\sqrt{10}} (1, 3)$ 13. $\dfrac{1}{\sqrt{3}} (1, -1, 1)$

15. It is already a unit vector.   17. $\frac{1}{2} (1, 1, 1, 1)$

19. $\dfrac{1}{\sqrt{10}} (0, 2, -2, 0, 1, -1)$ 21. Yes   23. Yes

25. Yes   27. $(1, 0, 0, 0), (0, 1, 0, 0), (0, 0, 1, 0), (0, 0, 0, 1)$.

29. Let $u = (1, 1, 0)$ and $v = (0, 1, 1)$. Then $u + v = (1, 2, 1)$, $||u|| = \sqrt{2}$, $||v|| = \sqrt{2}$, $||u + v|| = \sqrt{6}$. Note that $\sqrt{6} < \sqrt{2} + \sqrt{2}$.

31. $|\langle u, v \rangle| = 105$; $||u|| = \sqrt{21}$; $||v|| = 5\sqrt{21}$. Hence equality holds and u and v are linearly dependent.

33. Since $\langle 0, v \rangle = 0$, 0 is in S. Also if s_1, s_2 are in S, then $\langle s_1 + s_2, v \rangle = \langle s_1, v \rangle + \langle s_2, v \rangle = 0 + 0 = 0$, so $s_1 + s_2$ is in S. Similarly, ks_1 is in S for all scalars k. So S is a subspace of V; it is the subspace orthogonal to v. If $V = \mathbb{R}^2$, this subspace is the line perpendicular to the vector v. If $V = \mathbb{R}^3$, this subspace is the plane perpendicular to v.

35. 1   37. No.

39. Let $\langle u, u \rangle = a + ib$. By (ii), $\langle u, u \rangle = \overline{\langle u, u \rangle}$ and hence $a + ib = a - ib$. Thus $b = 0$ and $\langle u, u \rangle = a$ is real.

41. Let $z = a + ib$ be a complex number and $\text{Re}(z) = a$ denote the real part of z. Then $z + \bar{z} = 2\,\text{Re}(z)$, $\text{Re}(z) \leqslant |z|$, and $z\bar{z} = |z|^2$. Also, for any complex numbers z_1, z_2, we have

$|z_1 z_2| = |z_1| |z_2|$ and $\overline{z_1 z_2} = \bar{z}_1 \bar{z}_2$. By (v), $0 \leq \langle x\mathbf{u} + \mathbf{v}, \ x\mathbf{u} + \mathbf{v} \rangle$ for all *complex* numbers x. Now, use the above facts and the new conditions (i)–(v) above as well as Exercises 39, 40 to get

$$0 \leq |x|^2 \langle \mathbf{u}, \ \mathbf{u} \rangle + 2|\langle \mathbf{u}, \ \mathbf{v} \rangle| \, |x| + \langle \mathbf{v}, \ \mathbf{v} \rangle.$$

The rest of the proof is as indicated in the text for the case of real scalars.

Exercises 4.4 (page 177)

1. $\left(\dfrac{1}{\sqrt{2}}, \dfrac{1}{\sqrt{2}} \right), \left(-\dfrac{1}{\sqrt{2}}, \dfrac{1}{\sqrt{2}} \right)$ **3.** $\dfrac{1}{\sqrt{17}} (-1, 4), \ \dfrac{1}{\sqrt{425}} (20, 5)$

5. $\dfrac{1}{\sqrt{2}} (1, 0, 1), \ \dfrac{1}{\sqrt{6}} (-1, 2, 1), \ \dfrac{1}{\sqrt{3}} (1, 1, -1)$

7. $\dfrac{1}{\sqrt{2}} (1, 1, 0, 0), \ \dfrac{1}{\sqrt{2}} (1, -1, 0, 0), \ (0, 0, 0, 1), \ (0, 0, 1, 0)$

9. $\sqrt{\tfrac{2}{3}} (1, 0, 1), \ \dfrac{1}{\sqrt{21}} (-1, 3, 2), \ \dfrac{1}{\sqrt{14}} (2, 1, -4)$

11. Yes.   **13.** $\dfrac{1}{\sqrt{2}} (1 - x^2), \ \dfrac{1}{\sqrt{2}} (1 + x^2), \ x, \ x^3$

15. Suppose that $\mathbf{v}_1, \ldots, \mathbf{v}_n$ are *nonzero* vectors in an inner product space V and that $\langle \mathbf{v}_j, \mathbf{v}_i \rangle = 0$ whenever $j \neq i$. Then $\{\mathbf{v}_1, \ldots, \mathbf{v}_n\}$ is linearly independent. For, suppose that

$$\alpha_1 \mathbf{v}_1 + \cdots + \alpha_i \mathbf{v}_i + \cdots + \alpha_n \mathbf{v}_n = \mathbf{0}.$$

Then,

$$0 = \langle \mathbf{0}, \ \mathbf{v}_i \rangle = \langle \alpha_1 \mathbf{v}_1 + \cdots + \alpha_i \mathbf{v}_i + \cdots + \alpha_n \mathbf{v}_n, \ \mathbf{v}_i \rangle$$
$$= \alpha_i \langle \mathbf{v}_i, \ \mathbf{v}_i \rangle = \alpha_i ||\mathbf{v}_i||^2.$$

So $\alpha_i ||\mathbf{v}_i||^2 = 0$ and hence each $\alpha_i = 0$ (since $\mathbf{v}_i \neq \mathbf{0}$). Thus, $\mathbf{v}_1, \ldots, \mathbf{v}_n$ are linearly independent.

17. $1, \ \sqrt{3}(2x - 1), \ \sqrt{5}(6x^2 - 6x + 1)$ **19.** $\dfrac{1}{\sqrt{13}} (3x + 2), \ \sqrt{\tfrac{3}{13}} (7x - 4)$

21. Let $\mathbf{u} = \alpha_1 \mathbf{v}_1 + \cdots + \alpha_i \mathbf{v}_i + \cdots + \alpha_n \mathbf{v}_n$. Then $\langle \mathbf{u}, \ \mathbf{v}_i \rangle = \alpha_i \langle \mathbf{v}_i, \ \mathbf{v}_i \rangle = \alpha_i$. Thus,

$$\mathbf{u} = \sum_{i=1}^{n} \langle \mathbf{u}, \ \mathbf{v}_i \rangle \mathbf{v}_i.$$

Exercises 4.5 (page 185)

1. $y = \tfrac{3}{2}x - \tfrac{2}{3}$

3. $y = 1.3x + 1.1$. Note that the given points actually lie *on* this line.

5. $y = -\tfrac{3}{4}x^2 + \tfrac{7}{20}x + \tfrac{91}{20}$ **7.** $y = -1.043x^2 + 4.891x - 2.086$

9. Substituting the values of $\mathbf{v}_j$ into the equation $c_1\mathbf{v}_1 + c_2\mathbf{v}_2 + \cdots + c_m\mathbf{v}_m = \mathbf{0}$, we get

$$c_1[\langle x_1, x_1 \rangle, \langle x_2, x_1 \rangle, \ldots, \langle x_m, x_1 \rangle]^t + \cdots$$
$$+ c_m[\langle x_1, x_m \rangle, \langle x_2, x_m \rangle, \ldots, \langle x_m, x_m \rangle]^t = [0, \ldots, 0]^t.$$

Equating the ith coordinates of both sides of this equation, we get the desired conclusion.

11. $\det(M^t M) = (\det M^t)(\det M) = (\det M)(\det M) \neq 0$, since M is nonsingular; hence $M^t M$ is nonsingular.

13. Not quite. (See Exercise 14.)

CHAPTER 5

Exercises 5.1 (page 194)

1. Yes   3. No   5. Yes   7. Yes   9. Yes

11. $T(\mathbf{x} + \mathbf{y}) = T((x_1, x_2) + (y_1, y_2)) = T((x_1 + y_1, x_2 + y_2))$
$\qquad = (x_1 + y_1, -(x_2 + y_2), (x_1 + y_1) - (x_2 + y_2))$
$\qquad = (x_1, -x_2, x_1 - x_2) + (y_1, -y_2, y_1 - y_2) = T(\mathbf{x}) + T(\mathbf{y})$.
$T(a\mathbf{x}) = T(a(x_1, x_2)) = T((ax_1, ax_2)) = (ax_1, -ax_2, ax_1 - ax_2)$
$\qquad = a(x_1, -x_2, x_1 - x_2) = aT(\mathbf{x})$.

13. $T(\mathbf{x} + \mathbf{y}) = \mathbf{0} = \mathbf{0} + \mathbf{0} = T(\mathbf{x}) + T(\mathbf{y})$; $T(a\mathbf{x}) = \mathbf{0} = a \cdot \mathbf{0} = aT(\mathbf{x})$.

15. $T(\alpha\mathbf{x} + \beta\mathbf{y}) = T(\alpha(x_1, x_2) + \beta(y_1, y_2)) = T((\alpha x_1 + \beta y_1, \alpha x_2 + \beta y_2)) = (0, \alpha x_2 + \beta y_2)$
$\qquad = (0, \alpha x_2) + (0, \beta y_2) = \alpha T((x_1, x_2)) + \beta T((y_1, y_2)) = \alpha T(\mathbf{x}) + \beta T(\mathbf{y})$.

17. Since matrices have the distributive property, we get:
$$T_A(X + Y) = A(X + Y) - (X + Y)A = AX + AY - XA - YA$$
$$= (AX - XA) + (AY - YA) = T_A(X) + T_A(Y).$$
Since all matrices A commute with scalar multiplication, we have:
$$T_A(\alpha X) = A(\alpha X) - (\alpha X)A = \alpha(AX) - \alpha(XA) = \alpha[AX - XA] = \alpha T_A(X).$$

19. For any $\mathbf{u} \in U$, there exist scalars $\alpha_1, \alpha_2, \ldots, \alpha_n$ such that $\mathbf{u} = \alpha_1\mathbf{u}_1 + \alpha_2\mathbf{u}_2 + \cdots + \alpha_n\mathbf{u}_n$ because $S = \{\mathbf{u}_1, \ldots, \mathbf{u}_n\}$ is a basis for U. Thus for any $\mathbf{u} \in U$,
$$T(\mathbf{u}) = T(\alpha_1\mathbf{u}_1 + \alpha_2\mathbf{u}_2 + \cdots + \alpha_n\mathbf{u}_n) = \alpha_1 T(\mathbf{u}_1) + \cdots + \alpha_n T(\mathbf{u}_n).$$

21. This follows at once from the definition of spanning. Note that every vector in the subspace spanned by the set $T(S)$ is a linear combination of the vectors $T(\mathbf{u}_1), \ldots, T(\mathbf{u}_n)$.

23. Let A be an arbitrary $m \times n$ matrix and $X = \begin{bmatrix} x_1 \\ \vdots \\ x_n \end{bmatrix}$, $Y = \begin{bmatrix} y_1 \\ \vdots \\ y_n \end{bmatrix}$ be $n \times 1$ column vec-

tors. Then, since matrices have the distributive property, we get: $A(X + Y) = AX + AY$. Since matrices commute with scalars, we have: $A(\alpha X) = \alpha(AX)$. So matrix multiplication is a linear transformation on the space of $n \times 1$ column vectors.

25. From the derivative formulas $D(f+g)(x) = D((f+g)(x)) = D(f(x)+g(x)) = (D(f))(x)+(D(g))(x)$ and $(D(\alpha f))(x) = D(\alpha f(x)) = \alpha(Df)(x)$ we see immediately that D is linear.

27. $T(x^3 - 3x + 1) = D^3(x^3 - 3x + 1) - 2D^2(x^3 - 3x + 1) + D(x^3 - 3x + 1)$
$$= 6 - 2(6x) + (3x^2 - 3) = 3x^2 - 12x + 3.$$

29. We know that $\int_0^1 (f+g)(x)dx = \int_0^1 (f(x)+g(x))dx = \int_0^1 f(x)dx + \int_0^1 g(x)dx$ and
$\int_0^1 (\alpha f)(x)dx = \int_0^1 \alpha f(x)dx = \alpha \int_0^1 f(x)dx.$ Thus L is linear.

Exercises 5.2 (page 204)

1. $\begin{bmatrix} 2 & -1 \\ -6 & 3 \end{bmatrix} \begin{bmatrix} 4 \\ 8 \end{bmatrix} = \begin{bmatrix} 0 \\ 0 \end{bmatrix}$

3. Range of T_A consists of all vectors of the form $\begin{bmatrix} 2 & -1 \\ -6 & 3 \end{bmatrix} \begin{bmatrix} x_1 \\ x_2 \end{bmatrix} = \begin{bmatrix} 2x_1 & -x_2 \\ -6x_1 & +3x_2 \end{bmatrix}.$

Letting $x = 2x_1 - x_2$, we see that range of T_A consists of all vectors of the form $\begin{bmatrix} x \\ -3x \end{bmatrix}$;

that is, range of T_A is the subspace spanned by $\begin{bmatrix} 1 \\ -3 \end{bmatrix}$. Thus $\begin{bmatrix} 1 \\ 5 \end{bmatrix}$ is not in the range of T_A.

5. Kernel of T_A consists of all vectors $\begin{bmatrix} x_1 \\ x_2 \end{bmatrix}$ such that $2x_1 - x_2 = 0$. Thus kernel of T_A is

spanned by the vector $\begin{bmatrix} 1 \\ 2 \end{bmatrix}$, and $\left\{ \begin{bmatrix} 1 \\ 2 \end{bmatrix} \right\}$ forms a basis for the kernel of T_A.

7. Kernel of $T = \{0\}$. Range of $T = \mathbb{R}^2 = $ all of the Euclidean plane.
   Dim(Kernel of T) + Dim(Range of T) = $0 + 2 = 2 = $ Dim $\mathbb{R}^2 = $ Dim(Domain of T).

9. Kernel of $T = U$. Range of $T = \{0\}$.
   Dim(Kernel of T) + Dim(Range of T) = Dim(U) + 0 = Dim(U) = Dim(Domain of T).

11. Kernel of T consists of all vectors $\begin{bmatrix} x_1 \\ x_2 \\ x_3 \\ x_4 \end{bmatrix}$, where $x_1 = -\frac{5}{19}x_2$, $x_3 = -\frac{1}{19}x_2$,

$x_4 = -\frac{11}{19}x_2$. Thus, kernel of T is the one-dimensional subspace spanned by the vector
$\begin{bmatrix} -\frac{5}{19} \\ 1 \\ -\frac{1}{19} \\ -\frac{11}{19} \end{bmatrix}$. Range of T is all of $\mathbb{R}^3$.

Dim(Kernel of T) + Dim(Range of T) = $1 + 3 = 4 = $ Dim($\mathbb{R}^4$) = Dim(Domain of T).

13. D is clearly linear from its definition. Kernel of D is the set of all polynomials of degree zero, i.e., the constant polynomials. Range of D is P_{n-1}. Note that
Dim (Kernel D) + Dim (Range D) = $1 + (n-1) = n = $ Dim $(P_n) = $ Dim (Domain D).

15. We already know that $\{T(\mathbf{u}_1), T(\mathbf{u}_2), \ldots, T(\mathbf{u}_n)\}$ spans the range of T. Thus, we must show that $T(\mathbf{u}_1), \ldots, T(\mathbf{u}_n)$ are linearly independent if and only if Kernel of $T = \{\mathbf{0}\}$. Suppose that Kernel of $T = \{\mathbf{0}\}$ and that $\mathbf{0} = \alpha_1 T(\mathbf{u}_1) + \cdots + \alpha_n T(\mathbf{u}_n)$. Then $\mathbf{0} = T(\alpha_1 \mathbf{u}_1 + \alpha_2 \mathbf{u}_2 + \cdots + \alpha_n \mathbf{u}_n)$ and hence, $\mathbf{0} = \alpha_1 \mathbf{u}_1 + \alpha_2 \mathbf{u}_2 + \cdots + \alpha_n \mathbf{u}_n$. Thus, $\alpha_1 = \alpha_2 = \cdots = \alpha_n = 0$ (since $\mathbf{u}_1, \ldots, \mathbf{u}_n$ are linearly independent). Therefore, $T(\mathbf{u}_1), T(\mathbf{u}_2), \ldots, T(\mathbf{u}_n)$, must be linearly independent. Conversely, suppose $T(\mathbf{u}_1)$, $T(\mathbf{u}_2), \ldots, T(\mathbf{u}_n)$ are linearly independent. Let $\mathbf{u}$ be a vector in U such that $T(\mathbf{u}) = \mathbf{0}$. Since $\{\mathbf{u}_1, \mathbf{u}_2, \ldots, \mathbf{u}_n\}$ is a basis for U, there exist scalars $\alpha_1, \ldots, \alpha_n$ such that $\mathbf{u} = \alpha_1 \mathbf{u}_1 + \alpha_2 \mathbf{u}_2 + \cdots + \alpha_n \mathbf{u}_n$. So $\mathbf{0} = T(\mathbf{u}) = T(\alpha_1 \mathbf{u}_1 + \alpha_2 \mathbf{u}_2 + \cdots + \alpha_n \mathbf{u}_n) = \alpha_1 T(\mathbf{u}_1) + \cdots + \alpha_n T(\mathbf{u}_n)$. But since $T(\mathbf{u}_1), \ldots, T(\mathbf{u}_n)$ are linearly independent, we must have $\alpha_1 = \alpha_2 = \cdots = \alpha_n = 0$. So $\mathbf{u} = \mathbf{0}$ and hence Kernel of $T = \{\mathbf{0}\}$.

Exercises 5.3 (page 210)

1. $\begin{bmatrix} 1 & 0 & 0 \\ 0 & 1 & 0 \end{bmatrix}$ 3. $\begin{bmatrix} 1 & 5 \\ 0 & 1 \end{bmatrix}$ 5. $\begin{bmatrix} 0 & 0 & 0 & 0 \\ 1 & -1 & 0 & 0 \\ 0 & 0 & 1 & -1 \end{bmatrix}$

7. $\begin{bmatrix} 1 & 0 & 0 \\ 0 & 1 & 0 \\ 0 & 0 & 1 \end{bmatrix}$ 9. $\begin{bmatrix} 0 & 0 \\ 1 & 0 \\ 0 & 1 \end{bmatrix}$

13. Since $\{\mathbf{u}_1, \ldots, \mathbf{u}_n\}$ is a basis of U, $\mathbf{u}$ can be expressed in at least one way in the form $\mathbf{u} = a_1 \mathbf{u}_1 + \cdots + a_n \mathbf{u}_n$. Suppose that we also have $\mathbf{u} = b_1 \mathbf{u}_1 + \cdots + b_n \mathbf{u}_n$. Subtracting the last two equations, we get $(a_1 - b_1) \mathbf{u}_1 + \cdots + (a_n - b_n) \mathbf{u}_n = \mathbf{0}$, and hence $a_1 = b_1, \ldots, a_n = b_n$. (Why?)

Exercises 5.4 (page 216)

1. Let $T = \frac{1}{2} T_1 T_2 - 2 T_2 T_1$. Then $T(x_1, x_2) = (-3x_2, -3x_1)$.

3. $\begin{bmatrix} 2 & 0 \\ 0 & 2 \end{bmatrix}$ 5. $\begin{bmatrix} 0 & 2 \\ 2 & 0 \end{bmatrix}$ 7. $\begin{bmatrix} \frac{1}{2} & 0 \\ 0 & \frac{1}{2} \end{bmatrix}$

9. Let $T = \frac{1}{2} T_1 T_2 - 2 T_2 T_1$. Then $T(x, y, z) = (\frac{3}{2}(y-z), 2(x-z), \frac{3}{2}(y-z))$.

11. $\begin{bmatrix} 0 & 0 & 1 \\ 0 & 1 & 0 \\ 0 & 0 & 1 \end{bmatrix}$ 13. $\begin{bmatrix} 0 & -1 & 1 \\ 0 & 0 & 0 \\ 0 & -1 & 1 \end{bmatrix}$ 15. T_2 has no inverse.

17. $\begin{bmatrix} 1 & -1 & 1 \\ -2 & 0 & 1 \end{bmatrix}$

19. $ST(x, y, z) = (3x - y, 6x - 2y, 4x - 2y + z)$; $TS(x, y) = (x, y)$.

21. Let $p_1(x) = a_1 x^2 + b_1 x + c_1$ and $p_2(x) = a_2 x^2 + b_2 x + c_2$. Then

$$T((p_1 + p_2)(x)) = T((a_1 + a_2)x^2 + (b_1 + b_2)x + (c_1 + c_2))$$
$$= [(a_1 + a_2) - (b_1 + b_2)]x^2 + [(a_1 + a_2) + (c_1 + c_2)]x + [(a_1 + a_2) + (b_1 + b_2)]$$
$$= [(a_1 - b_1)x^2 + (a_1 + c_1)x + (a_1 + b_1)] + [(a_2 - b_2)x^2 + (a_2 + c_2)x + (a_2 + b_2)]$$
$$= T(p_1(x)) + T(p_2(x)).$$

Also

$$T((\alpha p_1)(x)) = T((\alpha a_1)x^2 + (\alpha b_1)x + \alpha c_1)$$
$$= (\alpha a_1 - \alpha b_1)x^2 + (\alpha a_1 + \alpha c_1)x + (\alpha a_1 + \alpha b_1)$$
$$= \alpha[(a_1 - b_1)x^2 + (a_1 + c_1)x + (a_1 + b_1)] = \alpha T(p_1(x)).$$

23. Let T_1 and T_2 be linear transformations. Then if $\mathbf{v}$ and $\mathbf{w}$ are vectors, we have:

$$(T_1 + T_2)(\mathbf{v} + \mathbf{w}) = T_1(\mathbf{v} + \mathbf{w}) + T_2(\mathbf{v} + \mathbf{w}) = T_1(\mathbf{v}) + T_1(\mathbf{w}) + T_2(\mathbf{v}) + T_2(\mathbf{w})$$
$$= (T_1(\mathbf{v}) + T_2(\mathbf{v})) + (T_1(\mathbf{w}) + T_2(\mathbf{w}))$$
$$= (T_1 + T_2)(\mathbf{v}) + (T_1 + T_2)(\mathbf{w}).$$

If α is a scalar, we have

$$(T_1 + T_2)(\alpha \mathbf{v}) = T_1(\alpha \mathbf{v}) + T_2(\alpha \mathbf{v}) = \alpha T_1(\mathbf{v}) + \alpha T_2(\mathbf{v})$$
$$= \alpha(T_1(\mathbf{v}) + T_2(\mathbf{v})) = \alpha(T_1 + T_2)(\mathbf{v}).$$

25. Suppose we have linear transformations: $S: U \to V$, $T: V \to W$. Then TS is defined, and if $\mathbf{x}$ and $\mathbf{y}$ are vectors in U we have $TS(\mathbf{x} + \mathbf{y}) = T(S(\mathbf{x} + \mathbf{y})) = T(S(\mathbf{x}) + S(\mathbf{y})) = T(S(\mathbf{x})) + T(S(\mathbf{y})) = TS(\mathbf{x}) + TS(\mathbf{y})$. Also, if α is a scalar, then $TS(\alpha \mathbf{x}) = T(S(\alpha \mathbf{x})) = T(\alpha S(\mathbf{x})) = \alpha T(S(\mathbf{x})) = \alpha TS(\mathbf{x})$.

27. Using Theorem 5.5, first verify that T is *one-to-one* and *onto* if and only if Range $T = U$. Next, note that any function that is *one-to-one* and *onto* has an inverse function, and conversely. In fact, T^{-1} itself is a linear transformation.

29. Suppose $AT = TA = I$ and $BT = TB = I$, where I is the identity transformation. Then, $B = BI = B(TA) = (BT)A = IA = A$.

Exercises 5.5 (page 221)

1. $SI_n S^{-1} = S(I_n S^{-1}) = SS^{-1} = I_n.$

3. Let $A = I_2 = \begin{bmatrix} 1 & 0 \\ 0 & 1 \end{bmatrix}$, let $B = \begin{bmatrix} 0 & -1 \\ 1 & 0 \end{bmatrix}$. Then det A = det B = 1, but A is not similar to B from Exercise 1.

5. The given statement is true. For, suppose $B = SAS^{-1}$. If A has an inverse, then B is invertible, in fact $B^{-1} = SA^{-1}S^{-1}$. If B has an inverse, then A is invertible, in fact $A^{-1} = S^{-1}B^{-1}S$. So A is invertible if and only if B is invertible; that is, A is nonsingular if and only if B is.

7. Yes. $B = SAS^{-1}$, where $S = \begin{bmatrix} 0 & 1 \\ 1 & 0 \end{bmatrix}$.

9. Yes. $B = SAS^{-1}$, where $S = \begin{bmatrix} 0 & 0 & 1 \\ 0 & 1 & 0 \\ 1 & 0 & 0 \end{bmatrix}$.   **11.** $\begin{bmatrix} -1 & 1 & 0 \\ 0 & 0 & 0 \\ -1 & 0 & 1 \end{bmatrix}$ **13.** $\begin{bmatrix} 1 & 0 & 1 \\ 0 & -1 & 1 \\ 1 & -1 & 0 \end{bmatrix}$

15. $\begin{bmatrix} -\frac{1}{2} & -1 & -\frac{1}{2} \\ -\frac{1}{2} & 0 & \frac{1}{2} \\ -\frac{1}{2} & 0 & \frac{1}{2} \end{bmatrix}$ **17.** $\begin{bmatrix} \frac{1}{2} & \frac{1}{4} & -\frac{1}{4} \\ -\frac{1}{2} & \frac{1}{4} & -\frac{1}{4} \\ 0 & \frac{1}{2} & \frac{1}{2} \end{bmatrix}$ **19.** $\begin{bmatrix} \frac{1}{2} & 1 & \frac{1}{4} \\ \frac{1}{2} & -1 & -\frac{3}{4} \\ -1 & 0 & \frac{1}{2} \end{bmatrix}$

21. The rank of a matrix is the dimension of its range when it is viewed as a linear transformation. Dimension is preserved when an invertible linear transformation is applied.

23. $\begin{bmatrix} 1 & 0 \\ 0 & 1 \end{bmatrix}$ and $\begin{bmatrix} 1 & 0 \\ 1 & 1 \end{bmatrix}$ are row equivalent but not similar.

Exercises 5.6 (page 228)

1. Not orthogonal.   **3.** Orthogonal.   **5.** Not orthogonal.

7. Orthogonal.   **9.** Orthogonal.   **11.** Not orthogonal.

13. $\begin{bmatrix} 0 & 0 & 1 \\ \frac{\sqrt{3}}{2} & \frac{1}{2} & 0 \\ \frac{1}{2} & -\frac{\sqrt{3}}{2} & 0 \end{bmatrix}$ **15.** $\begin{bmatrix} \frac{5}{13} & 0 & \frac{12}{13} \\ 0 & \frac{12}{13} & \frac{-5}{13} \\ 1 & 0 & 0 \end{bmatrix}$

17. Yes   **19.** T is orthogonal.

21. Imitate the argument used in Example 1.

23. $\det A = \cos^2 \phi + \sin^2 \phi = 1$ (see Exercise 21).

25. $\dfrac{\langle T(\mathbf{v}),\ T(\mathbf{w}) \rangle}{\|T(\mathbf{v})\| \cdot \|T(\mathbf{w})\|} = \dfrac{\langle k\mathbf{v},\ k\mathbf{w} \rangle}{\sqrt{\langle k\mathbf{v},\ k\mathbf{v} \rangle} \cdot \sqrt{\langle k\mathbf{w},\ k\mathbf{w} \rangle}} = \dfrac{k^2 \langle \mathbf{v},\ \mathbf{w} \rangle}{k^2 \sqrt{\langle \mathbf{v},\ \mathbf{v} \rangle} \cdot \sqrt{\langle \mathbf{w},\ \mathbf{w} \rangle}}$
$= \dfrac{\langle \mathbf{v},\ \mathbf{w} \rangle}{\|\mathbf{v}\| \cdot \|\mathbf{w}\|}.$

27. No. Since $k > 1$, lengths are not preserved.

29. Yes, since it preserves length.   **31.** No. Use Exercises 24–26.

CHAPTER 6

Exercises 6.1 (page 238)

1. (a) $\lambda^2 - 6\lambda + 8 = 0$ (b) $\{2, 4\}$ (c) $\left\{ \begin{bmatrix} 1 \\ -1 \end{bmatrix},\ \begin{bmatrix} 1 \\ 1 \end{bmatrix} \right\}$

3. (a) $\lambda^2 - 8\lambda + 16 = 0$ (b) $\{4\}$ (c) $\left\{ \begin{bmatrix} 3 \\ 2 \end{bmatrix} \right\}$

5. (a) $\lambda^2 - 0.8\lambda - 0.2 = 0$ (b) $\{1, \ -0.2\}$ (c) $\left\{ \begin{bmatrix} 1 \\ 1 \end{bmatrix}, \ \begin{bmatrix} -7 \\ 5 \end{bmatrix} \right\}$

7. (a) $\lambda^2 - 5\lambda + 8 = 0$ (b) No real eigenvalues.

9. (a) $\lambda^3 - 2\lambda^2 + \lambda = 0$ (b) $\{1, \ 0\}$ (c) $\left\{ \begin{bmatrix} 1 \\ 0 \\ 0 \end{bmatrix}, \ \begin{bmatrix} 1 \\ 1 \\ 1 \end{bmatrix} \right\}$

11. $\left\{ \begin{bmatrix} 1 \\ 1 \end{bmatrix} \right\}, \left\{ \begin{bmatrix} -7 \\ 5 \end{bmatrix} \right\}$

13.

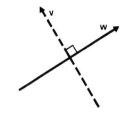

Eigenvectors are **w** and **v**, where $\langle \mathbf{v}, \mathbf{w} \rangle = 0$. The corresponding eigenvalues are $+1$ and -1.

15.

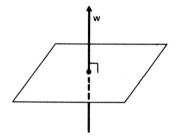

Eigenvectors are **w** and the set of all vectors in the plane perpendicular to **w**. The corresponding eigenvalues are $+1$ and -1.

17. Same diagram as in Exercise 15; The eigenvectors are the same as in Exercise 15 but this time with corresponding eigenvalues 1 and 0.

19. The characteristic polynomial is $(\lambda - 2)(\lambda - 3)(\lambda - 5)$ and the eigenvalues are 2, 3, 5. The bases for the eigenspaces associated with $\lambda = 2$, $\lambda = 3$ and $\lambda = 5$ are, respectively,

$$\left\{ \begin{bmatrix} 0 \\ 0 \\ 1 \end{bmatrix} \right\}, \left\{ \begin{bmatrix} 1 \\ -1 \\ 0 \end{bmatrix} \right\} \quad \text{and} \quad \left\{ \begin{bmatrix} 1 \\ 1 \\ 0 \end{bmatrix} \right\}.$$

21. The characteristic polynomial is $(\lambda + 1)(\lambda - 2)(\lambda - 4)$ and the eigenvalues are $-1, 2, 4$. The bases for the eigenspaces associated with $\lambda = -1$, $\lambda = 2$, and $\lambda = 4$ are, respectively,

$$\left\{ \begin{bmatrix} 1 \\ 0 \\ 0 \end{bmatrix} \right\}, \quad \left\{ \begin{bmatrix} 0 \\ 1 \\ -1 \end{bmatrix} \right\}, \quad \text{and} \quad \left\{ \begin{bmatrix} 0 \\ 1 \\ 1 \end{bmatrix} \right\}$$

23. The characteristic polynomial is $(\lambda - 1)(\lambda - 2)(\lambda - 3)$ and the eigenvalues are 1, 2, 3. The corresponding bases for the associated eigenspaces are $\left\{ \begin{bmatrix} 1 \\ 0 \\ 0 \end{bmatrix} \right\}, \left\{ \begin{bmatrix} 2 \\ 1 \\ 0 \end{bmatrix} \right\}, \left\{ \begin{bmatrix} 3 \\ 2 \\ 2 \end{bmatrix} \right\}.$

25. $\begin{bmatrix} 4 & 0 & 1 \\ -2 & 1 & 0 \\ -2 & 0 & 1 \end{bmatrix}$ 27. $\{1, 2, 3\}$ 29. $\begin{bmatrix} 10 & -9 & 0 & 0 \\ 4 & -2 & 0 & 0 \\ 0 & 0 & -2 & -7 \\ 0 & 0 & 1 & 2 \end{bmatrix}$

31. 4 is the only real eigenvalue.

33. Suppose $A\mathbf{v} = \mathbf{0}$, $\mathbf{v} \neq \mathbf{0}$. If A were invertible, then $\mathbf{v} = A^{-1}(A\mathbf{v}) = A^{-1}\mathbf{0} = \mathbf{0}$, which is a contradiction. So, if $\lambda = 0$ is an eigenvalue of A, then A is not invertible. Conversely, suppose A is not invertible. Then kernel of A is not zero. So there is a *nonzero* vector corresponding to the eigenvalue 0.

35. Suppose that $AP = PB$. Equating corresponding entries, we see that all the entries in the last row of P are zero and hence P is singular. Therefore, A and B are not similar.

37. There are no eigenvectors for this rotation since there are no *real* eigenvalues.

39. 1 and 4 (see Exercise 38).

41. This follows from the expansion of det $(\lambda I_3 - A)$.

Exercises 6.2 (pages 249)

1. $D = \begin{bmatrix} 1 & 0 \\ 0 & 2 \end{bmatrix}$, $P = \begin{bmatrix} 1 & 1 \\ 2 & 1 \end{bmatrix}$ 3. $D = \begin{bmatrix} 1 & 0 \\ 0 & 0 \end{bmatrix}$, $P = \begin{bmatrix} 1 & 1 \\ 1 & -1 \end{bmatrix}$

5. $D = \begin{bmatrix} \sqrt{6} & 0 \\ 0 & -\sqrt{6} \end{bmatrix}$, $P = \begin{bmatrix} 1 & 1 \\ \dfrac{\sqrt{6}}{2} & -\dfrac{\sqrt{6}}{2} \end{bmatrix}$

7. $D = \begin{bmatrix} 1 & 0 & 0 \\ 0 & -1 & 0 \\ 0 & 0 & 3 \end{bmatrix}$, $P = \begin{bmatrix} 2 & 0 & 0 \\ 2 & 2 & 0 \\ -3 & -1 & 1 \end{bmatrix}$

9. $D = \begin{bmatrix} -1 & 0 & 0 \\ 0 & -1 & 0 \\ 0 & 0 & 2 \end{bmatrix}$, $P = \begin{bmatrix} 1 & 1 & 3 \\ 0 & -1 & 1 \\ -1 & 0 & -3 \end{bmatrix}$

11. The characteristic polynomial is $\lambda^2 - \lambda + 1$, which has no *real* roots. So $\begin{bmatrix} 2 & -3 \\ 1 & -1 \end{bmatrix}$ has no eigenvectors and thus is not similar to a diagonal matrix.

13. The characteristic polynomial is $\lambda^3 - \lambda^2 - \lambda - 2 = (\lambda - 2)(\lambda^2 + \lambda + 1)$, which has some *nonreal* roots. So the given matrix is not similar to a diagonal matrix.

15. $D = \begin{bmatrix} 4 & 0 & 0 \\ 0 & 2 & 0 \\ 0 & 0 & 2 \end{bmatrix}$, $P = \begin{bmatrix} 1 & 0 & 1 \\ 1 & 0 & -1 \\ 0 & 1 & 0 \end{bmatrix}$

17 and **19.** Not similar to a diagonal matrix.

21. $D = \begin{bmatrix} 1 & 0 & 0 \\ 0 & 2 & 0 \\ 0 & 0 & 3 \end{bmatrix}$, $P = \begin{bmatrix} 1 & 2 & 1 \\ 1 & 3 & 3 \\ 1 & 3 & 4 \end{bmatrix}$

23. $D = \begin{bmatrix} 2 & 0 & 0 & 0 \\ 0 & 2 & 0 & 0 \\ 0 & 0 & -3 & 0 \\ 0 & 0 & 0 & -3 \end{bmatrix}$, $P = \begin{bmatrix} 1 & 0 & 0 & 0 \\ 0 & 1 & 1 & -1 \\ 0 & 0 & 1 & 0 \\ 0 & 0 & 0 & 1 \end{bmatrix}$

25. $B = \left\{ \begin{bmatrix} 1 \\ 0 \end{bmatrix}, \begin{bmatrix} 0 \\ 1 \end{bmatrix} \right\}$, $[T]_B = \begin{bmatrix} 1 & 0 \\ 0 & 0 \end{bmatrix}$

27. $\begin{bmatrix} 5 & 0 & 0 \\ 0 & 3 & -2 \\ 0 & -2 & 3 \end{bmatrix}$

29. $(P^{-1}AP)^2 = (P^{-1}AP)(P^{-1}AP) = (P^{-1}A)(PP^{-1})(AP) = (P^{-1}A)I_n(AP) = (P^{-1}A)(AP) = P^{-1}A^2P$. Use induction to show that $(P^{-1}AP)^k = P^{-1}A^kP$ for all positive integers k.

31. $A^{10} = \begin{bmatrix} \frac{1}{2}[3^{10} + 1] & \frac{1}{2}[3^{10} - 1] \\ \frac{1}{2}[3^{10} - 1] & \frac{1}{2}[3^{10} + 1] \end{bmatrix}$

33. $PD = P(\lambda I) = \lambda(PI) = \lambda P$; $DP = (\lambda I)P = \lambda(IP) = \lambda P$. Hence $PD = DP$ and thus $D = P^{-1}DP$.

35. The entries of D^2 are the squares of the entries of D.

37. The standard matrix for a $90°$ rotation is $\begin{bmatrix} 0 & -1 \\ 1 & 0 \end{bmatrix}$; its characteristic polynomial is $\lambda^2 + 1$ which has no roots in $\mathbb{R}$; its complex roots are $\{i, -i\}$. Let $P = \begin{bmatrix} i & -i \\ 1 & 1 \end{bmatrix}$; then $P^{-1} \begin{bmatrix} 0 & -1 \\ 1 & 0 \end{bmatrix} P = \begin{bmatrix} i & 0 \\ 0 & -i \end{bmatrix}$.

39. Let $A = \text{diag}(\alpha_{11}, \alpha_{22}, \ldots, \alpha_{nn})$. Then $P_A(\lambda) = (\lambda - \alpha_{11})(\lambda - \alpha_{22}) \cdots (\lambda - \alpha_{nn})$ and hence $P_A(\alpha_{ii}) = 0$ for all i. Moreover, $P_A(A) = \text{diag}(P_A(\alpha_{11}), \ldots, P_A(\alpha_{nn})) = 0$.

Exercises 6.3 (page 256)

1. $\{0, 2\}$

3. $\left\{ \dfrac{-1 + 3\sqrt{17}}{4}, \dfrac{-1 - 3\sqrt{17}}{4} \right\}$

5. $\{0, 0, 3\}$

7. $\{0, 2, 5\}$

9. $\{0, 3, 3, 3\}$

11. (1) $D = \begin{bmatrix} 2 & 0 \\ 0 & 0 \end{bmatrix}$, $P = \begin{bmatrix} \dfrac{1}{\sqrt{2}} & \dfrac{1}{\sqrt{2}} \\ \dfrac{-1}{\sqrt{2}} & \dfrac{1}{\sqrt{2}} \end{bmatrix}$

(3) $D = \begin{bmatrix} \dfrac{-1+3\sqrt{17}}{4} & 0 \\ 0 & \dfrac{-1-3\sqrt{17}}{4} \end{bmatrix}$, $P = \begin{bmatrix} \dfrac{3+3\sqrt{17}}{a} & \dfrac{3-3\sqrt{17}}{b} \\ \dfrac{12}{a} & \dfrac{12}{b} \end{bmatrix}$,

where $a = \sqrt{306 + 18\sqrt{17}}$, $b = \sqrt{306 - 18\sqrt{17}}$.

(5) $D = \begin{bmatrix} 3 & 0 & 0 \\ 0 & 0 & 0 \\ 0 & 0 & 0 \end{bmatrix}$, $P = \begin{bmatrix} \dfrac{\sqrt{3}}{3} & \dfrac{-\sqrt{2}}{2} & \dfrac{\sqrt{6}}{6} \\ \dfrac{\sqrt{3}}{3} & 0 & \dfrac{-\sqrt{6}}{3} \\ \dfrac{\sqrt{3}}{3} & \dfrac{\sqrt{2}}{2} & \dfrac{\sqrt{6}}{6} \end{bmatrix}$

(7) $D = \begin{bmatrix} 2 & 0 & 0 \\ 0 & 5 & 0 \\ 0 & 0 & 0 \end{bmatrix}$, $P = \begin{bmatrix} \dfrac{\sqrt{2}}{2} & 0 & \dfrac{\sqrt{2}}{2} \\ -\dfrac{\sqrt{2}}{2} & 0 & \dfrac{\sqrt{2}}{2} \\ 0 & 1 & 0 \end{bmatrix}$

(9) $D = \begin{bmatrix} 3 & 0 & 0 & 0 \\ 0 & 3 & 0 & 0 \\ 0 & 0 & 3 & 0 \\ 0 & 0 & 0 & 0 \end{bmatrix}$, $P = \begin{bmatrix} \dfrac{1}{\sqrt{3}} & \dfrac{-1}{\sqrt{3}} & 0 & \dfrac{1}{\sqrt{3}} \\ \dfrac{-1}{\sqrt{3}} & 0 & \dfrac{1}{\sqrt{3}} & \dfrac{1}{\sqrt{3}} \\ 0 & \dfrac{1}{\sqrt{3}} & \dfrac{-1}{\sqrt{3}} & \dfrac{1}{\sqrt{3}} \\ \dfrac{1}{\sqrt{3}} & \dfrac{1}{\sqrt{3}} & \dfrac{1}{\sqrt{3}} & 0 \end{bmatrix}$

13. This can be proved readily by mathematical induction.

15. Suppose A is symmetric and P is orthogonal. Then $B^t = (P^{-1}AP)^t = (P^tAP)^t = P^tA^t(P^t)^t = P^tA^tP = P^{-1}AP = B$. Hence B is symmetric.

17. Let $A = \begin{bmatrix} \alpha & \beta \\ \beta & \gamma \end{bmatrix}$ be a real matrix. The characteristic polynomial of A is $\lambda^2 - (\alpha + \gamma)\lambda + (\alpha\gamma - \beta^2)$. The discriminant of this quadratic polynomial is:

$$(-(\alpha + \gamma))^2 - 4(\alpha\gamma - \beta^2) = (\alpha - \gamma)^2 + 4\beta^2 \geqslant 0.$$

This polynomial always has real roots and it will have multiple roots *only* if $\alpha = \gamma$ and $\beta = 0$. In this case, A is already a diagonal (in fact, scalar) matrix.

19. $A^* = \begin{bmatrix} 1+i & -i \\ 3 & 1-i \end{bmatrix}$, $(A^*)^t = \begin{bmatrix} 1+i & 3 \\ -i & 1-i \end{bmatrix}$

21. $(A^*)^t = \begin{bmatrix} 3 & 1-2i \\ 1+2i & 1 \end{bmatrix} = A$

Exercises 6.4 (page 265)

1. xy 3. $53x^2 - 72xy + 32y^2$ 5. $16x^2 - 24xy + 9y^2$ 7. $2x^2 - 3xy + 4y^2$

9. $\begin{bmatrix} 0 & \frac{1}{2} \\ \frac{1}{2} & 0 \end{bmatrix}$ 11. $\begin{bmatrix} 53 & -36 \\ -36 & 32 \end{bmatrix}$ 13. $\begin{bmatrix} 16 & -12 \\ -12 & 9 \end{bmatrix}$ 15. $\begin{bmatrix} 2 & -\frac{3}{2} \\ -\frac{3}{2} & 4 \end{bmatrix}$

17–24. Use the notation $[x, y]A\begin{bmatrix} x \\ y \end{bmatrix} + N\begin{bmatrix} x \\ y \end{bmatrix} + f = 0$.

17. $A = \begin{bmatrix} 0 & \frac{1}{2} \\ \frac{1}{2} & 0 \end{bmatrix}$, $N = [0 \ \ 0]$, $f = -2$

19. $A = \begin{bmatrix} 53 & -36 \\ -36 & 32 \end{bmatrix}$, $N = [0 \ \ 0]$, $f = -80$

21. $A = \begin{bmatrix} 16 & -12 \\ -12 & 9 \end{bmatrix}$, $N = [-60 \ \ -80]$, $f = 100$

23. $A = \begin{bmatrix} 2 & -\frac{3}{2} \\ -\frac{3}{2} & 4 \end{bmatrix}$, $N = [-7 \ \ 2]$, $f = 7$

25. Hyperbola   27. Ellipse   29. Parabola   31. Ellipse

33.

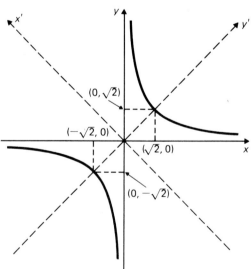

The new equation is $\frac{1}{2}(y')^2 - \frac{1}{2}(x')^2 = 2$.

35.

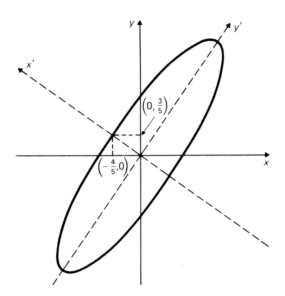

The new equation is $\dfrac{(y')^2}{4^2}+\dfrac{(x')^2}{1^2}=1.$

37.

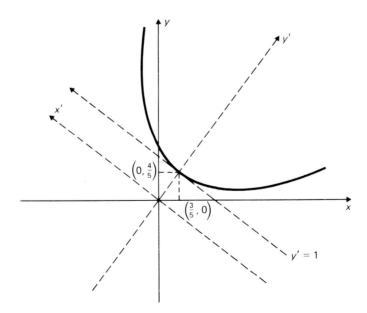

The new equation is $y'=\frac{1}{4}(x')^2+1.$

39. The new equation is $\left(3+\dfrac{\sqrt{13}}{2}\right)(x')^2 + \left(3-\dfrac{\sqrt{13}}{2}\right)(y')^2 + d'x' + e'y' + 7 = 0$. Proceed as in Example 7 to find d', e' and to complete the square for finding the standard form of this ellipse; then sketch it.

41. Let A be the matrix described in Theorem 6.9. The eigenvalues for the matrix A corresponding to a circle must be the same; that is, A is similar to a scalar multiple of $I_2 = \begin{bmatrix} 1 & 0 \\ 0 & 1 \end{bmatrix}$. But we know that in this case A must already be diagonal, so that the quadratic form associated with A has 0 for its xy-coefficient, i.e., it has no xy-term.

43. Let P be the matrix of rotation by some angle θ. Suppose $a'(x')^2 + 2b'(x'y') + c'(y')^2 + d'x' + e'y' + f = 0$ is the new equation obtained from the original equation $ax^2 + 2bxy + cy^2 + dx + ey + f = 0$ by rotating through the angle θ. Then $\begin{bmatrix} a' & b' \\ b' & c' \end{bmatrix} = P^{-1} \begin{bmatrix} a & b \\ b & c \end{bmatrix} P$.

So $(b')^2 - a'c' = -\det \begin{bmatrix} a' & b' \\ b' & c' \end{bmatrix} = -\det \left[P^{-1} \begin{bmatrix} a & b \\ b & c \end{bmatrix} P \right] = -\det \begin{bmatrix} a & b \\ b & c \end{bmatrix} = b^2 - ac.$

So the discriminant is invariant under rotation.

45. Let $ax^2 + 2bxy + cy^2 + dx + ey + f = 0$ be a quadratic equation such that at least one of the numbers a, b, c is not zero. We can rotate axes to put this equation in the form: $a'(x')^2 + c'(y')^2 + d'x' + e'y' + f = 0$. This equation may have no solutions or may be one of the degenerate cases, but if it turns out to be a "genuine" conic section then it is clear that

  i) It will be a hyperbola if a' and c' have different signs, i.e., if $a'c' < 0$.

  ii) It will be an ellipse if a' and c' have the same signs, i.e., if $a'c' > 0$.

  iii) It will be a parabola if either a' or c' is equal to zero, i.e., if $a'c' = 0$.

But from Exercise 43 we find that $b^2 - ac = -a'c'$. Therefore, the original equation $ax^2 + 2bxy + cy^2 + dx + ey + f = 0$ will be

  i) a hyperbola if $b^2 - ac > 0$;

  ii) an ellipse if $b^2 - ac < 0$;

  iii) a parabola if $b^2 - ac = 0$.

47. Degenerate conic

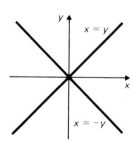

49. Degenerate conic

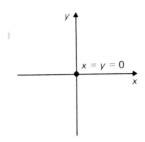

51. Degenerate conic

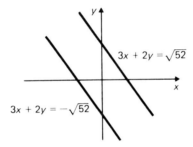

53. Degenerate conic

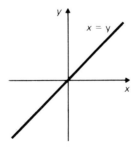

Exercises 6.5 (page 273)

1. Ellipsoid (in particular a sphere)   **3.** Elliptic paraboloid

5. Elliptic cone   **7.** Hyperbolic paraboloid

9. $A = \begin{bmatrix} 1 & 0 & 0 \\ 0 & -1 & 0 \\ 0 & 0 & -1 \end{bmatrix}$, $K = \begin{bmatrix} 0 & 0 & 0 \end{bmatrix}$

11. $A = \begin{bmatrix} 36 & 0 & 0 \\ 0 & 4 & 0 \\ 0 & 0 & 9 \end{bmatrix}$, $K = \begin{bmatrix} 0 & 0 & 0 \end{bmatrix}$

13. $A = \begin{bmatrix} 2 & 0 & 0 \\ 0 & -3 & 0 \\ 0 & 0 & 6 \end{bmatrix}$, $K = \begin{bmatrix} 0 & 0 & 0 \end{bmatrix}$ **15.** $P = \begin{bmatrix} \frac{1}{\sqrt{2}} & \frac{-1}{\sqrt{2}} & 0 \\ \frac{1}{\sqrt{2}} & \frac{1}{\sqrt{2}} & 0 \\ 0 & 0 & 1 \end{bmatrix}$; hyperbolic paraboloid

17. $P = \begin{bmatrix} \frac{1}{\sqrt{2}} & \frac{1}{\sqrt{2}} & 0 \\ 0 & 0 & 1 \\ \frac{1}{\sqrt{2}} & \frac{-1}{\sqrt{2}} & 0 \end{bmatrix}$; hyperbolic cylinder **19.** $P = \begin{bmatrix} 0 & \frac{-1}{\sqrt{2}} & \frac{1}{\sqrt{2}} \\ \frac{3}{\sqrt{10}} & \frac{-1}{\sqrt{20}} & \frac{-1}{\sqrt{20}} \\ \frac{1}{\sqrt{10}} & \frac{3}{\sqrt{20}} & \frac{3}{\sqrt{20}} \end{bmatrix}$; hyperbolic cylinder

21. $P = \begin{bmatrix} \frac{-1}{\sqrt{2}} & \frac{1}{\sqrt{6}} & \frac{1}{\sqrt{3}} \\ 0 & \frac{-2}{\sqrt{6}} & \frac{1}{\sqrt{3}} \\ \frac{1}{\sqrt{2}} & \frac{1}{\sqrt{6}} & \frac{1}{\sqrt{3}} \end{bmatrix}$; elliptic hyperboloid of two sheets

23. This is a direct result of the spectral theorem (Theorem 6.6).

Exercises 6.6 (page 277)

1. $y_1 = c_1 e^x + c_2 e^{2x}$
$y_2 = 2c_1 e^x + c_2 e^{2x}$

3. $y_1 = c_1 e^{5x} - 2c_2 e^{-x}$
$y_2 = c_1 e^{5x} + c_2 e^{-x}$

5. $y_1 = c_1 e^{3x} - c_2 e^{-3x}$
$y_2 = c_1 e^{3x} - c_1 e^{-3x}$
$y_3 = c_1 e^{3x} + (c_1 + c_2)e^{-3x}$

7. $y_1 = -2e^x + 3e^{2x}$
$y_2 = -4e^x + 3e^{2x}$

9. $y_1 = 3e^{5x} - 4e^{-x}$
$y_2 = 3e^{5x} + 2e^{-x}$

11. $y_1 = \frac{2}{3}e^{3x} + \frac{1}{3}e^{-3x}$
$y_2 = \frac{2}{3}e^{3x} - \frac{2}{3}e^{-3x}$
$y_3 = \frac{2}{3}e^{3x} + \frac{1}{3}e^{-3x}$

13. $y_1 = 3c_1 e^{2x} - c_2 e^{-x}$

$\quad\ y_2 = c_1 e^{2x}$

$\quad\ y_3 = -3c_1 e^{2x} + c_2 e^{-x}$

15. $y_1 = c_1 e^{3x} + c_2 e^x$

$\quad\ y_2 = -c_1 e^{3x} + c_2 e^x$

$\quad\ y_3 = c_3 e^{2x} + c_4$

$\quad\ y_4 = -c_3 e^{2x} + c_4$

17. $y = c_1 e^{2x} + c_2 e^{-4x}$

19. $D(f + g) = f' + g' = D(f) + D(g)$; $D(cf) = cf' = cD(f)$ for all constants (i.e., scalars) c.

Exercises 6.7 (page 281)

1. Let $A_{11} = \begin{bmatrix} 3 & 0 \\ 0 & 3 \end{bmatrix} = 3I_2$, $\qquad A_{12} = \begin{bmatrix} 1 & 2 \\ 0 & 1 \end{bmatrix}$, $\qquad A_{13} = \begin{bmatrix} -1 \\ 2 \end{bmatrix}$,

$A_{21} = \begin{bmatrix} 0 & 0 \\ 0 & 0 \end{bmatrix} = 0_2$, $\qquad A_{22} = \begin{bmatrix} 1 & 0 \\ 0 & 1 \end{bmatrix} = I_2$, $\qquad A_{23} = \begin{bmatrix} 0 \\ 0 \end{bmatrix}$,

$A_{31} = \begin{bmatrix} 0 & 0 \end{bmatrix}$, $\qquad A_{32} = \begin{bmatrix} 0 & 0 \end{bmatrix}$, $\qquad A_{33} = \begin{bmatrix} 1 \end{bmatrix}$,

$B_{11} = \begin{bmatrix} 1 & 2 & 4 \\ 1 & -1 & 3 \end{bmatrix}$, $\qquad B_{12} = \begin{bmatrix} 1 & 5 \\ 0 & -2 \end{bmatrix}$, $\qquad B_{13} = \begin{bmatrix} 1 \\ 0 \end{bmatrix}$,

$B_{21} = \begin{bmatrix} 4 & 1 & -1 \\ 0 & 0 & 1 \end{bmatrix}$, $\qquad B_{22} = \begin{bmatrix} 0 & 1 \\ 1 & 0 \end{bmatrix}$, $\qquad B_{23} = \begin{bmatrix} 0 \\ 0 \end{bmatrix}$,

$B_{31} = \begin{bmatrix} 1 & 0 & 1 \end{bmatrix}$, $\qquad B_{32} = \begin{bmatrix} 0 & 1 \end{bmatrix}$, $\qquad B_{33} = \begin{bmatrix} 0 \end{bmatrix}$.

Then $AB = \begin{bmatrix} A_{11}B_{11} + A_{12}B_{21} + A_{13}B_{31} & A_{11}B_{12} + A_{12}B_{22} + A_{13}B_{32} & A_{11}B_{13} + A_{12}B_{23} + A_{13}B_{33} \\ A_{21}B_{11} + A_{22}B_{21} + A_{23}B_{31} & A_{21}B_{12} + A_{22}B_{22} + A_{23}B_{32} & A_{21}B_{13} + A_{22}B_{23} + A_{23}B_{33} \\ A_{31}B_{11} + A_{32}B_{21} + A_{33}B_{31} & A_{31}B_{12} + A_{32}B_{22} + A_{33}B_{32} & A_{31}B_{13} + A_{32}B_{23} + A_{33}B_{33} \end{bmatrix}$

$= \begin{bmatrix} 3B_{11} + A_{12}B_{21} + A_{13}B_{31} & 3B_{12} + A_{12}B_{22} + A_{13}B_{32} & 3B_{13} \\ B_{21} & B_{22} & B_{23} \\ B_{31} & B_{32} & B_{33} \end{bmatrix}$

$= \left[\begin{array}{ccc:cc:c} 6 & 7 & 12 & 5 & 15 & 3 \\ 5 & -3 & 12 & 1 & -4 & 0 \\ \hdashline 4 & 1 & -1 & 0 & 1 & 0 \\ 0 & 0 & 1 & 1 & 0 & 0 \\ \hdashline 1 & 0 & 1 & 0 & 1 & 0 \end{array}\right].$

Moreover, $A^2 = \begin{bmatrix} 3^2 I_2 & 3A_{12} + A_{12} & 3A_{13} + A_{13} \\ A_{21} & A_{22} & A_{23} \\ A_{31} & A_{32} & A_{33} \end{bmatrix} = \left[\begin{array}{cc:cc:c} 9 & 0 & 4 & 8 & -4 \\ 0 & 9 & 0 & 4 & 8 \\ \hdashline 0 & 0 & 1 & 0 & 0 \\ 0 & 0 & 0 & 1 & 0 \\ \hdashline 0 & 0 & 0 & 0 & 1 \end{array}\right]$

$$3.\ AB = \begin{bmatrix} -4 & 3 & -1 \\ 5 & 0 & 0 \\ 2 & -6 & 2 \\ -2 & 0 & 0 \\ 3 & 3 & -1 \end{bmatrix}, \quad \text{no matter which partitioning we use.}$$

5. This follows at once from the rule for block multiplication.

CHAPTER 7

Exercises 7.1 (page 290)

1. No   **3.** No   **5.** Yes   **7.** Yes

9. The matrix in Exercise 3 is *not* an incidence matrix.

$$11.\ \begin{bmatrix} 0 & 1 & 0 \\ 0 & 0 & 1 \\ 1 & 1 & 0 \end{bmatrix}^2 = \begin{bmatrix} 0 & 0 & 1 \\ 1 & 1 & 0 \\ 0 & 1 & 1 \end{bmatrix} = \text{2-stage dominance matrix for no. 5.}$$

$$\begin{bmatrix} 0 & 1 & 0 \\ 0 & 0 & 1 \\ 1 & 1 & 0 \end{bmatrix} + \begin{bmatrix} 0 & 1 & 0 \\ 0 & 0 & 1 \\ 1 & 1 & 0 \end{bmatrix}^2 = \begin{bmatrix} 0 & 1 & 1 \\ 1 & 1 & 1 \\ 1 & 2 & 1 \end{bmatrix} = \text{Power matrix; 3 } \textit{is leader.}$$

$$13.\ \begin{bmatrix} 0 & 0 & 1 \\ 1 & 0 & 0 \\ 0 & 1 & 0 \end{bmatrix}^2 = \begin{bmatrix} 0 & 1 & 0 \\ 0 & 0 & 1 \\ 1 & 0 & 0 \end{bmatrix} = \text{2-stage dominance matrix.}$$

$$\begin{bmatrix} 0 & 0 & 1 \\ 1 & 0 & 0 \\ 0 & 1 & 0 \end{bmatrix} + \begin{bmatrix} 0 & 0 & 1 \\ 1 & 0 & 0 \\ 0 & 1 & 0 \end{bmatrix}^2 = \begin{bmatrix} 0 & 1 & 1 \\ 1 & 0 & 1 \\ 1 & 1 & 0 \end{bmatrix} = \text{Power matrix; } \textit{no leader.}$$

Note that the cube of the matrix is I_3, so there is no leader at any stage.

$$15.\ \begin{array}{c} \\ A \\ B \\ C \\ D \end{array} \begin{array}{cccc} A & B & C & D \\ \end{array} \\ \begin{bmatrix} 0 & 1 & 0 & 1 \\ 0 & 0 & 1 & 0 \\ 1 & 0 & 0 & 0 \\ 0 & 1 & 0 & 0 \end{bmatrix}$$

16. No

17.
$$\begin{bmatrix} 0 & 1 & 0 & 1 \\ 0 & 0 & 1 & 0 \\ 1 & 0 & 0 & 0 \\ 0 & 1 & 0 & 0 \end{bmatrix}^2 = \begin{bmatrix} 0 & 1 & 1 & 0 \\ 1 & 0 & 0 & 0 \\ 0 & 1 & 0 & 1 \\ 0 & 0 & 1 & 0 \end{bmatrix} = \text{2-stage dominance.}$$

$$\begin{bmatrix} 0 & 1 & 0 & 1 \\ 0 & 0 & 1 & 0 \\ 1 & 0 & 0 & 0 \\ 0 & 1 & 0 & 0 \end{bmatrix} + \begin{bmatrix} 0 & 1 & 0 & 1 \\ 0 & 0 & 1 & 0 \\ 1 & 0 & 0 & 0 \\ 0 & 1 & 0 & 0 \end{bmatrix}^2 = \begin{bmatrix} 0 & 2 & 1 & 1 \\ 1 & 0 & 1 & 0 \\ 1 & 1 & 0 & 1 \\ 0 & 1 & 1 & 0 \end{bmatrix} = \text{Power matrix.}$$

18. Yes, A

19.

Player	Power
(1) Carter	6
(2) Kelly	3
(3) Thompson	1
(4) O'Brian	0

21.

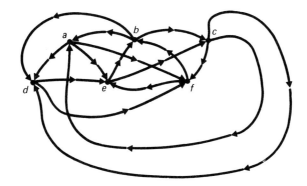

Exercises 7.2 (page 298)

1.

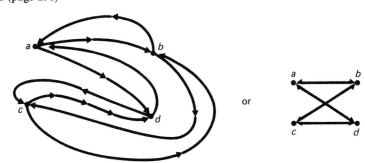   or

It *is* a perfect communication network.

3. There are no liaisons in either Exercise 1 or Exercise 2.

5.

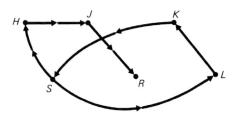

This *is* a connected graph; J, H and S are liaison individuals.

7.
$$\begin{bmatrix} 0 & 1 & 1 & 1 & 1 & 0 & 1 & 0 \\ 1 & 0 & 0 & 1 & 1 & 0 & 0 & 0 \\ 1 & 0 & 0 & 0 & 0 & 1 & 0 & 0 \\ 0 & 1 & 0 & 0 & 0 & 0 & 0 & 0 \\ 0 & 1 & 0 & 0 & 0 & 0 & 0 & 0 \\ 1 & 0 & 0 & 1 & 0 & 0 & 0 & 0 \\ 1 & 0 & 0 & 0 & 0 & 0 & 0 & 1 \\ 0 & 0 & 0 & 0 & 0 & 0 & 1 & 0 \end{bmatrix}$$

9. 4 stages; 3 stages

11. The liaison cities are 1 and 7.

13. Let $B_0 = A_i \rightarrow B_1 \rightarrow B_2 \rightarrow \cdots \rightarrow B_{k-1} \rightarrow A_j = B_k$ be a communication path from A_i to A_j such that it is of "minimal length," that is, we have used the smallest possible number of stages, k. We want to show that $k \leqslant n-1$. Suppose that $k \geqslant n$. Then, since we have n individuals in the entire communication network and since the number of B_t's is at least $n+1$ ($0 \leqslant t \leqslant k$ and we are assuming $k \geqslant n$), we must have $B_p = B_q$ for some p, q, where $0 \leqslant p < q \leqslant k$. But then the path $B_0 = A_i \rightarrow B_1 \rightarrow \cdots \rightarrow B_p \rightarrow B_{q+1} \rightarrow B_{q+2} \rightarrow \cdots \rightarrow B_{k-1} \rightarrow A_j = B_k$ is a communication path from A_i to A_j and its length is strictly less than k. But we chose k to be the *smallest* possible such length. Thus we cannot have $k \geqslant n$. Therefore, $k \leqslant n-1$.

Exercises 7.3 (page 305)

1. Yes   **3.** Yes   **5.** No   (a_{21} is always 0)

7. Yes   **9.** No   ($\frac{1}{2} + \frac{1}{3} \neq 1$)

11. We have $p^{(3)} = p^{(0)} T^3$. In this case, T is given by $T = \begin{matrix} C \\ D \end{matrix} \begin{matrix} C & D \\ \begin{bmatrix} \frac{2}{5} & \frac{3}{5} \\ \frac{1}{5} & \frac{4}{5} \end{bmatrix} \end{matrix}$ and $P^{(0)} = \begin{bmatrix} 0 & 1 \end{bmatrix}$.

So $p^{(3)} = \begin{bmatrix} 0 & 1 \end{bmatrix} \begin{bmatrix} \frac{32}{125} & \frac{93}{125} \\ \frac{31}{125} & \frac{94}{125} \end{bmatrix} = \begin{bmatrix} \frac{31}{125} & \frac{94}{125} \end{bmatrix}$.

Thus, the probability that it will be D three days later is $\frac{94}{125}$.

13.

City	Probability
Springfield	0.3234
Portland	0.3536
Middletown	0.323

15. (1) $(\frac{2}{5}, \frac{3}{5})$ (3) $(\frac{2}{3}, \frac{1}{3})$ (5) Not regular

(7) $(\frac{1}{4}, \frac{3}{4})$ (9) Not a transition matrix

17.
$$\begin{bmatrix} 1-a & 0 & a & 0 \\ b & 0 & 1-b & 0 \\ 0 & 1-c & 0 & c \\ 0 & d & 0 & 1-d \end{bmatrix}^2 = \begin{bmatrix} (1-a)^2 & a(1-c) & a(1-a) & ac \\ b(1-a) & (1-b)(1-c) & ab & c(1-b) \\ b(1-c) & cd & (1-b)(1-c) & c(1-d) \\ bd & d(1-d) & d(1-b) & (1-d)^2 \end{bmatrix}$$

Since a, b, c, d are all in the open interval $(0, 1)$, none of the numbers a, b, c, d, $(1-a)$, $(1-b)$, $(1-c)$, $(1-d)$ is zero, so none of their pairwise products is zero. Thus the matrix on the right has only *positive* entries and the original matrix is regular.

19. $\begin{bmatrix} \frac{2}{5} & \frac{3}{5} \\ \frac{2}{5} & \frac{3}{5} \end{bmatrix}$ **21.** $\begin{bmatrix} \frac{3}{4} & \frac{1}{4} \\ \frac{3}{4} & \frac{1}{4} \end{bmatrix}$ **23.** $\begin{bmatrix} \frac{3}{4} & \frac{1}{4} \\ \frac{3}{4} & \frac{1}{4} \end{bmatrix}$ **25.** $\begin{bmatrix} \frac{1}{5} & \frac{2}{5} & \frac{2}{5} \\ \frac{1}{5} & \frac{2}{5} & \frac{2}{5} \\ \frac{1}{5} & \frac{2}{5} & \frac{2}{5} \end{bmatrix}$

27. No. *In the long run*, out of every 223 transitions, he will visit Springfield 65 times, Portland 88 times and Middletown 70 times. (See the solution to Exercise 31 below.)

29. Suppose $\begin{bmatrix} a & b & c \end{bmatrix} \begin{bmatrix} 0.25 & 0.5 & 0.25 \\ 0.4 & 0.6 & 0 \\ 1 & 0 & 0 \end{bmatrix} = \begin{bmatrix} a & b & c \end{bmatrix}$, where $a + b + c = 1$. Then we have

the homogeneous system of linear equations:

$$\begin{bmatrix} a & b & c \end{bmatrix} \begin{bmatrix} -0.75 & 0.5 & 0.25 \\ 0.4 & -0.4 & 0 \\ 1 & 0 & -1 \end{bmatrix} = \begin{bmatrix} 0 & 0 & 0 \end{bmatrix}.$$

Solving this system gives $a = 4c$, $b = 5c$. Since $a + b + c = 1$, we have $a = 0.4$, $b = 0.5$, $c = 0.1$.

31. (11) $\begin{bmatrix} \frac{2}{5} & \frac{3}{5} \\ \frac{1}{5} & \frac{4}{5} \end{bmatrix}$ is regular; its fixed vector is $(\frac{1}{4}, \frac{3}{4})$.

(12) $\begin{bmatrix} 0 & 0.6 & 0.4 \\ 0.5 & 0 & 0.5 \\ 0.3 & 0.7 & 0 \end{bmatrix}$ is regular; its fixed vector is $(\frac{65}{223}, \frac{88}{223}, \frac{70}{223})$.

(See the solution to Exercise 27 above.)

(14) $\begin{bmatrix} 0.4 & 0.6 \\ 0.7 & 0.3 \end{bmatrix}$ is regular; its fixed vector is $(\frac{7}{13}, \frac{6}{13})$.

$\begin{bmatrix} 0.7 & 0.3 \\ 0.5 & 0.5 \end{bmatrix}$ is regular; its fixed vector is $(\frac{5}{8}, \frac{3}{8})$.

Exercises 7.4 (page 313)

1. Absorbing   **3.** Absorbing   **5.** Absorbing

7. Neither   **9.** Regular   **11.** Neither

13. $[2]$ **15.** $\begin{bmatrix} \frac{15}{8} & \frac{5}{4} \\ \frac{5}{4} & \frac{5}{2} \end{bmatrix}$ **17.** $\begin{bmatrix} \frac{9}{7} & \frac{3}{7} & \frac{1}{7} \\ \frac{6}{7} & \frac{9}{7} & \frac{3}{7} \\ \frac{9}{7} & \frac{3}{7} & \frac{8}{7} \end{bmatrix}$ **19.** $\begin{bmatrix} \frac{5}{2} \end{bmatrix}$

21. $\begin{bmatrix} 14 \\ 15 \\ 12 \\ 7 \end{bmatrix}$ **23.** $[1]$ **25.** $\begin{bmatrix} 1 \\ 1 \end{bmatrix}$ **27.** $\begin{bmatrix} \frac{3}{7} & \frac{4}{7} \\ \frac{2}{7} & \frac{5}{7} \\ \frac{3}{7} & \frac{4}{7} \end{bmatrix}$

29. (1) $\begin{bmatrix} 1 & 0 \\ \frac{2}{3} & \frac{1}{3} \end{bmatrix}$ (3) $\begin{bmatrix} 1 & 0 \\ 0.3 & 0.7 \end{bmatrix}$ (5) $\begin{bmatrix} 1 & 0 \\ 0 & 1 \end{bmatrix}$

(7) Not absorbing   (9) Not absorbing   (11) Not absorbing

31. Number the states of this game as follows:

State	1	2	3	4	5	6
Number of dollars player A has	5	0	1	2	3	4

States 1 and 2 are absorbing states corresponding to the situations where player A has won or lost the game, respectively. Thus the transition matrix is

$$\begin{bmatrix} 1 & 0 & 0 & 0 & 0 & 0 \\ 0 & 1 & 0 & 0 & 0 & 0 \\ 0 & \frac{1}{2} & 0 & \frac{1}{2} & 0 & 0 \\ 0 & 0 & \frac{1}{2} & 0 & \frac{1}{2} & 0 \\ 0 & 0 & 0 & \frac{1}{2} & 0 & \frac{1}{2} \\ \frac{1}{2} & 0 & 0 & 0 & \frac{1}{2} & 0 \end{bmatrix}.$$

The game starts in state 5.

33. Since the game starts in state 5, it is likely to last for six flips of the coin (the entry in N corresponding to state 5).

35. $1/3$ **37.** 0.26

39. The transition matrix in canonical form is

$$\begin{array}{c} \\ C \\ E \\ S \end{array} \begin{array}{ccc} C & E & S \\ \begin{bmatrix} 1 & 0 & 0 \\ 0.1 & 0.7 & 0.2 \\ 0.2 & 0.4 & 0.4 \end{bmatrix}. \end{array}$$

The fundamental matrix F is

$$F = \left[\begin{bmatrix} 1 & 0 \\ 0 & 1 \end{bmatrix} - \begin{bmatrix} 0.7 & 0.2 \\ 0.4 & 0.4 \end{bmatrix} \right]^{-1} = \begin{matrix} & E & S \\ E & \begin{bmatrix} 6 & 2 \\ 4 & 3 \end{bmatrix} \end{matrix}.$$

Thus the average number of generations until the offspring of a member of class E attends college is $6 + 2 = 8$. Similarly, the average number of generations for class S is $4 + 3 = 7$.

INDEX